THE COLOR HANDBOOK OF HOUSE PLANTS

THE COLOR HANDBOOK OF HOUSE PLANTS

Edited by
ELVIN McDONALD
JACQUELINE HERÍTEAU
FRANCESCA MORRIS

Hawthorn Books, Inc./Wentworth Press, Inc.
NEW YORK

ELVIN McDONALD **JACQUELINE HERITEAU** **FRANCESCA MORRIS**

ELVIN McDONALD, *Director*
has written many well-known books on gardening, is Senior and Garden Editor for *House Beautiful,* and is often seen on television. He was born on a farm in Oklahoma, directed *The Good Housekeeping Illustrated Encyclopedia of Gardening,* and lives and gardens with his three children in New York.

Editor: Jacqueline Heriteau

Contributing Editor: Francesca Morris

Design: Susan Lusk, Denise Weber
Photos: Frank Lusk, Elvin McDonald

Associate Editors: William C. Mulligan, Dorothy Chamberlain, Maxine Krasnow, Ann Lemoine

Typographer: P. Baronne & Sons

Color Separations: Sun Graphics

Printed by Suburban Publishers, Inc., West Pittston, Pennsylvania

For technical assistance, the Editors thank the research staff of The Hyponex Company, Inc., Copley, Ohio 44321.

The photos in this book were taken in the homes of the editors, and on location at Greenleaves and Hunter Florists, New York, and in Fantastic Gardens, and the Keil Brothers, Robert Heller and Tropic Greenhouses.

THE COLOR BOOK OF HOUSE PLANTS

Library of Congress Catalog Card Number: 75-37337
ISBN: 0-8015-7441-X

1 2 3 4 5 6 7 8 9 10

Table of Contents

Be a Great Indoor Gardener

House plants, unlike plants that grow outdoors, depend entirely on you for everything they need to live. The basics of temperature, humidity, watering, and light are covered in this chapter. Once you realize how simply these relate to plants, you will be able to grow almost anything successfully. All it takes is common sense—and a little love. Succeeding chapters go into the refinements on care that make the difference between plants that merely survive and plants that actually thrive.

THE RIGHT ENVIRONMENT: Moist, fresh air, moderate temperatures, the right amount of light guarantee shiny, healthy leaves, loads of bright blooms on the flowering plants, and the look of a thriving jungle for your indoor garden. Not all homes automatically provide these conditions, of course. The indoors just isn't the outdoors, the plants' natural habitat. But air can be moistened with a mister, with pebble beds, by grouping plants, and in the process, overheating will be modified. And—surprise—light to fill each plant's particular need, (see Chapter 7) can be found in most homes. You just have to know where and how to find it.

HUMIDITY: The moisture in the air surrounding your house plants is measured in degrees of relative humidity. The average home in winter has only 5%, hardly enough for a cactus. Plants need 30 to 60% humidity. In winter, you can't provide too much humidity for them, yourself, or your furniture. Below are some ways to deal with such conditions.

Battery-powered mister (above) refreshes leaves and increases relative humidity around plants with little effort on your part. Hand-operated, pistol-handled misters (opposite) are easy—and fun, like a water pistol—to use.

Portable electric humidifier helps keep winter-heated homes at the 30 to 60% humidity in which plants thrive.

Open the doors and windows: Whether your winter climate is mild or severe, you can, and should, open a door or two and a window in each room for some period daily. Some plants suffer in drafts—Chapter 7 tells which—so don't open windows near them. Plants thrive on fresh air, just as you do.

Use a humidifier: If your home has a humidifier as part of its heating system, use it from the time the heat goes on until it goes off. If you have a lot of plants, invest in a portable electric humidifier (see photograph). You will still find that plants noted as benefiting from frequent misting continue to benefit from hand misting, but the humidifier will help keep things green. If you are uncertain about needing an electric humidifier, borrow or buy a humidity indicator (hygrometer). Or buy a digital thermometer; it will measure humidity and temperature in your growing areas. If humidity is less than 20% during the heating season, leaf edges will brown and plants droop unless you install an electric humidifier, or mist by hand often, and group moisture-loving plants on trays filled with moist pebbles. With an electric humidifier, twice-weekly misting will be enough.

A humidity indicator, called a hygrometer, accurately records amount of moisture in the air around the plants in your home. It works like a thermometer.

Plants grouped on pebble tray. Keep tray filled, but keep water level well below pot bottoms. Water plants as usual. Pebble trays help keep atmosphere moist.

WATERING: In Chapter 7 you will find information about the range of soil moisture each plant requires. Keep your house plants in soil in that range, and you will have a flourishing garden.

The rule of thumb for watering is this: Only a few plants thrive when they are either very wet or very dry. Most prefer to be just nicely moist, somewhere between wet, after watering, to slightly damp, at which point most need to be watered again.

Don't take literally advice to let a plant dry out *completely* between waterings. This isn't good practice, even with cacti or bulbs like gloxin-

Cape primrose, left, is barely wilted, and it will recover easily. Plant at right may live; leaf edges will brown.

ias and amaryllis during their resting period. If the phrase "nicely moist" puzzles you, think about a sponge. It is saturated—wet—when water will run from it without squeezing when you pick it up. A dry sponge will yield not a drop of water, no matter how hard you squeeze. A sponge that is nicely moist gives up a few drops of water when you squeeze lightly. Keep these three stages of the sponge in mind as you feel the surface soil of a potted plant. Compare it to the feel of the sponge. With experience, you will recognize moisture content by the look of the surface soil in each pot. You can also tell whether a pot is dry or moist by its weight—a dry pot is much lighter. If you want readings at lower pot levels, use a solid-state moisture meter, an electronic device that accurately measures moisture in soil.

The way plant leaves hang tells you, too, whether water is needed. If they are barely wilted, as those of the Cape primrose pictured at left above, the plant needs water and probably should have been watered earlier. If they are drooping, like those of the plant on the right, the plant is in trouble. Emergency measures include plunging the whole pot into a container full of water and misting the leaves. Leave the plant until it is soaked; then let it drain, and put it in a shaded, airy spot in moderate temperatures (60 to 70) for a few days to recover.

A plant as badly wilted as the second one may not recover.

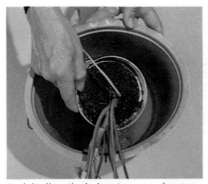

Soak badly wilted plant in a pot of water. Remove when beads of moisture show on soil surface; drain, and place in shaded spot to recuperate.

Top watering with water at room temperature is the rule for most plants. After an hour, pour off any excess that remains in the saucer.

Bottom watering is recommended for some plants. The flexible nozzle shown here bends up or down and makes reaching into pot interiors easier.

HOW TO WATER: Most plants are watered from the top. Some benefit from bottom watering; these are specified in Chapter 7. When you water, be thorough. When plants are quite dry, pour on enough water so that some seeps into the saucer. An hour later, remove saucer water the plant has not reabsorbed. Figure out how much water big plants need—a quart, half a canful. Then you won't spend a long time after the hour wait emptying big saucers. The plant tells you exactly how much it needs; whatever it doesn't absorb in an hour is unneeded. Add less each successive watering until you know the right amount.

Bathing (Chapter 5, page 39) isn't a part of the watering routine, though the plant gets watered in the process. Frequent bathing helps keep plants in hot, dry rooms clean and healthy; but the main purpose of bathing is to discourage pests and keep plants beautiful.

Mulches on indoor plants can lessen watering chores—handy when you have lots and lots of plants. Mosses and pebbles are the prettiest.

Hints: Small pots dry out almost daily in winter; big pots weekly or every 10 days. Well-drained sandy soils dry out more quickly than moisture-retaining humusy soils. Plants with many leaves use more water than plants with few. Thin leaves dry out more quickly than thick, fleshy ones. Plants in hot, dry rooms need watering and misting more often than do those in cool, airy rooms.

Light-intensity chart at right gives a thumbnail view of the types of plant that flourish in the various ranges of light available for plants growing in the average home.

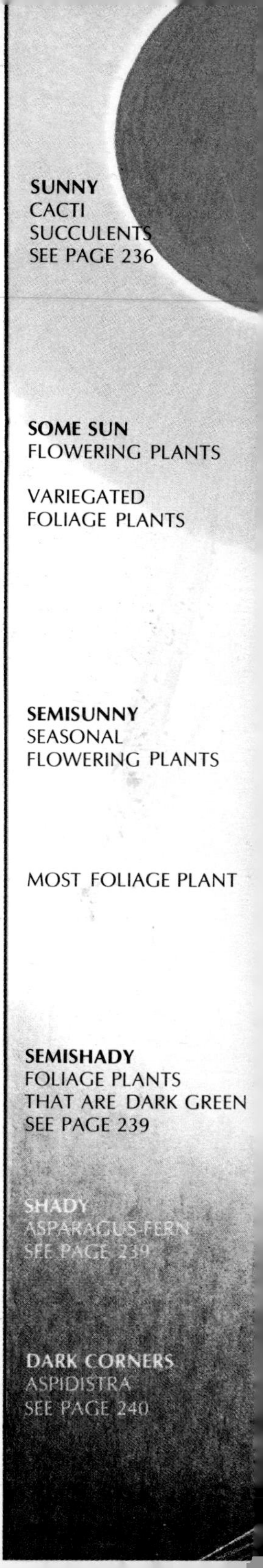

SUNNY
CACTI
SUCCULENTS
SEE PAGE 236

TEMPERATURE: Providing temperatures comfortable for your plants is a problem usually only in winter. Most plants like the same conditions as people (Chapter 7 describes plants' specific needs): a daytime range between 68 and 75 degrees, with a drop of 7 to 10 degrees at night. Even tropical plants, like African violets, suffer no harm at 62 degrees. Air-conditioning has little ill effect on healthy plants. Nor does reasonable summer heat, because the air tends to be moist. Most plants don't like sudden extreme changes of temperature, especially cold or hot drafts. If you have well-lighted areas that are consistently cool in winter, see plants for cool locations, Chapter 11.

SOME SUN
FLOWERING PLANTS

VARIEGATED
FOLIAGE PLANTS

LIGHT FOR YOUR PLANTS: When you bring home a new plant, you must decide where it is to live, and this must be determined by its light requirements. Consult Chapter 7, and place it where it will have the light it needs. A plant has to adjust to change, so give it time. If it doesn't thrive, try more or less light until you find the perfect spot. Most plants flourish in an east or west window that gets full morning or afternoon sun; many do as well in a bright north window. If a plant needs even dimmer light, place it a few—or several—feet from the window. White walls or mirrors nearby reflect the sun and increase light intensity. Increase window sill growing spaces with one of the new extendable shelves. These stack to make double-deck growing shelves.

SEMISUNNY
SEASONAL
FLOWERING PLANTS

MOST FOLIAGE PLANT

Some plants flourish in the interior of rooms if some sunlight falls on them during the day. Chapter 11 lists plants successful in dim light.

Be wary of summer light. Full exposure to sun, especially in a south window, may burn plants in summer that could live there in winter. An awning or a leafed-out tree or vine outdoors can act as a screen; or move the plant to the side of the window or back a few feet.

Most plants will thrive in fluorescent-light gardens, discussed in the next chapter.

SEMISHADY
FOLIAGE PLANTS
THAT ARE DARK GREEN
SEE PAGE 239

SHADY
ASPARAGUS-FERN
SEE PAGE 239

DARK CORNERS
ASPIDISTRA
SEE PAGE 240

2
Artificial Light
If You Have No Sun

Plants can't grow without light, but they don't seem to care whether it is from the sun or is man-made. Even if you have sunny windows, there may be dark corners in your home where you would like to have thriving, flowering plants. Artificial light is the answer. It can be from fluorescent tubes or incandescent bulbs, either ordinary or special plant-growth types. Setups are simple, the rewards infinite.

FLUORESCENT-LIGHT GARDENS: Fluorescent tubes provide the most efficient and least costly means of growing plants under artificial light. Fortunately, these fluorescent tubes give off very little heat and thus don't dry out the air around your plants. Even ceiling fluorescents in offices will supplement natural light and benefit plants. Certain foliage plants such as *Dracaena fragrans* and aspidistra, placed within 6 feet of the fixtures, live well with no other light, provided they are lighted the duration of the business day. A real fluorescent-light garden sets plants within a few inches of the tubes, as in the unit shown opposite, where each shelf is lighted by two 20-watt tubes. A timer that will turn the lights on and off automatically, whether or not you are at home, is a help. It also assures uniform *days* and *nights*. Most plants, such as the flowering African violets shown here, along with lipstick vine, leopard plant, philodendron, and bromeliads, do well with 15 to 16 hours of light daily, followed by 8 to 9 hours of darkness.

Timer (above) automatically switches lights on and off, for "days" of uniform duration. Fluorescent-light garden (opposite) cheers and uses an otherwise dark, wasted hallway space.

FLUORESCENT FIXTURES: Prefabricated units for growing plants under lights may be tabletop units with a reflector with two 20-watt tubes, decorative shelf gardens (page 12), or utilitarian carts like the one pictured opposite. It has three 2-by-4 foot shelves, lighted by two 40-watt fluorescent tubes in each of three reflectors. To add lights for plants in an existing bookcase, or in the space between a kitchen countertop and the wall-hung cabinets above, install fluorescent strip fixtures sold by electric-supply houses. The space between the tubes and the surface on which pots will be placed should be about 18 inches. The photograph below shows how to boost small or light-loving plants closer to the tubes. Do not let plants touch the tubes, or growth may be damaged. If a fan is used to circulate the air, a fluorescent-light garden can grow even in a closet.

BEST FLUORESCENTS FOR PLANTS: Despite contrary claims, plants seem to grow equally well under ordinary fluorescents or under special agricultural tubes. Light intensity counts more than the type of light. A good combination to use for a light garden is one Cool White tube and one Warm White tube in each fixture. Or use one Cool White tube with one of the special plant fluorescents that cast a pink glow. Experiment with various tubes in different combinations. Replace old tubes yearly. Dust all tubes monthly.

Prefabricated fluorescent-light garden (opposite) requires floor space 2 by 4 feet, and gives 24 square feet of growing space. Upside-down pots (above) boost plants closer to lights.

LIGHT GARDENING: For a list of plants recommended for use in fluorescent-light gardens, see Chapter 11. Since the "sun" shines every day in a light garden, plants remain in constant growth all year and therefore tend to need somewhat more watering and feeding. They benefit from misting, as do other house plants. Low-light foliage plants (see the list in Chapter 11) do well when placed at the ends and sides of a fluorescent-light garden, where there is less light; flowering types do best directly under the tubes. Light gardens may be operated all year, or in warm weather you can move the plants outdoors. A light garden is the perfect place to sprout seeds for your outdoor garden and a good place to nurture gift plants, such as azaleas and gloxinias (opposite).

Table lamp with two ordinary 60-watt incandescent bulbs burned 6 to 8 hours daily supplements natural light and helps two African violets and a cactus thrive.

INCANDESCENT LIGHT FOR PLANTS: Incandescent (ordinary) light bulbs do not only use electricity less efficiently than do fluorescents, but they heat and dry the atmosphere. Nevertheless, they can be useful to the indoor garden. Desk and table lamps come readily to mind. In an office, they usually burn at least 8 hours daily, and in homes, they burn 6 to 8 hours during the long, dark nights of winter, when plants are most likely to need supplementary light.

Small, low-light plants (see list, Chapter 11) adapt and grow beautifully within the circle of brightest light cast on a desk or table by a lamp that is burned 6 to 8 hours a day. Bulb wattage must be at least 100; 200 would be better. Flowering plants such as African violets will need some supplementary daylight. Pretty foliage plants such as heartleaf philodendron, pothos, small-leaved English ivy, and 'Florida Beauty' dracaena do well on lamplight alone. Low-light miniature plants that need high humidity can also be grown in this kind of illumination. Plant them in small terrariums or bell jars, which will provide the moist atmosphere necessary for many miniatures. Try miniature fern (*Polystichum tsus-simense*), miniature gloxinia (*Sinningia pusilla*), selaginella, and miniature rex begonias.

Although fluorescent fixtures sometimes include sockets for two or three incandescents, it is a waste of electricity to use these two kinds of light together.

FLOODLIGHTS: You can give large plants that live in dark corners a real boost by shining one or more floodlights on them. These are available in sizes from 75 to 300 watts, with built-in reflectors. Because of the heat generated, it is best to use these only in porcelain (ceramic) sockets. Do not confuse spotlights with floodlights; spots concentrate the light too much. The smaller the wattage of the flood, the closer it can be placed to the foliage without burning it. The 75-watt size may be placed in a range of 1 to 2 feet from sturdy foliage plants. Set at twice this distance for fragile flowers like the pink azalea and red begonia shown here. Place larger floods lighting tree-size plants about 3 feet from the leaves. Fixtures for floodlights can be ceiling- or wall-mounted individual units, part of a ceiling track-lighting system, or attached to the top of an adjustable photographer's light stand. Although up lighting (from the floor) is dramatic, plants do better if light comes from above or the side, so that it strikes surfaces of the leaves. For a large tree such as a weeping fig, a palm, or a tall, columnar cactus, two floods may be needed, one directly over the plant and one to the side. Rotate the plant a quarter turn weekly, so that all sides receive light. How long a flood should burn each day depends on whether it is the sole source of light (if so, burn 14 to 16 hours daily) or supplements the natural light (burn 6 to 8 hours daily). Floodlighted plants (except cacti) need daily misting to counteract the light's drying effect.

Incandescent floodlight attached to top of mirrored room divider in entryway benefits growth and dramatizes beauty of plants. Pink azalea (top) and Rieger begonia (bottom) are in silver pedestal.

3
Soils and Food for Your Plants

There's a key to the kind of house plant you admire most—big, lush-leaved beauties shining with health and bright with color. Soil is this key. The right soil does more than just hold the plant up. It controls the availability of the water and food you give the plant and even influences the amount of humidity in the air around the pot. There is nothing mysterious, however, about soils used for potting house plants. Their general and specific qualities are described below.

POTTING SOILS: Plants grow beautifully in soil that is loose enough to let roots develop freely, retains nutrients and water, and is in the right pH balance. To do all this, it must contain material that drains well and stays fluffy, so roots can develop (sand, perlite, for instance); material that acts as a sponge to retain water (humus and vermiculite); organic matter that includes nutrients and trace minerals. Cacti, foliage and flowering plants, and terrarium plants need these materials in different percentages; good potting soils, whether commercial or homemade, supply these trace minerals and nutrients.

ALL-PURPOSE SOIL: All-purpose potting soil sold commercially is a fairly evenly balanced mixture of the elements described above, and it includes nutrients. It meets the needs of most house plants and is the soil used for potting most foliage as well as many flowering plants.

CACTUS SOIL: Nature has developed plants suited to their environment. Cacti and other succulents evolved in areas where little rain falls and the sandy soils don't retain water well. These plants do need water, but their systems compensate for their arid environment. Thick leaves and stems store water, and shallow feeder roots take instant advantage of every drop that falls. In soils that hold water (humusy potting soils), cacti may soak up too much moisture. They flourish in soils that contain lots of sand or other drainage material, such as perlite.

To pot and make potting soils: back row, marble chips, sand, vermiculite; third row, charcoal, perlite, pebbles; second row, peat moss and humus soil. Two front rows include commercial all-purpose potting soil, soil for blooming plants, for cacti and succulents, and for terrariums and bottle gardens.

TERRARIUM SOILS: Terrariums, bottle gardens, and other closed containers are used to grow plants that need lots of moisture in air and soil. Soils for terrarium plants must hold water well, so these have a high percentage of materials that act as sponges — humus and vermiculite. They have sand or perlite, for drainage, and a smaller percentage of earth than does all-purpose soil.

AFRICAN-VIOLET/BLOOMING SOIL: The African-violet, is the most popular plant grown for flowering, so soil for flowering and fruiting plants has come to be called African-violet soil. It contains enough humus to keep the soil evenly moist, and it is slightly acid, to encourage best growth from azalea, gardenia, citrus, and other plants.

The ball test is used to determine the composition of potting soil. Pack a handful of damp soil as though you were making a snowball.

PASTEURIZING: Making your own potting mixtures is a happy, paying proposition only if you have work space, storage room for supplies, and the patience to pasteurize the soil. Commercial potting soils are well-balanced, inexpensive; some contain plant food for about 6 weeks; and all are pasteurized before you buy them. If you begin with garden soil as a base for a homemade mixture, be aware that it probably contains organisms, in particular nematodes, harmful to plants. Don't be tempted into skipping pasteurizing soil to be used for African violets. They are very susceptible to nematodes. And be sure to pasteurize soils for all seedlings, which are susceptible to damping-off (see page 49).

The only practical way for the homeowner to pasteurize soil is in an oven or in a barbecue that has a hood and a temperature gauge. The gauge is important. Heats higher than 180 degrees can kill everything beneficial in the soil. Heat the oven to 180 degrees; place the soil in a large kettle; add 1 cup of water for each 4 quarts of soil; bake 45 minutes. Turn the soil onto some clean newspaper, and let it aerate for 24 hours before using it.

It's really much easier to begin with pasteurized products. Other safe garden elements offered in packages include charcoal chips to keep wet terrarium soils pure and fresh-smelling, marble chips and pebbles for bottom drainage of containers, sand and perlite for soil drainage, humus and vermiculite to hold water.

20

Ball test shows the effect of packing on two types of soil. All-purpose soil will ball when packed; but sandy soil will crumble, won't form a ball.

USING GARDEN SOILS: At times garden soils are sandy, humusy, or heavy with clay. Use the snowball test to determine which yours is. Packed as pictured, well-balanced soil will form into a ball that crumbles easily under pressure, whereas sandy soil won't ball, and clayey soil will ball so firmly it won't crumble. To create a balanced loam, add both sand and humus to clay soils, and add humus to sandy soils. Keep adding the missing elements until you have a soil that balls properly and crumbles easily. If you are beginning a potting recipe with a commercial mixture, it already is in good balance, and it is likely that nothing need be added.

Recipe for all-purpose mix: Combine equal parts soil, sand (or perlite), and peat moss. Most foliage plants will grow in this; also geraniums.

Recipe for cactus mix: Combine 1 part soil, 1 part peat moss, and 2 parts sand (or perlite).

Recipe for African-violet/blooming mix: Combine equal parts soil, sand (or perlite), well-rotted leaf mold (or vermiculite), and acid peat moss.

Recipe for terrarium/bottle-garden mix: Combine equal parts soil, sand (or perlite), vermiculite, sphagnum peat moss, and charcoal chips.

Potting air plants: See Bromeliads, page 77; Orchid, page 148.

Renewing soil: To keep plants growing and blooming, potting soils need periodic renewal. Plants use up soil nutrients (foods); water compacts the soil and drains nutrients; and in time the soil becomes too acid. Acid soil locks up plant foods so plants can't absorb it and makes feeding almost useless. Even acid-loving plants languish in stale soil. Repot small plants often; add fresh soil to large plants yearly. (Repotting and top-dressing information is given on pages 41 and 43.)

You can repot at any season. The best time to repot is in spring before growth begins. At other seasons, repotting may check growth briefly, but that moment of quiet is followed by a burst of activity.

Hints: Chapter 7 notes some plants that do best when pot bound, when roots have outgrown the pot. Remove these from their pots; replenish soil; repot in the same container. Some plants hate transplanting: If possible, top-dress them instead of repotting. When repotting, the rule for container size is one size larger.

FEEDING: There are two basic types of house plant food on the market: One is used for flowering fruiting plants and the other, called all-purpose, is used for all other plants. Both the blooming type and the all-purpose are sold in preparations that can be used every time you water or at periodic intervals. Both are excellent. The every-time-you-water-(continuous) food will give slightly better results. Which you choose should depend on your temperament: If you don't want to bother keeping track of when you last fed the plants, use an every-time plant food. If it's easy for you to remember when the next feeding is due, use one of the compositions intended for periodic feeding.

Most plants need additional food in periods of major growth and feeding every three or four weeks in periods when growth is slow. It is easy to understand that plants would respond best to heavier feeding during the time of maximum growth.

Plant food for blooming plants is often packaged in purple and is called African-violet food. African violets have been the most grown of flowering indoor plants, so the plant food that best promotes their blooming has come to be identified with the food to be used for flowering and fruiting plants. Plant foods for blooming plants (1-1-1 or 10-10-10) generally include equal quantities of the three nutrients most needed: Nitrogen (N), Phosphates (P), and Potash (K). The photographs opposite illustrate the purpose of each. Fed this balanced mixture, blooming plants grow big flowers in colors far more brilliant than those of underfed plants. The nitrogen encourages rich-green leaves. The phosphates help a good root system to develop and promote luxuriant flowering. The potash helps promote bloom, gives strength to stems, and is vital in making plants resistant to diseases.

All-purpose plant food for foliage and other indoor plants is packaged in three different compositions. For every-time use, it generally provides twice as much phosphate as nitrogen or potash, 1-2-1.

All-purpose plant foods for periodic use are balanced—combinations of 5-10-5 or 7-6-19. The 7-6-19 composition is meant to promote foliage growth in particular and is high in potash, to ward off disease and to aid in flowering. The smaller quantity of phosphates, which promote root growth primarily, reflects the fact that many house plants don't require big root systems. The 5-10-5 mixture is a balanced composition high in phosphates. Choose the 5-10-5 food for young plants, where lots of root growth is desirable. For older plants, use a 7-6-19 composition to encourage good health and plentiful foliage. For a flowering plant, change when budding is due to a flowering-type plant food.

A shortage of nitrogen shows in stunted growth and yellow leaves. Too much nitrogen shows in an overabundance of foliage growth, no flowers, and can leave plants weakened and susceptible to diseases. Symptoms of shortage of phosphates are stunted plants, foliage too dark a green, and leaf stems with a purple cast when they should be green. Shortages of potash show in dwarfed plants and leaves that yellow and die at the tips and the edges.

Digging In

All-purpose plant food ingredients are always listed in the same order. In 5-10-5, for instance, content is always:

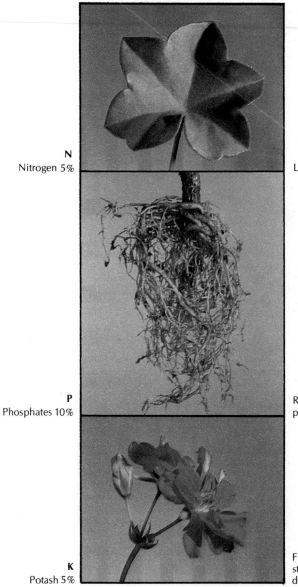

N
Nitrogen 5%

Leaf production

P
Phosphates 10%

Root and flower production

K
Potash 5%

Flower production, strength in stems, disease resistance

What Went Wrong?

Even though you follow the general and specific care guidelines in this handbook, insects may attack. Attend to them in time. Inspect each plant regularly, so that you will catch the earliest signs of trouble. A safe, easy way to discourage insects is to spray periodically with aerosol insect spray. Or bathe plants (as shown in the photograph opposite) every 2 to 4 weeks in tepid water to which a little mild soap has been added; rinse with clean water.

RED SPIDER MITE: This tiny mite, one of the worst of indoor-plant pests, is not readily seen with the naked eye. Under a 10-power microscope, you would discover the mite is reddish. A major problem in coping with red spider mite is that it infests ornamental trees, shrubs, and flowers outdoors, as well as agricultural crops, so it's always lurking somewhere nearby, just waiting for the right conditions to attack. And the right conditions are air —hot, cool, or in between—that is stale and dry. Early signs of mite attack are leaves paler than usual, with a white or graying flecking of the surface. In later stages, you will notice fine spider webs. When you first see these signs, shower the plant well, especially undersides of leaves, with tepid water. Repeat every day. Meanwhile, try to improve the atmosphere in your garden. Except for a few of the terrarium plants, most kinds need fresh air that circulates freely. If constant showering, misting, and increased fresh air do not stop red spider, spray with a miticide (available where garden supplies are sold); follow directions on the container.

Shiny green leaves of English ivy are healthy; yellow, gray, and brown ones show damage caused by red spider mites.

APHIDS: These soft-bodied insects are about ⅛ inch long, are usually green, and cluster on tender new growth, flower buds included, especially of chrysanthemums, anemones, cinerarias, and tulips; to wash off the insects, shower the plants, in sink or tub, every few days. If the aphids persist, treat them with a pesticide (see page 28).

CYCLAMEN MITE: Though these tiny mites are too small to be seen, the damage they cause to African-violets and columnea is readily detected. The symptom is malformed new growth. Leaf and flower stems thicken and curl or twist unnaturally. In African-violets, new leaves may be unusually hairy; columnea stems form a scaly brown surface. Treat these pests with miticide (page 28). Use only pasteurized soil for potting these plants.

MEALYBUG: These have grayish-white, oblong bodies about 3/16 inch long. Masses of cottony white eggs are usually found on the underside of leaves and in crevices between leaves and stems. Coleus is especially susceptible; mealybugs are most difficult to control on plants like amaryllis and palm because they burrow between leaves. To control, touch each insect with a cotton swab dipped in rubbing alcohol. Weekly washing with tepid, sudsy water helps, but a pesticide (page 28) may be required.

SCALE: These have oblong bodies about 3/16 inch long, usually tan or brown. They may be found on stems and leaves, both upper and lower surfaces. Cane-stemmed and angelwing begonias, birds-nest ferns, ficus, and palms are most susceptible. If there are a few scale insects, remove each either with your fingernail or with the tip of a sharp knife. Otherwise, treat with a pesticide (page 28). Citrus scale is similar in size, but it is grayish-white and very hard shelled. Treat these insects as described here.

THRIPS: These tiny black insects are like minute snips of thread. Indoors they favor gloxinias; outdoors, gladiolus. They eat away leaf and flower tissue, leaving only a thin, almost transparent, grayish spot. Frequent spraying with tepid water helps, but a pesticide may be needed to get rid of them. (page 28).

WHITEFLY: You can tell you have them because they fly up like animated flecks of ash when you disturb a plant. Common pests of the outdoor garden, they migrate indoors on house plants that have summered out, or on clothing. Specially susceptible are fuchsia, lantana, basil, and tomato leaves. They are tricky to dispose of because the minute you pick up the plant, they abandon it. To control, quickly plop a plastic bag over the infested plant, take it outdoors, and wash it well; repeat this procedure every few days until the whiteflies have disappeared. Or use a pesticide (page 28).

Upper left: Mature mealybugs gather on stems, as seen on this coffee plant, and under leaves. Inspect susceptible plants often. Upper right: Young mealybugs and eggs will soon kill this aralia leaf. Wash away with mild soap and water; rinse with clean water. Repeat at 5-day intervals until bugs are gone. Lower left: Whiteflies favor tomato (shown), fuchsia, lantana, and basil; for control, see page 26. Lower right: Aphids cluster on new browallia growth. Rinse off with water; check plant daily.

Left: Three ways to control insects on house plants. Top: Wash all leaf and stem surfaces in tepid water with a little mild soap (not detergent); rinse with clean water. Center: If insects persist on plant small enough to handle as shown, dip in pesticide solution; wear rubber gloves. Bottom: Aerosol pesticides are easiest to use. Follow label directions.

CONTROLLING INSECTS: The photographs on this page show the three most popular ways of controlling insect pests on house plants. Washing all exposed plant parts in tepid water to which a little mild soap has been added is safe and surprisingly effective; rinse off the soap with clean water. Repeat every 4 or 5 days until the insects are gone. If they persist, dipping the plant in, or spraying it with a pesticide may be necessary. Read the label carefully before you buy a pesticide and before you use it. Pesticides containing synthetic pyrethrins are especially effective. Malathion may be needed for a bad case of mealybugs. For red spider mite, you will have to use a miticide, so designated on the label. Use pesticide aerosols only in a well-ventilated room. Keep the nozzle about 12 inches from the plant; be sure to mist all surfaces. To prepare a pesticide dip, mix liquid or powdered concentrate (malathion, for example, available from nursery or garden center) with water according to the container directions. Wear waterproof rubber gloves. Some growers find that pest strips hung to discourage household flies also control most house-plant pests. Follow package directions and renew as directed.

LIGHT, LACK OF: Plants in need of more light display various symptoms, but generally speaking, they appear spindly—gardeners sometimes refer to such plants as leggy, meaning that there is too much space along the stems between leaves. Sun-loving plants like geraniums almost always grow spindly indoors in winter, especially if they are too warm. African violets grow long, weak leaf stems that reach in the direction of the strongest light available. There will be few flowers on such plants. Ficus trees such as weeping fig and rubber tree will drop quantities of older leaves if they are moved from ample to poor light. Within reason, however, they will adapt. Relatively low-light plants, such as

Light-starved scented rose geranium (right) is spindly or leggy in comparison with healthy plant (left) grown in ample sunlight.

spathiphyllum, will exist as long as a year in a dark corner; then they will go into rapid decline if they are not moved to better light. If you cannot give light-starved plants more sun, the answer is artificial light, either alone or as a supplement to poor natural light. For large plants, use floodlights overhead or to the side. Fluorescents may be used for plants 12 inches tall or less. For information on the various uses of artificial light, see Chapter 2.

African violet placed on the sill of a sunny south or west window in hot summer weather will burn as this one has. Trim off damaged growth; reduce light.

LIGHT, TOO MUCH: The sunburned African violet pictured at the left shows damage typical when too much sun shines directly on the leaves. This occurs most often when plants are within a few inches of a sunny south or west window, especially in hot summer weather. Excess sun also sometimes bleaches the entire plant to a sickly or yellowish green—a reaction typical of dracaena and Chinese evergreen. Piggyback plant given too much light grows unnaturally compact and turns a sickly yellowish-green. Move such plants to less light.

Asparagus-fern turns yellow if soil dries out severely or in air that is hot, dry, and stale. Trim off dead stems.

Brown, dead patches in piggyback leaves result from dry soil, too much direct sun, or air that is hot, dry, and stale.

White crust on this pot is caused by natural mineral salts. Remove by scrubbing pot with a stiff brush; rinse with clean water.

ENVIRONMENTAL PROBLEMS: Several major problems are the result of house plants' growing in air that is too hot and too dry and does not circulate freely. Temperature and humidity are discussed in Chapter 1 (pages 7 and 11). If your plants show dead leaf tips and edges and withered flower buds, it will pay to evaluate the indoor climate. Although a few house plants require coolness in winter (see list in Chapter 11), most will tolerate considerable heat if it is combined with moist, fresh air that circulates freely. Meeting this requirement is easier said than done, especially in an apartment where the heat cannot be controlled. In many apartments that are centrally heated in winter and cooled in summer, the same stale air is continually recirculated, heated or cooled in the process, but not freshened. For best growth, plants need some fresh air, but tropicals (many house plants are tropicals) suffer when really cold air blows on them in winter. It is better to open a door or window in another room, so the fresh air warms to room temperature before it reaches the plants. This is less difficult to do in a private dwelling, where entry doors open to the outdoors and fresh air is admitted in the daily comings and goings. In most apartments, access doors open to a hallway, where the air is likely to be even more stale than that within. The more plants you grow, the more moisture will be given off by moist soil. If small plants are grouped on trays of wet pebbles, the humidity will be increased. However, fresh circulating air is essential. In small rooms or where artificial light is used for growing plants, a small circulating fan may be needed.

Moss growing on soil surface of ginger plant indicates overwatered, poorly drained soil that has become too acid.

DISEASES AND POT PROBLEMS: When a house plant fails to grow well, it is natural to suspect it may have a disease. Actually, few diseases attack. The problem most often lies with insects or an unfriendly environment. Such an environment is usually directly or indirectly responsible for diseased plants. Powdery mildew attacks in air that is humid, warm in the daytime, cool at night, and circulates poorly. To eliminate the mildew, increase air circulation, and spray or dust the infected plant with a fungicide, such as horticultural dusting sulfur. Rots of various kinds usually occur when soil drains poorly and the plant also is subject to careless watering habits. For example, if you wait to water a plant until it has wilted severely, and you let this happen again and again, eventually the root system will disintegrate until it can no longer absorb moisture. Rotted roots and stems result; but you may be able to salvage healthy tip growth for cuttings, to perpetuate the plant. Petiole rot of African violets occurs when leaf stems rest on a moist pot rim incrusted with plant-food salts. To prevent this, keep pot rims clean. African violets fed and watered from below instead of from the top, or allowed to wilt from dryness between waterings, are liable to petiole rot. White incrustation on the outside walls of clay pots (photograph at right, opposite) is a build-up of mineral salts from the soil and from excess feeding. Remove by scrubbing pot wall with a stiff brush; then rinse with clean water. Green moss on surface soil indicates overwatered and poorly drained soil that has become too acid. Repot plant in fresh, well-drained soil in a container with good drainage.

The unsightly spots on this rex-begonia leaf are caused by powdery mildew, a disease. Spray with fungicide to control.

African-violet leaf stems show petiole rot, the result of resting on a constantly damp, rough surface such as clay-pot rim.

HEALTH GROOMING:

An easy way to improve the health of your plants is to remove all the yellowed or dead leaves, withered flowers, and any rotting stems. A plant that appears to be unhealthy often can be put into show condition with simple grooming tricks. Follow all the grooming by a sponge bath or shower. It pays to form the habit of grooming your plants frequently. It's a pleasant, soothing activity; more important, it places you in one-to-one contact with each plant, so you can tell if it needs special attention.

This scented geranium is healthy, but old brown leaves should be removed; otherwise, they may harbor both insects and disease.

Stems of this Swedish-ivy have grown old and woody. To renew, root stocky tip cuttings of healthy growth; discard old plant.

OLD AGE AND HOUSE PLANTS: There are times when the only thing to do about a failing plant is to take healthy tip cuttings and discard the old plant as soon as the cuttings have rooted and begun healthy growth. This may sound heartless, but it is not. It is a shame to give growing space to a plant that is past its prime and struggling to barely survive. This happens often with such hanging-basket plants as Swedish-ivy (see photograph at right, above), wandering Jew, and piggyback. Swedish-ivy stems grow hard, brittle, and woody with age until they seem no longer able to produce healthy, vigorous leaf and new stem growth. With Swedish-ivy, it is a simple matter to take tip cuttings, root them, and plant several in a hanging basket. Grow them alongside the old plant until the cuttings have produced a mass of foliage big enough to fill the corner. Treat wandering Jew the same way. Piggyback is short-lived by nature; it's best always to have some young ones coming along to replace those that grow past their prime. Coleus also is prettiest while plants are young. When they are a year old, root tip cuttings in water—they root in a week or two—and these will become colorful, vigorous young plants. Replace wax begonias every year, too. Make tip cuttings of stocky new growth that sprouts from the base of the plants. The best geranium and poinsettia plants also are started annually from tip cuttings. To keep older plants going, cut old, woody stems back to 6 or 8 inches; this promotes sturdy growth. Replace tall-growing plants that have lost lower leaves (dumbcane and zebra plant, for example) by rooting cuttings for new plants.

WATERING PROBLEMS: Every time you let the soil of a potted plant dry out severely, the plant suffers a certain amount of stress. The outward signs vary, depending on the individual plant's physical make-up. Since, by their very nature, cacti and other succulents are able to store moisture, they are slow to show signs of stress from underwatering. Some plants wilt when dry (spider plant, for example), but stress signs—yellowed, dying leaf tips and edges—may not show up for several days or weeks. Most plants, however, react almost immediately when the soil is allowed to become completely dry between waterings. Older leaves and flowers turn yellow and die, sometimes showering the surface beneath with withered leaves and petals (see poinsettia photograph below, center). Overwatering, like underwatering, causes some plants to immediately drop older leaves and flower buds, while other plants show no signs of stress for several weeks or months. Overwatering also causes leaf tips and edges to die back. You must judge which caused your particular problem by checking the soil moisture against the information given for the plant in Chapter 7. In practice, large plants in small pots are likely to be underwatered, and small plants in large pots are likely to be overwatered.

CHANGE OF ENVIRONMENT: Some plants are sensitive to being moved from one environment to another, especially if they love fresh air. The geranium below, right, was perfectly healthy when it was wrapped for mailing. However, lack of air circulation and constant darkness for several days have caused most of the leaves to turn yellow. They will quickly fall from the plant; but with care, it will recover.

Every time spider plant dries out severely, about ½ inch of the leaf tip will die back.

If flowering poinsettia wilts from dry soil, most of the older leaves will turn yellow and fall off.

Yellowed leaves on young geranium are the result of plant's being wrapped and in the mail for several days.

AFRICAN-VIOLET PROBLEMS: The African violet is one of the best of all flowering house plants. It will be beautiful all year round only if you pay attention to its little peculiarities. Water African violets *only* with water at room temperature. In winter, cold water taken directly from the faucet and spilled on the leaves or applied to the soil will cause ugly yellow or white circles and spots to form on the foliage (photograph below, left). If the plants are in direct sunlight at the time of watering, drops of water (even at room temperature) spilled on the leaves may cause similar spotting. This is one reason some growers prefer to water African violets only from the bottom (see Chapter 1, page 10, for bottom-watering photograph). However, if you water them from the bottom, water them from the top every fourth time, so that excess plant-food salts will be washed down and out of the pot. Because African-violet foliage is so sensitive to water, plants are best kept indoors all year; if you wish to move them outdoors in warm weather, place them on a porch or in some other area where they will be protected from rainstorms. Another problem with these plants has to do with their habit —more pronounced in some varieties than in others — of producing many offsets. This may be fine if you want to propagate one plant into many in a hurry, but if your primary goal is to have each plant covered with flowers, it is best to remove an offset as soon as it begins to grow at the base of a mature leaf. At first, the tiny leaves may appear to be flower buds; but with experience you will learn to tell which is which. If the new growth is the start of an offset, remove it (African-violet specialists call it a sucker) with the tip of a sharp knife. Larger offsets (photograph below, right) may be cut off with a knife, saved and rooted if you wish. African-violet stems (see photograph) sometimes grow tall and bare; if this happens, unpot, work old soil away from the top, and repot in fresh soil. Set the plant low enough in the new soil to cover the bare stem.

Cold water dropped on African-violet leaves or used to moisten soil causes ugly spots to form.

Remove African-violet offsets, called suckers, when small, to keep the parent plant healthy and blooming.

34

Coleus is prized for its colorful foliage; pinching off flower buds encourages leaf growth.

RESTING PLANTS: Sometimes a plant with a lackluster appearance needs a rest, described usually as a period of dormancy. This need is more pronounced in some plants than in others: when it is important to success with the plant, a rest period is noted in the care section for each plant in Chapters 7 or 8. Kinds with tuberous roots—amaryllis and gloxinias, for example—are rested by withholding water (and all plant food) until the leaves wither and die down. This is called drying off. They are then set away to rest for about 8 weeks in a dark place such as a closet. Check the soil from time to time; keep it barely moist. If it dries out completely, tubers may shrivel and die. After the rest period, unpot the plant, remove old soil, and repot (in the same container) in fresh soil. Tropical foliage plants in natural light grow less rapidly in the short days of late fall and winter. This is especially true during long periods of cloudy weather or in a room where temperatures remain generally below 70 degrees. If these conditions exist, water less (but don't let the soil become bone-dry) and feed about half as much as you would normally. When sunnier, longer days arrive at the end of winter, vigorous new top growth will signal the need for more water and for plant food. Any plant that flowers heavily for several weeks or months, African violets included, will perform best if given a rest for a month or two. During this time, withhold food and water slightly less—but not so little as to wilt the foliage. If the plant flowers on new growth—as do wax begonia, geranium, flowering maple, and shrimp plant—the rest period is a good time to prune back gangly or too large stems. At the end of a rest period, unpot the plant, remove some of the old soil, and repot in fresh soil. Keep the soil nicely moist, but take care not to saturate it until new growth is obvious; at that time, you can resume normal feeding and watering.

Hints for healthy plants: To grow the handsomest house plants and enjoy them the most, try to limit your collection to a size you will be able to care for well without neglecting any of the plants. Then you will be less likely to over- or underwater, to let insect pests or disease go unnoticed, or to fail to keep leaves free of dust. You'll also have time to pick off dead leaves and flowers and to pinch out tip growth of plants that grow rapidly—such as the coleus pictured above. Coleus in particular needs frequent pinching to encourage branching and prevent flowering, which, if permitted, channels strength to insignificant flowers instead of to beautiful leaves.

35

Digging In

Once you understand what makes house plants grow or not grow, which we have discussed in earlier chapters, you are ready to dig in. The real fun begins as you shop for plants, carry them home, and see how much life they contribute to the rooms where you live. To keep your plants in top form, follow guidelines in this chapter for grooming, bathing and showering, containers, repotting, top-dressing, pruning—and more.

HOW TO BUY A PLANT: Hundreds of different house plants are available from such local sources as nurseries, garden centers, florists, plant shops, supermarkets, and variety stores. If you can't find what you want locally, write for the catalogs of mail-order specialists. Their selections are virtually unlimited; orders are processed and shipped immediately except during weather that would be too cold for the plants' safety. When you shop for plants locally, watch for

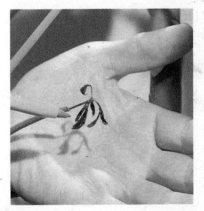

these good and bad signs: *Bad:* Plants displayed on the sidewalk in front of a store when temperatures are below 55 degrees. *Good:* Fresh green tip growth; older leaves shiny and clean. *Bad:* Dry soil and wilted leaves. *Good:* Some unopened buds on flowering-type plants. *Bad:* Mealybugs, red spider mites, or other insects on leaves and stems. *Good:* Clean pots with soft, nicely moist surface soil. *Bad:* Stems that wobble loosely in the pot. The photograph opposite illustrates an important point: At the same price, which of the Swedish-ivies is the better buy? Our choice is the smaller, younger plant; it will grow bigger and better. The other one is already past its prime; decline is inevitable.

Blackened tips of schefflera (above) show it has been badly treated—over- or underwatered, chilled or overheated. Plants you buy should have firm, green new leaves. To learn which Swedish-ivy, opposite, is the better to buy, see text.

This spathiphyllum has healthy, green new growth; few leaves have dead tips. Grooming and a shower will make it look like an expensive florist plant.

Contrast spathiphyllum leaf on left after shower with dusty leaf on right. Cleaning the foliage is one of the best ways to keep plants healthy.

GROOMING: To look their best, plants need grooming, just as we do. One of the benefits of growing house plants is the soothing, quiet time spent in caring for them. It is therapeutic, a natural tranquilizer. The best time for grooming your plants is when you can do it at your leisure. If you have plants in your kitchen or laundry room, groom them while you wait for the teakettle to boil or the machine to finish its cycle. Grooming plants in living areas is all the more enjoyable if you work to the accompaniment of your favorite recordings. After all, growing and caring for plants is a pleasure; if the care ceases to be enjoyable, you probably have too many plants. If you do your grooming at night, give yourself good light in which to work; otherwise, you might cut off a flower bud instead of a dead leaf. Although some dead leaves and flowers fall naturally or at the slightest touch of your fingers, others need to be clipped off with a pair of sharp scissors. If dead growth is twiggy or woody, use a pair of pruning shears (see page 45). Heavy kitchen shears are useful when the time comes to remove the tough, fibrous base of a yellowed or dead palm frond. Trimming out dead fronds from a fern, especially one with many stems, is tricky; unless you work carefully in good light, it is hard to tell which stems are dead (cut off near the soil) and which should be let alone. To remove yellowed, old leaves from around an African violet, use the blade of a sharp knife—taking care to cut only the stem of the leaf you wish to remove; cut through it as close to the main stem as possible. After an amaryllis flower has wilted, but before a seed pod has begun to form, cut through the bulb, taking care not to cut into the leaves. If several flowers are growing on a stem and some of them wither before others, as often happens with African-violet plants, the new blooms will look considerably better if the old ones are clipped. Prompt removal of dead flowers and leaves not only improves the appearance of plants, but helps ward off disease attacks. If less than half of a leaf is yellowed or dead, at the tip or along the edges use sharp scissors to trim away only the discolored part, plus enough of the green to shape the leaf to its natural form. This tends to halt the dieback and also improves the appearance of your plant.

The same spathiphyllum after grooming and showering might command twice the original price. Its plain pot and saucer are hidden by a basket cachepot.

BATHING AND SHOWERING: House plants grow and look better if they are bathed and showered often enough to keep leaves free of dust and grime. With small plants, this is easy; carry them to the kitchen sink, and rinse the leaves above and below, as well as the stems, with water at room temperature or slightly warmer. Set aside to drain until dripping stops. African violets bathed in this manner should not be placed in direct sun until the foliage is completely dry. Don't overlook cacti at bath time; they collect dust and grime just as other plants do—but take care not to saturate the soil. Plants too large for a kitchen sink may be bathed in a utility sink or bathtub or in the shower. If the water pressure is strong, regulate it, so that tender growth won't be damaged. Plants too large to move may be given a sponge bath, following this procedure: Soak and wring out a piece of clean, soft, cotton cloth or paper toweling. Hold part of the cloth or paper in one hand, part in the other, and sandwich leaves between, so that both upper and lower surfaces are cleaned. Large-leaved plants, such as rubber trees and palms, are fairly simple to clean in this manner. A tree-size plant with many small leaves, such as weeping fig, is tedious to clean; frequent feather-dusting will help. Leathery, hard-faced leaves may be given a coating of commercially prepared leaf luster. Do not use milk or cooking oil to shine leaves.

Pot drainage varies. In clay pot (left) cover with chip of broken pot placed curved side up. Use a layer of pebbles (clear pot) for plastic pot with smaller hole. This is called crocking.

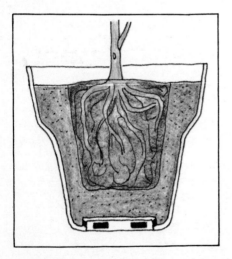

Potting a plant: Newer pots need no crocking because drain holes are smaller and placed around the edges of the pots. Add a layer of soil; position rootball so plant grows at same level as before. Add soil to top; firm with fingers; leave space of ½ inch to 1 inch for watering small pots; as much as 3 inches in giant pots.

DRAINAGE AND CONTAINERS:

For plants that require moisture holding soils — African-violet and terrarium soils—choose containers of plastic, glass or metal. Drainage must be very good, because no moisture will escape from sides. For plants best dryish or susceptible to overwatering, choose porous clay pots. Air in soil is vital. As air circulates from bottom to top, it can do this best when drainage holes are in pot sides, just above pot bottoms. A layer of gravel in the bottoms is not essential for pots under 3 inches. Use pebbles or marble chips to prevent the soil's running through drainage holes. A layer of pebbles or marble chips in bottoms of larger pots helps to improve air circulation; it is a must for containers without drainage holes. Even if plants are never overwatered, without this layer, soil may lack the air plants need. For small pots, use ½ inch of pebbles; for large pots, up to 3 inches of marble chips. For pots without drainage holes, double drainage material, and add a layer of charcoal chips to keep soil fresh. These layers are musts for terrariums and bottle gardens. Pot saucers hold excess water. Cachepots, to serve as saucers and hide tops of plain pots, must be large enough to let the air circulate around the plants.

40

POTTING AND REPOTTING: Getting your hands into the soil as you pot or repot is satisfying when you are a gardener at heart. Newly repotted plants usually spurt into vigorous growth after a brief period of readjustment. Spring and early summer are excellent times for repotting most plants. However, repot in a container one size larger when growth is active and roots are cramped, or growth will slow or stop. Plants that seem to need repotting but are "sulking" often burst into new life when repotted with fresh soil. Repot in original container.

To find out if roots are pot bound, unpot the plant and have a look. For small plants, the kitchen sink is a good place to do this if you plug the drain. When unpotting large plants, work on several thicknesses of newspaper. A few hours before repotting, moisten the plant's soil—lightly, because mud isn't easy to handle. To unpot, first loosen the root ball. Tap the edge of the pot sharply in two or three places against the edge of the sink. Work your fingers around the stems, palm facing the soil, and flip the plant; it should slide into your hand. If it doesn't, rap pot a few more times on the sink, and try again. If this fails, slide a sharp knife around the inside of the container, just as you loosen a baked cake. Fill the pot with drainage material and soil, and plant as in the lower photograph opposite.

These rex begonias grow in a glass bowl without a drainage hole. Layer of gravel with charcoal chips helps keep soil fresh and allows air to reach the roots.

This calathea has filled its pot with stems, a sure sign that the roots are also cramped for space.

By contrast, this miniature spider plant still has room to expand. To make sure, remove pot, check roots.

If the roots of the unpotted plant form a solid network and the larger ones coil around and around the soil, repotting is in order. If the soil crumbles away from the roots of its own accord, you do not need a larger pot size: Repot in the original container, using fresh soil. If the plant needs a larger pot, select one a size larger than the pot it was growing in. (Measure the diameter across the pot top.) When in doubt, play it by eye. If plant and pot you have selected look well balanced, the pot is probably the right size. By rule of thumb, the diameter of the pot should be equal to about ⅓ the height of the upright plant, or ¼ the width of a plant that spreads horizontally. Thus a 9-inch begonia would need a 3- or 4-inch pot.

To encourage new root growth, use a sharp knife to make a few slashes around the old root ball. At the same time, remove the old soil and any dead or damaged roots.

Pots under 5 inches in diameter do not require a layer of drainage material in the bottom. If the pots are larger, add a half-

The same calathea removed from its pot. Roots so thickly bind the soil that it stands alone, shaped like the pot.

Before repotting in a pot one size larger, remove old soil to release roots; if soil is hard, wash some off.

Position plant in new pot at same level it grew before. Using hands, work in fresh soil all around.

After repotting the plant, groom it by trimming dead leaf tips and brown edges. Shape leaves naturally.

Finally, water the soil well, and mist the leaves, to clean them and to help relieve transplant shock.

inch layer of broken clay pieces, or pebbles, or marble chips. Put in enough potting soil (a scoop helps) so the stem of the plant will be positioned at about the same height above the soil as it was growing before. Hold the plant in position in the pot with one hand while you add soil with the other. Gently but firmly work the soil around the roots. Continue to add soil until the pot is just about filled. Then press down the soil all over its surface with your fingers to remove air pockets left around the roots. To make watering easy, leave ½ to 1 inch of space between the soil surface and the top of the pot. After repotting, water the soil well, and mist the leaves. Use sharp scissors to trim away browned and dead stems and tips. Let the plant rest a few days in semilight to recover.

TOP-DRESSING: Large plants growing in heavy pots are difficult to repot. Top-dressing is an easy alternative. Use your fingers to remove the top 2 to 3 inches of soil; replace this with fresh potting soil. You can top-dress like this annually for 2 or 3 years before repotting is necessary.

To top-dress large plant, remove 2 or 3 inches of old soil; replace with fresh.

PINCHING: Pruning done with your fingers is called pinching. Coleus (left), Swedish-ivy, and wandering Jew are good plants to practice on, because they almost always need lots of pinching. Pinch the growing tips just in front of a node on the stem or in front of one of a pair of leaves. Two new branches will form here, and when they grow a little, their tips can be pinched out. Soon you will see one stem become two, four, and so on. Pinching often develops a bushy, compact plant. It works only on plants that have leaf buds all along the stems; removing the tip of a fern or palm frond only spoils its appearance. Pinching is especially important for growing full, not stringy, hanging-basket plants such as Swedish-ivy and wandering Jew.

Pinching out tip growth encourages bushy, compact, well-branched growth. Here, bloom tip of coleus is being pinched.

STANDARDS AND TOPIARY FORMS: When house plants that normally grow as bushes are trained to grow as small trees, they are called standards or topiaries. Tree-form roses cultivated in outdoor gardens are the most popular standards, but their development involves complicated grafting techniques. House-plant standards are much easier. Kinds you can train this way include avocado, geranium, fuchsia, rouge berry, lantana, flowering maple, coleus, and sometimes English ivy. Here is the procedure: Select a vigorous young plant, preferably with one sturdy upright stem. Insert in the pot a strong bamboo stake the height you wish your tree to be—probably 2 to 4 feet. As the stem grows taller, tie it all along the stake. Remove any branches that begin to grow along the stem. When the stem reaches the top of the stake, pinch out the tip. When branches at the top grow to 2 or 3 inches, pinch out their tips. Continue pinching until the plant has formed a head, or tree, shape. After the top has several branches and a fair quantity of leaves, remove all leaves along the trunk; rub off any that later start to grow there. If you are training fuchsia or English ivy to standard form, it will help if you nail or screw an inverted wire hanging basket to the stake's top. Pinch out the tip of the main stem as soon as it grows just above where the basket is attached. Future branches can be trained all around until they hide the support. Other topiary shapes, best suited to plants with a trailing habit, are discussed in Chapter 7: see Ivy, English, page 126.

CUTTING BACK: If a plant that needs a good deal of pinching is neglected, it will grow tall and spindly. This frequently happens with aluminum plant, coleus, and geranium. Be brave. Take shears or scissors in hand, and cut back all the stems to about 8 inches. You can use what you remove as cuttings. When new growth sprouts, pinch it back often.

PRUNING: All house plants having woody stems need to be pruned from time to time, just as do trees and shrubs growing outdoors. For this procedure, you will need a pair of sharp pruning shears. Outdoor pruning is done to thin out crowded and crossing branches; indoors, the intention usually is to encourage growth and to produce a plant with shorter, sturdier branches. Cut off tips just above a node on the stem (the point at which leaves are—or were—growing). New growth should occur at this point or just below it. Pruning is also done to remove dead twigs and branches. See the photographs at right for details.

Weeping fig tree has lots of twigs and small branches that are leafless. Dead ones should be pruned.

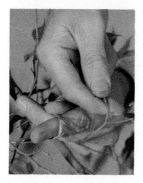

Bent dead twig breaks; live one bends.

Use sharp pruning shears to remove dead branches.

The pruning is nearly completed. Removing dead wood makes the tree look better and encourages new growth.

STAKING: House plants that grow tall, either naturally or because they are somewhat light-starved, will look and grow better if they are staked. For small plants, use thin bamboo stakes or the new clear-plastic plant supporters; for plants of medium size, use thick bamboo stakes; tree sizes, such as weeping fig, may require 1-by-1 inch wooden stakes of redwood or cypress, both of which are resistant to rot when they are placed in pots of moist soil. To tie a stem or trunk to a stake, you can use lengths of soft green plastic sold for this purpose or cut home-made ties from a dark-green plastic garbage bag. You can also use dark-green twist ties; but these must be tied loosely, so the wire imbedded in them won't strangle the stems as they grow. Select the thinnest stake you can find that will be strong enough to support the plant. If it is obtrusive, it will spoil the look of the plant. Insert the end of the stake into the pot as close to the main stem as possible without breaking major roots. Then loop and twist the tie tightly about the stake; then loosely tie it around the stem. The looseness is to allow for natural expansion of the stem as it grows. If a plant like the angelwing begonia shown in the photographs at the left has grown long, weak, or crooked stems, stake and tie it gently, or the stems will break. Sometimes a plant with long-straggly or floppy branches might be better cut back (see page 45) than staked. This is especially true of coleus and geraniums grown indoors.

This angelwing begonia droops awkwardly; flowers are hidden under leaves.

Push support stake to bottom of pot. White tub hides discolored clay pot.

Loop the tie first around stake, then loosely around stem, so that it can grow.

After staking, begonia stands up straight and flowers show clearly.

46

Climbing philodendrons need totem pole on which to attach their air roots.

Loop tie loosely around stem, and twist closed behind totem pole.

Roots along stem will clasp totem surface if it is kept moist by misting.

TOTEM POLES: Climbing philodendrons are at their most beautiful only when they have rough, moist surfaces on which to climb. Pieces of wood with bark attached and slabs of tree-fern fiber are sold for this use and are referred to among gardeners as totem poles. When you place a totem pole in the pot of a philodendron, tie the stem or stems of the plant to it as illustrated in the photographs above. If you keep the surface of the totem pole constantly moist by misting, air roots that grow naturally along the stems of climbing philodendrons will attach themselves to the rough surface.

HANGING BASKETS: Suspend hanging baskets from hooks (clear-plastic hooks are best) installed in the ceiling or from plant brackets (look for the clear-plastic kind) attached to wall or window frame. Holders by which baskets are suspended at various levels may be fashioned of clear-nylon cord, which is almost invisible, handcrafted macrame knotted from natural fibers, small chains, or wires. If you are investing in a plastic hanging basket, be sure the saucer is firmly attached. Classic wire hanging baskets lined with sheet moss look beautiful outdoors, where dripping water is no bother, but they are not suitable indoors. If you place a plant in a hanging ceramic container without a drainage hole, be careful not to overwater. The weight of a large hanging plant is something to reckon with—be sure the ceiling hook or wall bracket is anchored securely. It is no fun to come home and find your favorite basket plant fallen in a heap, with broken stems and soil scattered all over the floor or carpet. Potting soil for hanging-basket plants can be lightened by mixing 1 part vermiculite to 2 parts of the soil usually recommended for the plant.

How To Increase Your Plants without Spending Money

Most people who have a few house plants eventually own dozens, even hundreds. Why? Multiplying them is almost irresistible once you discover how easy and fascinating propagating plants can be. Watching baby rex begonias grow from slashes in a parent leaf is as much fun, almost, as watching kittens; and who could dislike acquiring for free a whole new rubber plant just by air-layering (opposite) the parent? Roots for new plants grow from various plant parts—leaves, branch tips, ends of half-ripened (not old, not new) wood, eyes in tubers, and parent roots, as well as seeds. Look at your house plants—and your neighbor's—with covetous eyes; almost all can become parents.

ROOTING MATERIAL: Plant parts will root in water, damp vermiculite, potting soil, sand, sphagnum, or peat moss. Water is the most convenient, but some cuttings root best other ways, as noted below. Plants root faster when a little dilute plant food is added. Mist other mediums. Damping-off, a fungus disease, can kill seedlings that grow in unpasteurized soils. Good commercial soils are pasteurized. If you make your own, pasteurize it (page 20). Use sulfur powder to protect cut ends of tuber cuttings. Rooting, or hormone, powders speed rooting in many plants.

Hints: Use sharp, clean knife or safety razor blade to take cuttings. Select healthy growth. Set in less light the first days, then in light suited to parent plant or in fluorescent light.

Roots for new plants will grow in water on a tip cutting (above) from an angelwing begonia in a pretty glass-ball container; in moss wrapping; on air layered *Dracaena* plant (opposite); or in damp vermiculite, soil, or sand.

49

Select stem ends that are firm to make tip cuttings for starting new plants.

Use a sharp knife to cut through node—place on stem where leaf grows.

This geranium yielded three cuttings. Old woody growth was discarded.

Remove leaves from part of stem to be inserted in rooting medium.

Cuttings may be rooted in a sterile medium such as perlite (shown) or vermiculite, or in a glass of water.

TIP CUTTINGS: You can multiply most upright and trailing house plants by rooting tip cuttings. Firm, healthy stems, neither soft and young nor woody and old, root best. Cuttings should have 4 to 6 leaves and at least 2 inches of stem to insert in the rooting medium —vermiculite, clean builder's sand, or just water. Use a sharp knife to cut through a node (shown in photograph top, right). Cut off lower leaves flush with stem, so they do not touch the rooting medium (this avoids rot). Place cuttings in the rooting material at once, except cactus: give these 24 hours to dry before planting. Cuttings in water usually don't wilt; in other mediums, use a plastic bag or glass cover to keep leaves firm. You can see the roots in water; in other mediums, check after a couple of weeks by gently pulling the cutting. If it resists, the roots probably have already formed. Transplant to a pot filled with moist potting soil (for correct soil, see Chapter 7). Cover with glass or plastic while the new roots are being established. Keep the soil moist; keep out of the sun. When new growth appears, remove the cover and the handle as directed in Chapter 7.

LEAF CUTTINGS: Some house plants have such a strong will to live that they are able to reproduce themselves by means of a single leaf cutting. Best known for this remarkable ability is the African violet. Other plants you can propagate this way include aspidistra, red and beefsteak begonias, Cape primrose, donkey-tail, echeveria, gloxinia, jade plant, peperomia, piggyback plant, snake plant, and waxplant. Select only healthy, mature leaves that are growing vigorously. Poke the base of the cut leaf stem ½ to 1 inch deep in a moist, sterile rooting medium such as vermiculite. Individual leaves may be planted in small pots, each covered with a drinking glass, fruit jar, or plastic bag. To prevent wilting, such covers serve as mini-greenhouses to maintain the high humidity needed for rapid rooting. Or use a clear-plastic sweater-storage box with lid as a mini-greenhouse for leaf cuttings.

Keep the soil constantly moist and the plant in a warm spot with bright light but no direct sun. After weeks or months, baby plants will sprout. When they are large enough to handle, divide (if more than one plant has sprouted from a single leaf), and transplant. If the parent leaf is still lively and green, you may root it again.

Cut African-violet leaves rooted in vermiculite soon sprout baby plants with clusters of tiny leaves, ready for potting.

Use knife tip to cut veins of begonia leaf. Weeks later, plantlets will grow in each cut.

BEGONIAS AND OTHER LEAF CUTTINGS: The wax and cane begonias such as angelwing are best increased by rooting tip cuttings, as above. Fancy-leaved and rex begonias can be multiplied by rooting leaf cuttings, like African violets; but a better method is this: Select a healthy, fresh leaf, and anchor it, face up, with a marble chip to moist African-violet soil. With a sharp, clean knife point, make one slash through each major vein. Plantlets will develop from most of the cuts in a few weeks. When all are growing sturdily, divide the parent leaf among the plantlets, giving each the largest possible portion. Plant these babies in African-violet potting soil, and for the first few days, set them in less light than the parent needs. Then provide requirements given in Chapter 7 as ideal for the parent plant to grow lustily.

Use a sharp knife to dig around and under offset; lift it free. This spider plant has many offsets.

ROOTING OFFSETS: Most plants multiply by producing babies, or offsets, in the soil, and rooting offsets is one of the easiest ways to multiply your plants. By the time leaves show above the ground, a root system has already formed. To remove an offset with the least disturbance to the rest of the plant, insert the blade of a sharp knife down, around, and under the offset. Avoid cutting off roots. Lift the offset (fill the hole) and pot immediately (page 41) in moist, sterile soil or in vermiculite. Water well, and keep out of direct sun, to prevent leaf wilt. Remove offsets when the parent plant is in active growth, usually in spring. Chapter 7 notes growth seasons that differ or are especially important. Plants in fluorescent-light gardens usually grow all year.

This single division of spider plant has been removed without any harm to the parent. If a hole is left, fill it with soil.

An entire plant may be removed from the pot and divided. This plant produced five healthy new divisions, ready to pot.

ROOT DIVISION: Some large single plants are actually made up of many individual offsets—for instance, the spider plant shown in the sequence pictured here. You can divide such a plant into small ones. Remove the plant from its pot. With your fingers and a sharp knife blade, work away enough soil to expose the root system. Carefully study the way the roots are connected; then gently cut away the offset, preserving as much root as possible. Cutting is better than tearing or breaking. Pot division; water well; keep shaded until it begins to grow.

Root division is the easiest way to get a lot of baby plants in a hurry. However, the babies look lonely planted separately in large pots and will take time to become big plants. If you plant several offsets in one container, you have an instant, mature-looking specimen.

DIVISION OF STEM OFFSETS: Some nearly stemless plants—for instance, African violets and bromeliads—develop offsets that grow as whorls or rosettes of leaves on the stems. The rosettes are tricky to propagate because it's hard to cut away enough stem to keep the rosettes intact without destroying the parent plant. Root them like leaf cuttings, but don't be upset if they fail. Offsets on African violets can interfere with flowering. If the offsets are small, rub them off; if they have grown several leaves, treat them as described above.

Plant each division in a clean pot of fresh soil, or group several in one large pot, water, and mist.

DIVISION OF TUBER OFFSETS: Some bulbs, such as amaryllis and oxalis, also form offsets in the soil. To divide these, remove the entire plant from the pot, so you won't slice into either the new or the old bulb when you make the cut. The best time to do this is after the plant's resting period but before new leaf growth is sizable. If you are careful to replant immediately and water well, bulb offsets such as these can be removed and planted in any season of the year.

DIVIDING TUBERS WITHOUT OFFSETS: Other plants that also grow from tubers—for example, tuberous begonia, cyclamen, and gloxinia—do not form offsets. To divide these, wait until the tuber grows large enough to produce two or more sprouts or eyes. (Sweet and white potatoes have similar eyes; treated as described below, they make interesting house plants and good children's

Spider-plant division has been repotted and groomed.

projects.) Eyes appear when the plant grows again after resting. With a sharp knife, slice cleanly through the tuber, assigning to each eye a generous segment of it. Coat cut surfaces with a fungicide such as horticultural dusting sulfur. Plant in moist soil suited to the parent. Each eye will sprout into a whole new plant.

You also can propagate a gloxinia or tuberous begonia by planting the tuber and encouraging all eyes to grow. When stems are 3 to 4 inches tall, cut off all but the strongest, and root tip cuttings of these.

Yet another way offsets develop is seen in the pregnant onion. On this plant, offsets form on top of the old bulb. When the offsets are large enough to handle, gently remove from the parent. Snuggle the base of each in moist soil to induce rooting; then transplant to soil.

PLANTING SEEDS: Seeds for the outdoor and indoor garden are sown the same way—but large, rectangular flats of pressed peat or cardboard or plastic are best for outdoor seedlings, while 4- or 5-inch pots make good starting beds for indoor seedlings. Sow indoor seeds, as well as outdoor seeds, in vermiculite, sphagnum moss, or pasteurized potting soil. Drop seeds about half an inch apart on slightly dampened growing medium; cover with a fine layer of sterile vermiculite or moss, and water lightly. Overwrap the flat or pot with plastic film, loosely, and set in dim light in warmth until seedlings have developed 2 or 4 sets of leaves. Feed; then

Newly planted seeds are grown in a plastic-enclosed pot, while sturdy seedlings (African violets) grow in the open air. They are ready to pot.

move pot to light suited to the plant's type and remove the plastic covering. Keep soil nicely damp, not soaked, turn the container often so seedlings will grow straight. As sturdy seedlings fill the growing area, remove spindly competitors for space. When seedlings are several inches high and crowding each other, transplant to 2- or 3-inch pots, depending on mature-plant size. If seedlings yellow, water with all-purpose plant food at half strength. Children love planting pantry seeds—dried beans, lentils, seeds of hot red peppers—and many dried herb seeds make handsome, if short-lived, foliage plants.

AVOCADO: No other seed grows quite like that of the avocado. Rinse the pit in clean water. About midway between pointed tip and base, poke three toothpicks into the pit. Place base down in a drinking glass or jar of water so toothpicks rest on its rim. Set in a dark place; keep water level around pit base until roots develop. Watch for a sprout. (See page 69.)

To sprout an avocado pit, suspend it in a jar or glass of water. Toothpicks hold the pit in place.

After the pit roots and sprouts, transplant to a pot of soil. It will grow into a house-plant tree.

AIR - LAYERING:
This is a safe way to propagate almost any thick-stemmed plant that has grown to be awkwardly tall, with a long, bare stem topped by leaves. The photographs on this page show the step-by-step procedure; the plant shown is *Dracaena fragrans*. Other dracaenas, except 'Florida Beauty,' may be air-layered; so may aralia, Chinese evergreen, cordyline, fatshedera, ficus, philodendron, pleomele, polyscias, schefflera, zebra plant. Rooting time varies according to the season (rooting is most rapid in spring and summer) and the kind of plant being air-layered. Check the plastic cover weekly, to be sure the sphagnum moss is moist; if it isn't, mist thoroughly; replace the plastic cover. When roots are readily visible, cut through stem an inch below, and pot the new plant. If the old part of the plant is given good care, new growth may sprout along the stem or from the base and form an interesting shape. You can try air-layering almost any plant; even if roots don't grow, it won't hurt to try.

Cut almost halfway through stem to be air-layered.

Use a wooden matchstick to hold the cut place open.

Surround the open cut with moistened sphagnum moss.

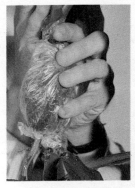

Wrap the moss in plastic; tie it at top and bottom.

Roots will grow quickly if the moss is kept moist.

After roots form, cut stem below; pot the new plant.

Dictionary of House Plants

The plants pictured and discussed in this book represent just about all the popular varieties to be found for sale right now, plus a few new and almost-forgotten old-fashioned kinds that grow unusually well indoors. The question "What plant is that?" can be answered by looking through the many pages of plant-identification photographs in this chapter. The plants included on pages 60 through 199 are cultivated either for foliage that is attractive every month of the year or for their habit of blooming constantly or periodically throughout the year. Plants that produce one burst of bloom annually, which may last for a few weeks or at most a month or two, are pictured and discussed in Chapter 8. Herbs to grow as house plants for fragrance and for use as seasonings are pictured and described in Chapter 9.

"WHAT PLANT IS THAT?" is a good question to ask if you don't know. Owning a plant whose name you do not know is unsettling, and besides, how will you know what kind of care it needs if you do not know its name? The correct horticultural names of plants are in Latin. They may sometimes be unfamiliar and difficult to pronounce, but the only way you can be sure what plant you are talking about is to use the official horticultural name, especially as common names vary greatly. Latin is, after all, the only universal language, and plants are universal in their appeal. This is one reason that plants break through communications barriers of all kinds—age, economic status, education, language, race. If you know and love plants, you can be sure of finding a friend and fellow plant lover.

COMMON NAMES: Most house plants have popular, or so-called common, names. These usually are more widely used than the official Latin titles. We have chosen to list the plants in Chapters 7, 8, and 9 by their best-known names, whether common or horticultural. In the case of *Spathiphyllum,* for instance, the Latin genus name is more commonly used than the popular names peace-lily and white flag. Since the genus *Ficus* has several species in cultivation and several popular names, we have listed it by the Latin name. Because more and more gardeners are finding it useful to know the horticultural names of plants, we have included this information at the end of each entry, along with a key to pronunciation. *Ornithogalum* looks impossible to pronounce, but try our key: or-nith-OG-uh-lum. Say it aloud three times, and the next time you see this plant in a friend's collection, in a nursery, or in a botanical garden, you will be able to rattle off *Ornithogalum* as easily as you might add, "That's sometimes called the pregnant onion." Not only do the Latin names of plants specify exactly what you are talking about but you can have fun with them.

HORTICULTURAL NAMES: The Latin names of all plants are formed about as our names are, except that we usually place the given name first, followed by the family or surname. With plants this is reversed. The plant's first name identifies its genus; the genus is roughly equivalent to our family or surname. The plant's second name, which follows that of the genus, identifies its species. Take *Dracaena marginata* — *Dracaena* is the plant's genus; *marginata* is its species. Sometimes there is a third name. This usually indicates a distinctly different plant that has special characteristics, but nevertheless belongs to the species. Such plants may be discovered growing in the wild along with plants typical of the species, or they may be discovered among cultivated plants. When such a discovery is made, the new variety is propagated, named, and put on the market—provided it seems worthy. An example of this triple name is *Dracaena deremensis warneckei*. The last name may also appear in single quotes as 'Warneckei.' Plants distinguished by quotes are called named varieties. New plants created in cultivation by controlled breeding are called cultivars. Their names also appear in single quotes, which are always used in technical journals and often by amateurs. The miniature gloxinia known as *Sinningia* 'Poupee' is an example.

FAMILY NAMES: Every plant, besides having a genus name in combination with a species and sometimes a variety or cultivar name, also has a family to which it belongs within the plant kingdom. Dracaenas, for example, belong to the Lily Family and share with all other members of this family certain characteristics. These are often not readily apparent except to botanists. More than 60 families are represented by the plants pictured and discussed in this book. The family richest in members that make excellent house plants is the Lily Family. The most prominent lily relatives included in these pages are aloe, asparagus fern, aspidistra, cordyline, dracaena, hyacinth, lily-turf, pregnant onion, pleomele, ponytail, scilla, snake plant, spider plant, tulip, and others — not to mention the chives we love to grow for those green snippings that add such flavor to scrambled eggs and other foods.

LABELS: Unless you are very familiar with a plant, it is quite helpful to label it. Wooden and plastic plant labels are usually available in the same places where plants are sold. Besides the plant's name, it is a good idea to include on the label where and when you acquired the specimen. If you don't like labels sticking up among your plants—and they certainly can be distracting—tuck the label for each plant under its saucer, or slip it down between the soil and the pot wall, with just the tip showing.

PLACING YOUR PLANTS: On each of the plant-identification pages that follow, essential information appears in a specific order. To give you a clue to the size of each plant shown, we have mentioned the size of the pot in which it is growing. This measurement is the diameter of the pot—that is, how wide it is from one side of the rim to the other. If the plant in the photograph is a small, young specimen that will eventually grow much larger, we have indicated this, suggesting where you might enjoy growing it while it is small and what kind of space you may need in the future for growing and displaying it.

In every case, we have told whether a plant is suited for placement on a sill, shelf, table, pedestal, floor, or in a hanging basket, a terrarium or a fluorescent-light garden. "Sill" means windowsill. In houses built since World War II, most windowsills are only a few inches deep. "Shelf" may be interpreted as a glass, Lucite, or Plexiglas shelf system installed in front of a window. Such a unit takes advantage of all available light and is ideal for a collection of fairly small plants that either grow upright or have trailing or creeping stems. Plants which have been suggested for display on a table are fairly small, about African-violet size, and especially attractive up close—the sort of plant you might enjoy on a coffee or lamp table. Certain taller plants displayed on a low table will spread their branches at a pleasant height over a couch, chair, or bed and look like a tree.

"Pedestal" means a stand that will elevate a plant so that its beauty can be better appreciated. Pedestals are recommended especially for plants with trailing or creeping stems, which look most attractive when they have plenty of room to dangle or cascade. A pedestal may be as ordinary as a 4-by-4-inch block of wood 12 inches tall or as simple as a stack of several upside-down pots. Found objects, such as clay flue and sewer tiles, as well as concrete conduit used for electrical wiring, also may be used for pedestals. Fancier pedestals of all sizes are available at specialty shops which stock plant containers. Or you can build cubes or pedestals of various sizes from half-inch marine plywood. Finish them to suit the room by painting them or covering them with wallpaper, peel-and-stick paper, or fabric. Plants do not need to have cascading or trailing stems to be effective on a pedestal; almost any beautiful plant will look more beautiful when displayed as if it were an important piece of sculpture, particularly if you up-light or down-light it at night (see page 17).

House Plants

Plants suggested for display on the floor usually are fairly sizable indoor shrubs or trees. One of these needn't necessarily stand alone. You will enjoy moving your plants around to see which look best together. If the environment—conditions of light, temperature, and humidity—remains essentially the same, plants won't mind a little change of location occasionally. One pleasing way to make a floor arrangement of plants is to group one that reaches toward the ceiling, one of about waist height, and one about knee high. Small plants can be placed on the floor, too. Three or four African violets in full bloom make a pretty floor display when you arrange them in a large, shallow container filled with pebbles. Viewing the plants from directly above gives you an interesting and unusual perspective.

Hanging-basket plants are ideal for display on a shelf or pedestal or at the edge of a table, where stems will be free to fall gracefully. Or suspend a pot in a handsome handcrafted macrame holder or a beautiful hand-thrown pottery container. Almost any plant of suitable size may be used; upright growth shows off the details of a good-looking holder. Fluorescent-light gardening is illustrated and discussed in Chapter 2. Plants that thrive in this light are so indicated throughout the book. Kinds that remain naturally low—African violets, for example—may be grown permanently in a fluorescent-light garden. If others outgrow the garden, you can move them to the natural light recommended for them in this chapter. Or you can cut them back several inches. Or you can start anew with tip cuttings.

FOR A LARGE COLLECTION: If you are just beginning as an indoor gardener, you are almost certain to discover that one plant leads to another—and another. Not too long ago, someone who had 50 house plants was considered slightly odd. Now it is not unusual for a gardener to grow as many as 300 in an apartment or house. Well-grown plants take time. The more you acquire or propagate, the more time you need to care for them. It has been suggested that plants are like people; but when it comes to caring for them, they actually are more like puppies or kittens, you must assume the sole responsibility of watering and feeding them and giving them the other care they need.

Another reality about collecting a large number of plants is that unless they are arranged and displayed thoughtfully, they may look like a jungle of weeds. Too much crowding robs individual plants of sufficient light and air—and attention. Sometimes a large collection of plants can be made more attractive simply by grouping all those of one kind. For example, instead of mixing ferns with other plants, assemble all the ferns in one area where the light is right for them. Display them at different heights, so they can be seen and appreciated.

The specific-care sections given in the following entries are self-explanatory. Whenever information may be less detailed than you may wish, we have added references to pages or chapters where all the information you require will be found.

AFRICAN VIOLET

Hybrid African violets; 4-inch pots.

Hybrid, rounded petals; 5-inch pot.

LIVING WITH IT: This is the most popular of all flowering house plants because it blooms effortlessly the year around. Almost the only difficulty with African violets is making a choice from the hundreds of varieties offered. To begin with, there are size variations: *miniatures* (6 inches or less from the tip of one leaf to the tip of the leaf growing opposite), *semiminiatures* (8 inches or less from leaf tip to leaf tip), and *standards* (all the others). There are a few trailing varieties, but they are hard to find.

There are also foliage variations. African-violet foliage generally is heart-shaped, but may be any shade of green, from pale green to dark olive. The reverse sides of the leaves can be white, green, or burgundy. Some leaves have flat surfaces; some are quilted; some curl inward in a spoon shape. There are also white-variegated green leaves and *supremes,* varieties with extra-large, unusually flat and stiff leaves.

And there are variations in flower colors: Besides white, colors run in shades of blue and red, palest to darkest, and some are edged in contrasting colors. There are corals and fuchsia-reds, but no yellow and no orange.

There are differences in flower type. There are the *single,* typical violet shape, the *semidouble,* and the fully *double. Star* varieties (all five petals equal in size, with pointed tips) also may be single, semidouble, or double. Petal edges of any of these many types may be frilled or ruffled, often in a contrasting color. Among the miniatures, several varieties have bell- or trumpet-shaped blooms.

60

AFRICAN VIOLET

African violets remain mostly between 2 and 4 inches tall, ideal for display on sill, shelf, table, pedestal, or in a hanging basket or a fluorescent-light garden (see Chapter 2). The miniatures are well suited to terrarium landscapes. To encourage the greatest bloom, sink the plant in its 2½-inch pot to the pot's rim in the terrarium soil. Miniatures growing outside terrariums may be planted in soil contained by a pocket in a chunk of Featherock or other stone planter. To give the effect of an outdoor garden indoors, group African violets in a pebble tray on the floor, in an arrangement with shrub- and tree-size house plants.

LIGHT: Ideal in winter is a sunny east or south window, in summer, a north or west window, year-round in a fluorescent-light garden. Some African violets find bright north light sufficient for all-year bloom. Too much hot, direct sun may turn leaves yellow or burn holes in them. Lack of light causes pale foliage with unnaturally long leaf stems and little or no flowering.

TEMPERATURE: Average house in winter; suffers below 60 degrees. Heat above 80 degrees reduces or may stop flowering. In the average winterheated house with low humidity, African violets grow well grouped in a pebble tray. Fill the tray with water to just below — not touching — pot bases. African violets prefer medium humidity, but they don't like misting. A cool-vapor humidifier helps them during winter heating. They appreciate fresh, circulating air; avoid hot or cold drafts. To clean the foliage, rinse it with water at room temperature; let dry completely before placing the plants in sun.

POTTING SOIL: African-violet (see Chapter 3). For best flowering, keep slightly pot-bound. Repot at least once a year.

WATERING NEEDS: Water often enough to keep the soil evenly moist. Use water at room temperature; ice-cold water would spot the leaves. Rain or distilled water is ideal. Soggy wetness or extreme dryness is likely to cause diseased roots. Bottom watering (see Chapter 1) usually is preferred, to prevent the build-up of mineral salts on surface soil; but every fourth time, water from above.

FEEDING: Feed blooming-type plant food all year, following the container directions.

PROBLEMS: Cyclamen mites and mealybugs may attack (see Chapter 4). Failure to bloom may be caused by lack of humidity, gas fumes, lack of light, stale air, hot or cold drafts, over- or underwatering. Baby plants (called suckers) that form at the base of old leaves are best removed as soon as they can be differentiated from flower buds; otherwise, there will be few flowers (see Chapter 4). African violets may "sulk" when moved: Be patient — they recover.

CONTAINERS: Standard plastic or clay pot, or hanging basket.

PROPAGATION: Plant seeds, make divisions, or root leaf cuttings.

Saintpaulia (saint-PAUL-ee-uh). Gesneriad Family. • *Saintpaulia* (African violet) A-1.

AGAVE

LIVING WITH IT:
The plant shown is in a 13-inch pot. Agaves are often confused with aloes, which have a similar form but belong to the Lily Family. The *Agave filifera* is very stiff, almost cactuslike. It is especially attractive displayed with cactus and leafy succulents such as kalanchoe. The most famous agave, the century plant *(A. americana)*, is said to bloom when 100 years old, then die. Actually, a century plant may bloom in 10 years and does not die after blooming. A mature century plant grows to tremendous size and is too big to recommend for the average house. Of the hundreds of varieties of agave, smaller species such as *A. filifera, A. miradorensis,* and *A. victoria-reginae* are better choices for window sill or tabletop. All agaves have thick, succulent leaves that form symmetrical rosettes. All make fine house plants while young and small enough. They tolerate neglect and adapt amazingly well to different kinds of light.

LIGHT: Ideal is a sunny south window. Acceptable is a sunny east or west window or 3 inches below the tubes in a fluorescent-light garden.
TEMPERATURE: Average house. Suffers below 45 degrees.
POTTING SOIL: Cactus mix (see Chapter 3).
WATERING NEEDS: Water about once a week in spring and summer; in other seasons water well, then not again until the surface soil is dry.
FEEDING: Use all-purpose plant food spring and summer, following container instructions; feed half as much in fall and winter.
PROBLEMS: If soaking wet and also cold, roots may rot.
CONTAINERS: Standard clay or plastic pot with drainage hole. A container without a drainage hole needs 1 or 2 inches of gravel in the bottom.
PROPAGATION: Remove and root offsets, in spring or summer.

Agave (ah-GAF-vee). Amaryllis Family • *Agave filifera* A-2; *A. victoria-reginae* A- 3.

LIVING WITH IT:
The flowering plant (*Anthurium andreanum*) here is in a 6-inch pot. It is a relative of the philodendron and calla lily. The flowering anthuriums have very attractive heart-shaped, waxy, long-lasting flowers of red, pink, or white and rather ordinary foliage.

Others have quite insignificant blooms and are grown for their velvety green, veined, and valentine-shaped leaves. Both types are at their best when displayed on a table, a shelf, or a sill. Young plants of smaller varieties do well in a large terrarium. All these plants like warmth and high

humidity—at least 50% in winter. *A. scherzerianum* (flamingo flower) usually has red flowers and is perhaps the most easily flowered. *A. clarinervum* and *A. crystallinum* are choice foliage types for home culture. If African violets thrive for you, you probably can grow anthuriums. They respond to frequent misting and are ideal choices for large terrariums where their need for warmth and humidity is met.

LIGHT: Best in winter is a sunny east or west window; in summer, bright but not direct sun; while small, plants grow well under fluorescent light.
TEMPERATURE: Average house. Suffers below 60 degrees.
POTTING SOIL: African-violet or terrarium (see Chapter 3).
WATERING NEEDS: Water about every 3 days, or often enough to keep the soil evenly moist. Dry spells cause dead leaf tips and margins.
FEEDING: Use all-purpose all year, following container directions. If flowering types fail to bloom, change to blooming plant food.
PROBLEMS: Hot, dry heat withers growth; cold and wet cause root rot.
CONTAINERS: Standard clay or plastic pot with drainage hole.
PROPAGATION: Remove and root offsets, in spring or summer.

Anthurium (an-THOO-ree-um). Calla Family • *Anthurium andreanum* (Flamingo flower) A-4; *A. scherzerianum* (Flamingo flower) A-5.

ARALIA

LIVING WITH IT:
The plant shown is in a 15-inch tub. Display young plants on a low table or the floor. In time, aralia will grow into a large, bold indoor shrub or tree. You can get the effect of a tree from a young aralia by setting the container on a pedestal about 3 or 4 feet tall. This elevates the foliage so it can spread above a chair or sofa, either to the side or behind it. Because aralia leaves grow large and are held in a more or less horizontal position, they probably will collect considerable dust and grime. About once a month, wipe them clean with a moist, soft cotton cloth or tissue. This benefits the plant and may be good therapy for you. Aralia is related to English ivy; in fact, it is so closely related genetically that a cross between the two produced another foliage plant, which is now well known as the popular house plant called fatshedera (also included in this book). Aralia, like English ivy, appreciates frequent misting and fresh, circulating air. Aralia's official name is *Fatsia japonica.*

LIGHT: Ideal is a sunny east or west window. Adapts to bright north light. Too much hot sun causes burnt spots on the leaves.
TEMPERATURE: Ideal is 60 to 70 degrees during the winter heating season; suffers over 75, under 50.
POTTING SOIL: All-purpose (see Chapter 3).
WATERING NEEDS: Water only often enough to keep the soil evenly moist; specimens in large tubs may need only a quart of water weekly. Mist often.
FEEDING: Feed all-purpose all year; follow container directions.
PROBLEMS: Hot, dry, stale air causes red spider mites (see Chapter 4).
CONTAINERS: Standard plastic or clay pot, or tub with drainage hole.
PROPAGATION: Root tip cuttings or air-layer in any season (see Chapter 6).

Fatsia (FAT-see-uh). Ginseng Family • *Fatsia japonica* (Aralia) A-6.

LIVING WITH IT:
The plant shown is in a 15-inch pot. Display young plants on sill, shelf, table, or—when very young—in a dish garden or a terrarium. When mature, plants will near the ceiling and may be displayed on a low table or set on the floor in a big tub. The very fine, elegant leaves (the botanical name of the plants is *Dizygotheca elegantissima*) grow large and coarse with age, spreading their bronzy-green segments to as much as 18 inches. Any light indoors sufficiently bright to read or do needlework by will do. What false aralia does not like is constantly being moved from one

location to another. Give a new plant the water and temperature it needs and time to adjust to its changed environment. It will probably shed several leaves in the beginning, but eventually will settle down and grow beautifully. This is one of the best of the tree-size house plants.

LIGHT: Ideal is 1 or 2 hours of direct sun daily or bright, reflected light most of the day. This plant, especially as it gets older, adapts amazingly easily to various kinds of light.
TEMPERATURE: Average house. Suffers below 50 degrees.
POTTING SOIL: All-purpose (see Chapter 3).
WATERING NEEDS: Water about every 3 days, or often enough to keep the soil always evenly moist. False-aralia plants resent either bone-dry or soggy-wet soil.
FEEDING: Feed all-purpose plant food year round; follow container directions for frequency of feeding.
PROBLEMS: Bone-dry soil and hot, dry, stale air.
CONTAINERS: Standard clay or plastic pot, or wooden, ceramic, or plastic tub with drainage. If there is no drainage hole, see Chapter 5.
PROPAGATION: Root cuttings, in spring or summer.

Dizygotheca (dizzy-GOTH-ick-uh). Ginseng Family • *Dizygotheca elegantissima* (False aralia) A-7.

ASPARAGUS FERN

Sprengeri asparagus-fern; 10-inch basket.   Asparagus setaceus; 4-inch pot.

LIVING WITH IT:
Although young asparagus-ferns may be grown on a sill, shelf, or table, they grow so quickly it is better to plan to display them in a hanging basket or on a pedestal. Here the graceful branches can cascade freely. Small asparagus-ferns, especially *Asparagus setaceus* (shown), are often included in

Meyeri asparagus-fern; 11-inch pot.

commercially planted dish gardens and terrariums, but these plants are definitely not well suited to such uses. Their root systems are so vigorous that smaller plants can't compete in the same planter. Besides, these need fresh air that circulates freely, rather than the close, and intensely humid atmosphere of a terrarium garden.

A. densiflorus sprengeri is the most popular of the asparagus-ferns. It clusters green, needlelike leaves in a random fashion on long stems. The effect is of a pleasant but indistinct mist of green foliage, attractive in a

Asparagus setaceus A-8.

66

window instead of curtains or blinds. In abundant light and fresh air, especially if placed outdoors in warm weather, sprengeri will bear tiny white flowers. These are followed by green berries that eventually turn lipstick-red.

Meyeri, like sprengeri (also a type of *A. densiflorus*), is fairly new. Its needles are clustered in dense, mostly upright or arching foxtail plumes. These compact plumes stand out clearly whether mixed with other plants or displayed alone. To dramatize the form of an older, many-plumed meyeri, set it on a pedestal; at night, shine a 75-watt floodlight on it, placing the fixture on the floor behind the pedestal. Meyeri often flowers indoors, but berries usually form only on plants that have flowered outdoors in warm weather.

A. setaceus (usually called plumosus) is most often cultivated by florists, who cut the delicate branches to place with bouquets of roses. This is the foliage most people call fern, thus the name asparagus-fern. When well grown, plumosus makes a beautiful hanging-basket plant that appears more fragile than it is.

LIGHT: Ideal is a sunny east or west window in winter; less direct sun is needed in summer. At the time of purchase, most asparagus-ferns have been growing in greenhouses with abundant sunlight. When they are placed in less light, a quantity of the needles may yellow and fall from the plants, even though you keep the soil moist. In time, however, asparagus-ferns will adapt to the light of a north window or similar brightness a few feet from a sunny east or west window. Young plants do well in fluorescent-light gardens.

TEMPERATURE: Ideal is 60 to 70 degrees during the winter heating season. Tolerates more heat in a pleasantly moist atmosphere where the air circulates freely. Avoid hanging near the ceiling in a hot, dry room.

POTTING SOIL: All-purpose (see Chapter 3).

WATERING NEEDS: Water often enough to keep the soil evenly moist. Grows poorly unless excess moisture drains freely and quickly from the container. If the soil dries out severely, even for a few hours, hundreds of the needles are likely to turn yellow and fall in a shower from the plant the first time you disturb it. This won't kill the plant, but does spoil its appearance. Mist often.

FEEDING: Feed all-purpose plant food all year; follow container directions for frequency of feeding.

PROBLEMS: In hot, dry, stale air, red spider mites are almost sure to infest asparagus-fern. Showering weekly and misting daily deters mites. Provide cooler temperatures and more fresh air. Mealybugs may also attack. See Chapter 4 for pest treatment.

CONTAINERS: Standard plastic or clay pot, or tub with drainage hole, or hanging basket.

PROPAGATION: Sow seeds or divide established plant, ideally in spring.

Asparagus (as-PAIR-uh-gus). Lily Family • *A. sprengeri* (spreng-er-EYE) A-9; *A.* meyeri (may-er-EYE) A-10.

ASPIDISTRA

LIVING WITH IT:
The plant shown is in an 8-inch pot. It will grow to be 2 feet tall and about as wide. Leaves are dark, plain green or green striped with white. It comes honestly by its name cast-iron plant, for if ever there was a house plant that thrives in a dark corner, this is it. It is widely used in the Deep South as a ground cover in the deep shade of old, towering trees, and was a stand-by in the darkened little-used Victorian parlor. Each slow-growing leaf has a long life and is very resistant to browning on tips and margins. While plant is small, shower with tepid water. Clean leaves of large plants with damp cotton. Display, according to size, on table, sill, or floor. Looks beautiful in a low, wide pot in a basket, with a saucer to catch excess moisture; spread florists' sheet moss over the soil surface to keep the soil evenly moist and to hide the edge of the pot.

LIGHT: Ideal is a bright north window or any daylight bright enough for reading or doing needlework. Tolerates even less light.
TEMPERATURE: Best not over 70 degrees in winter, but not below 50.
POTTING SOIL: All-purpose (see Chapter 3).
WATERING NEEDS: Water weekly, enough to keep soil evenly moist. Can be allowed to dry occasionally with little harmful effect.
FEEDING: Feed all-purpose plant food all year; follow container directions for frequency of feeding.
PROBLEMS: Bone-dry soil and simultaneously temperature that is too warm—over 75 degrees.
CONTAINERS: Standard clay or plastic pot, or decorative container.
PROPAGATION: Plant divisions, in late winter, spring, or summer. Leaf cuttings removed with the part attached to the root and inserted in moist soil.

Aspidistra (ass-pid-DIST-ruh). Lily Family • *Aspidistra* (Cast-iron plant) A-11.

LIVING WITH IT:
The plant shown is in an 11-inch pot; it will grow to ceiling height. Display on table or floor. The plant is grown from an avocado pit. Rooted avocados tend to shoot intó spindly, sparsely-leaved plants. To avoid this, follow one of two methods. First method: Stick the 3 toothpicks equidistant around a pit. Place, pointed end up and with at least ½ inch of base submerged, in a glass or jar of water. Keep in a dark closet; add water as needed. Move to light when sprout shows leaves. When plant is 8 inches tall, cut it back to 4 inches. When it is again 8 inches, pot in moist soil, leaving top third of pit exposed. Place in bright but sunless spot for a week; then move to better light (see below). Second method: Wash pit; let dry overnight. Pot in moist soil with top third of pit exposed. Place in east or west window; keep the soil evenly moist. Pinch growing tips often to induce branching.

LIGHT: Bright north, sunny east or west window. Needs 1 or 2 hours of direct sun daily, but don't place avocado plants in direct summer sunlight.
TEMPERATURE: Average house in winter; ideally not over 75 degrees. Some fresh air and frequent misting of the leaves make a better plant.
POTTING SOIL: All-purpose (see Chapter 3).
WATERING NEEDS: Water enough to keep evenly moist. Avoid extremes of wetness or dryness. Mist frequently.
FEEDING: Feed all-purpose all year, following container directions.
PROBLEMS: Hot, dry, stale air invites red-spider-mite attack. Mist throughout winter, and follow instructions in Chapter 4.
CONTAINERS: Standard clay or plastic pot, or tub. Repot to size larger as soon as roots begin to crowd container; cover pit.
PROPAGATION: Root pits, in any season (see above and Chapter 6).

Persea (purr-SEE-uh). Laurel Family • *Persea americana* (Avocado) A-12.

BABY'S TEARS

LIVING WITH IT:
The dark-green plant shown is in a 6-inch pot; the golden-green variety is in 5-inch pot. Display on table, sill, shelf, or as a small hanging-basket plant. Charming used as a ground cover around shrub- and tree-size house plants. Adapts to almost any kind of light, from that of a north window to that of 2 or 3 feet from a sunny south window. Needs constantly moist soil, as much humidity as possible, and fresh, moist air circulating freely. In a closed terrarium, the plant tends to grow spindly and unattractive. Baby's-tears likes to creep and expand over a moist surface. Planted in a 12-inch clay pot saucer filled with terrarium or humus potting soil and kept constantly moist, baby's-tears will quickly cover the surface. Occasional "mowing" with scissors, clipping only stray tips, will help baby's-tears grow into a compact mound of brilliant green. Mist often to maintain the high humidity the plant needs. A golden-leaved form is also available.

LIGHT: Ideal is a bright north or sunny east or west window. Also does well a few feet from a sunny south window.
TEMPERATURE: Average house temperature; preferably not warmer than 75 degrees in winter.
POTTING SOIL: Terrarium (see Chapter 3).
WATERING NEEDS: Water about every 3 days, or often enough to keep soil evenly moist at all times. Be sure the pot does not stand in water.
FEEDING: Feed all-purpose all year; follow container directions.
PROBLEMS: Dry soil, hot, dry heat, lack of fresh air wither leaves.
CONTAINERS: Standard clay or plastic pot with drainage hole, or hanging basket with drainage.
PROPAGATION: Plant divisions or root cuttings in water, any season.

Helxine (hell-ZYN-nee). Nettle Family • *Helxine* (Baby's tears) A-13.

Fancyleaf wax begonias: calla-lily (left) and 'Charm' (right); 4-inch pots.

Rieger begonia is a tuberous-rooted type that flowers all year; 8-inch pot.

LIVING WITH IT: Begonias are one of the largest groups of plants that thrive indoors. Some are beginner-easy, others difficult unless you know how to pamper them. Those shown on these four pages range from easy to difficult; they suggest the many sizes and leaf shapes you can grow. Most popular are the smallish wax begonias, hybrids of *Begonia semperflorens* (which means "always flowering"). Display on sill, shelf, table, pedestal, in a hanging basket or fluorescent-light garden. The waxy, cupped leaves may be fresh green or dark burgundy, the flowers white, pink, rose, or vivid red, single or double. Leaves of calla-lily begonia, a form of *semperflorens,* are partly or all white, furled like a calla lily. The green leaves of 'Charm' are splashed with white and yellow. Entirely different, but included here with the *semperflorens* types because it blooms lavishly all winter, is the Rieger. The best Rieger is Aphrodite, with clusters of red or pink 2-inch flowers.

LIGHT: Ideal is a sunny east or west window in winter.
TEMPERATURE: Ideal is 60 to 70 degrees during winter heating season. Suffers in hot, dry heat over 75 degrees or in temperatures below 55.
POTTING SOIL: African-violet (see Chapter 3).
WATERING NEEDS: Water well; after an hour, pour off excess in saucer; water again when a pinch of soil feels only slightly damp.
FEEDING: Feed blooming all year; follow container directions.
PROBLEMS: Hot, dry, stale air turns the leaf edges brown and withers the flower buds. If powdery mildew spots the leaves, see Chapter 4 for treatment.
CONTAINERS: Standard plastic or clay pot, or hanging basket.
PROPAGATION: Sow seeds, root tip cuttings, or divide in any season.

Begonia (be-GO-nee-uh). Begonia Family • *Begonia semperflorens* A-14; *Rieger begonia* A-15.

BEGONIA

LIVING WITH IT:
Begonia diadema (top) and 'Orange Rubra' (lower right) are in 3-inch pots. All the others are in 4-inch pots; these are, center row, left to right, 'Mme. Fanny Giron,' *B. bradei* and 'Catalina.' At lower left is 'Chiala rosea.' Display young angelwing or cane begonias on a sill, shelf, table, or in a fluorescent-light garden. Mature upright varieties several feet tall make showy floor plants; place kinds that have drooping branches on pedestal or in hanging basket. Begonias in this class are beautiful foliage plants; most bloom off and on all year.

Varieties with drooping branches are among the best of flowering plants for hanging baskets. The hairy-leaved begonias are much like angelwings; but foliage, stems, and flower buds are coated with soft hairs, often in a contrasting color.

LIGHT: Ideal is a sunny east or west window in winter; adapts to light of a bright north window; or stand near a fully sunny exposure.
TEMPERATURE: Ideal is 60 to 70 degrees during the winter heating season; suffers in hot, dry heat over 75 degrees or below 55 degrees.
POTTING SOIL: African-violet or all-purpose (see Chapter 3).
WATERING NEEDS: Water often enough to keep the soil evenly moist. Soggy wetness or extreme dryness causes many leaves to fall off.
FEEDING: Feed with blooming all year; follow container directions.
PROBLEMS: Virtually pest-free. Insufficient light or drafts of hot, dry air may prevent flowering.
CONTAINERS: Standard plastic or clay pot, or hanging basket.
PROPAGATION: Root tip cuttings, in any season.

Begonia (be-GO-nee-uh). Begonia Family • *Begonia bradei* A-16; *B. diadema* A-17.

LIVING WITH IT: Rhizomatous begonias in the photograph are, clockwise from top left: 'Fischer's Ricinifolia,' *B. manicata aureomaculata,* 'Verde Grande,' 'Cleopatra,' 'Leo Shippy.' Plant in the center is *B. fusco-maculata.* All are in 4-and 5-inch pots. Begonias of this type have fleshy, thick stems, which usually creep along the soil surface. In some varieties, these stems grow upright— *B. manicata aureomaculata,* for example. While small enough, display the plants on sill, shelf, table, or a fluorescent-light garden. Older plants look wonderful planted in a

hanging basket or placed on a pedestal. Begonias in this grouping including the old-fashioned beefsteak and star varieties, have beautiful foliage all year, and in season (usually late winter or spring) they send up tall, slender stems covered at the top with dainty pale-pink flowers. Miniatures like *B. bowerae* and *B. hydrocotylifolia* are ideal subjects for a fluorescent-light garden.

LIGHT: Ideal is a sunny east or west window in winter, or near a south window; needs less direct sun in summer. Adapts to north light.
TEMPERATURE: Average house in the winter; suffers in hot, dry heat.
POTTING SOIL: All-purpose or terrarium (see Chapter 3).
WATERING NEEDS: Water often enough to keep the soil evenly moist.
FEEDING: Feed all-purpose plant food in summer and autumn; blooming-type in winter and spring. Follow container directions.
PROBLEMS: Repot in fresh soil every 1 or 2 years, and thin out some of the old rhizomes; otherwise, the entire plant will go into decline.
CONTAINERS: Standard plastic or clay pot, tub, or hanging basket.
PROPAGATION: Roof leaf cuttings, or divide rhizomes, in any season.

Begonia (be-GO-nee-uh). Begonia Family • *Begonia* 'Fischer's Ricinifolia' A-18; *B. manicata aureo-maculata* A-19; *B. fusco-maculata* A-20.

BEGONIA

LIVING WITH IT:
Iron Cross begonia (far left) is in an 11-inch tub; the silverleaf *Begonia rex* (near left) is in an 8-inch pot. Display young plants on sill, shelf, table, in a terrarium or a fluorescent-light garden. Large, mature begonias of this type look good in a hanging basket or on a pedestal. Technically, Iron Cross is *Begonia masoniana,* and it's rhizomatous in habit (see page 73), as are the many varieties of *Begonia rex.* However, because they are cultivated almost entirely for their exquisite foliage and not for flowers, these begonias form a separate grouping. *Rex begonia* hybrids range in size from teacup miniatures to bushel plants with leaves 6 by 8 inches. The miniatures are perfect in terrariums. Iron Cross and the rexes thrive in fluorescent-light gardens. All need warmth, high humidity, and protection from drafts.

LIGHT: Ideal is a bright north window or a sunny east or west window in winter. Less light is needed in the summer.
TEMPERATURE: Average house in the winter. Suffers in dry heat over 75 degrees or below 55. Medium to high humidity is needed for perfect leaves. Frequent misting helps.
POTTING SOIL: African-violet or terrarium (see Chapter 3).
WATERING NEEDS: Keep evenly moist at all times. Mist often.
FEEDING: Feed all-purpose all year; follow container directions.
PROPAGATION: Hot, dry drafts or stale air inhibit growth and turn leaf edges brown. Soggy-wet soil and cold air combined cause leaf drop.
CONTAINERS: Standard plastic or clay pot, tub, or hanging basket.
PROPAGATION: Plant seeds or root leaf cuttings, or divide in any season.

Begonia (be-GO-nee-uh). Begonia Family • *Begonia masoniana* (Iron cross) A-21; *B. rex* A-22.

LIVING WITH IT:
The plant shown is in a 6-inch pot. Display on sill, shelf, or table. Although small, this spineless cactus is like a perfect piece of sculpture. Make an asset of it by placing it on a table under the light of a small, high intensity desk lamp. Although most of the year bishop's cap looks as it does here—if it is grown under ideal circumstances—in the summer, 2-inch golden-yellow, daisy-like flowers grow from the center. This species of *Astrophytum* is usually divided into five segments; but the related sand dollar (*A. asterias*) forms a perfectly rounded dome that is divided into eight segments. Both require the same culture. Ideally, they should receive full sun all day long. Less sun is acceptable. So is the light of a fluorescent garden; place 2 to 3 inches directly below the tubes. Be cautious about over- or underwatering, especially during the winter. In winter, cloudy weather brings growth to a halt, just when artificial heat can quickly dry the soil in a small clay pot.

LIGHT: Ideally, a sunny south window. Tolerates sunny east or west window. Or place under fluorescent lights, as described above.

TEMPERATURE: Average house in winter; suffers below 55 degrees.

POTTING SOIL: Cactus (see Chapter 3).

WATERING NEEDS: Water well, then again when surface soil feels dry.

FEEDING: Feed all-purpose plant food in spring, blooming in summer; follow container directions. Do not feed in fall and winter.

PROBLEMS: Soil that is either excessively dry or wet may cause cactus roots to become unhealthy, leading to rot.

CONTAINERS: Standard clay or plastic pot.

PROPAGATION: Plant seeds, preferably in spring or summer.

Astrophytum (as-troh-FYE-tum). Cactus Family ● *Astrophytum asterias* (Sand dollar) A-23; *A. myriostigma* (Bishop's cap) A-24.

BOUGAINVILLEA

LIVING WITH IT:
The plant shown is in a 3-inch pot. As a young plant, it is suitable for display on sill, shelf, table, in a hanging basket, or it can be trained as a bonsai. Although we tend to think of bougainvillea only as a climbing, thorny-stemmed vine of the tropics, it makes a fine house plant if it is confined to a medium-size pot and the stems are cut back often. The true flowers are slender white tubes, contained by the long-lasting bracts, which range from pure white, pale pink, and soft apricot, to brilliant hot pink, crimson, coppery orange, and bright purple. Although bougainvillea can be cultivated year round as a house plant, it blooms best if placed outdoors in full sun in summer. To maximize winter flowering, wait until spring to do any major pruning. Then pinch back the tips of new growth every few weeks until the end of July. This promotes growth. After July, do no more pruning or pinching, so wood grown during that period may ripen sufficiently to produce flower buds.

LIGHT: Ideal is full sun in an east, south, or west window; can do with less winter light if it summers out. Also fluorescent-light garden.
TEMPERATURE: Average house in winter. Suffers below 55 degrees.
POTTING SOIL: All-purpose (see Chapter 3).
WATERING NEEDS: Water thoroughly; then do not water again until the soil surface is approaching dryness.
FEEDING: In spring and summer, use all-purpose plant food; in fall and winter, use one that encourages blooming. Follow container directions.
PROBLEMS: Constantly moist to wet soil may discourage flowering.
CONTAINERS: Standard clay or plastic pot, or hanging basket.
PROPAGATION: Plant seeds, root tip cuttings or half-ripened wood, in summer.

Bougainvillea (boog-in-VILL-ee-uh). Four-O'Clock Family • *Bougainvillea* A-25.

Aechmea 'Silver King' in 11-inch tub.

Billbergia zebrina (left), 8-inch pot;
Neoregelia carolinae (right), 8-inch pot.

LIVING WITH IT: Bromeliads are among the most beautiful of all house plants. If they seem a little bizarre, it helps to remember they are ornamental forms of pineapple. In the tropics, where bromeliads grow wild, they are air plants (epiphytes) that usually grow perched among tree branches. The roots serve mainly as anchors to hold them in place, rather than as feeder systems. They exist on moisture they draw from the atmosphere and from rain water caught in the cup or vase formed in the center of the leaf rosette. Indoors, you have to play the role of rainmaker by daily misting them and keeping their cups filled with water; once a week, pour out water that has not evaporated, and refill the cups with fresh water. There is tremendous variety in bromeliads, not only in size, but in leaf shape and color and in the flowers. The photographs here and on page 79 will give you an idea of the different sizes and colors, but literally hundreds of bromeliads are in cultivation. They are wonderful plants to collect and are amazingly tolerant of various kinds of neglect.

Display young bromeliads of any kind, or the naturally small varieties such as cryptanthus, on a sill, shelf, or table, or in a terrarium or a fluorescent-light garden. Large bromeliads make breath-taking accent plants to display on a pedestal or in a hanging basket. Miniature bromeliads are often wired to a small slab of tree-fern bark, which is then suspended in the air. Daily misting of both bark and

BROMELIADS

bromeliads is vital, and once or twice a week submerge the bark with its plants in water for a few minutes; then remove, drain, and hang up again. Another way to grow and display these plants is to make a bromeliad tree. For this you will need a 5- or 6-foot piece of driftwood with two or more branches growing at interesting angles. Anchor base in a large pot or tub of sand; hide the sand at the top with a layer of pebbles or florists' sheet moss. Now you are ready to attach bromeliads of various sizes and kinds along the driftwood branches. Remove each plant from the pot in which it is growing, and wrap the roots in a handful or two of moistened, unmilled sphagnum moss. Secure to the driftwood branches by winding thin nylon cord around and around the moss-wrapped root system. Place the tree in suitable light (see the specific-care section, beginning on page 79). Mist the moss and the bromeliads daily. Strands of Spanish moss draped over the tree here and there are a picturesque and appropriate finishing touch because Spanish moss (*Tillandsia usneoides*) is also a bromeliad.

Approximately 1,800 different bromeliads have been indentified; new varieties are constantly coming into cultivation, both hybrids and natural species found growing wild in the tropics. Seven of the most readily available and best house-plant bromeliads are discussed in the text that follows. If you succeed with these, you will be ready to venture far beyond with these fascinating plants.

Aechmea (ECK-me-uh) is best known for its variety 'Silver King,' which has broad silver-and-green leaves and sends up a long-lasting head of pink bracts, from which the short-lived blue flowers grow. 'Foster's Favorite' has shiny dark-burgundy leaves. The blue flowers bloom from a gracefully arching stalk of long-lasting red berries.

Ananas (uh-NAN-us) *comosus* is the pineapple we eat. Florists often sell the dwarf form, which has a 12-inch rosette of stiff gray-green leaves crowned by a perfect miniature pineapple. When ripe, this gives off a delicious aroma. If left to mature, a baby pineapple plant will form on top of this small fruit, just as one does in the edible type. You can remove and plant this as you might the crown of leaves from a purchased pineapple. To do this, cut off the leaves with half an inch of the fruit attached; air-dry for 48 hours. Plant in barely moist soil, burying the dried fruit part and adding just enough soil to barely cover the base of the leaf rosette. Keep barely moist until the leaves begin to grow; then moisten the soil a little more. *Ananas comosus variegatus* is the showiest (see photograph opposite).

Billbergia (bill-BERJ-ee-uh) is best known as the living vase plant, an apt term since the leaves clasp tightly together for as much as 12 inches before they curve outward, away from each other. When the plant is not in flower, some gardeners like to place a cut orchid or other exotic bloom in the water contained by this living vase.

Cryptanthus (krip-TANTH-us), a ground hugger, is called earth stars for its starry shape. Small white flowers sometimes open from the center. These grow well in medium-wet terrariums.

Aechmea 'Silver King' A-26; *Ananas comosus* (Pineapple) A-27; *A. c. variegatus* (Variegated pineapple) A-28; *Billbergia zebrina* (Living vase) A-29; *Cryptanthus bivittatus minor* (Earth stars) A-30.

Ananas comosus variegatus, 11-inch tub.   *Cryptanthus bivittatus minor,* 4-inch pot.

Neoregelia (nee-oh-ruh-JEE-lee-uh) *carolinae* (see photograph, page 77) in bloom is truly exciting. The center leaves turn to glowing orange-red, surrounding dark-violet, white-edged flowers.

Tillandsia (till-AND-see-uh) is best known for its flaming-sword varieties. Showy flowers open from waxy, long-lasting brilliantly colored bracts. There are miniatures.

Vriesia (VREE-zee-uh) is prized both for its gloriously variegated and symmetrical rosettes of foliage and for its flaming-sword flowers.

LIGHT: Ideal is a sunny east or west window in winter, or near a south-facing, sunny window. Most bromeliads adapt well to a bright north window or similar brightness a few feet from a sunny exposure. They thrive in fluorescent-light gardens, but if the leaves touch a tube, ugly burns appear. Mature, flowering bromeliads last amazingly well in low-light areas. Floodlight them at night; it benefits them.

TEMPERATURE: Average house temperatures suit bromeliads. They survive near-freezing temperatures and heat of 80 degrees or more if there is moist, fresh air. Bromeliads prefer medium to high humidity, but tolerate dry air if the temperatures stay in a range between 60 and 72 degrees. If you want thriving, long-lived bromeliads that flower and multiply, use a humidifier in the room with them during the winter heating season, or mist well once or twice daily. Keep bromeliad leaves clean and healthy by showering with tepid water at least once a month. It is difficult to sponge the leaves clean since most have thorny edges and some have a feltlike surface coating that could be marred.

Neoregelia carolinae A-31; *Tillandsia* A-32; *Vriesia* A-33.

BROMELIADS

POTTING SOIL: Bromeliads, like epiphytic orchids, are usually planted in osmunda fiber, redwood bark, shredded fir, or chunks of tree-fern bark. These materials are available from bromeliad and orchid specialists. They will also grow well in unmilled sphagnum moss, perlite, vermiculite, and charcoal chips. Many florists and plant shops sell the more common bromeliads such as dwarf pineapple, variegated pineapple, and species of *Aechmea* and *Cryptanthus.* These will grow in almost any well-drained, standard, packaged potting mix, such as that labeled for cacti. Potting soil for any bromeliad must be spongy enough to drain excess moisture and to let roots breathe.

WATERING NEEDS: Keep the vase or cup formed in the center of each bromeliad filled with fresh water. Once a week, turn the plant upside down over a pail or sink, to drain any water that remains. Then turn the plant right side up, and fill the vase or cup with fresh water at room temperature. If you are using a coarse growing medium such as osmunda fiber, redwood bark, shredded fir, or chunks of tree-fern bark, drench this with water once or twice a week, but immediately empty any that drips into the saucer. If you are growing bromeliads in any of the other mediums suggested above, water often enough to maintain a range between moist and nearly dry. Overwatering will result in a soggy condition that may cause root rot and is definitely not to the liking of bromeliads.

FEEDING: Feed young bromeliads and those grown primarily for colorful foliage (species of *Cryptanthus,* for example) with an all-purpose plant food all year, mixed at about half the strength recommended on the container. Feed flowering-size bromeliads with a blooming-type plant food, also mixed at half the strength suggested on the container. Bromeliads benefit from having the leaves misted every 2 to 4 weeks with water to which plant food has been added at about half the strength recommended.

PROBLEMS: Given the care outlined here, bromeliads are virtually problem-free. Insects almost never attack them. There is considerable confusion about how to coax a nonblooming, mature bromeliad into flower. In recent years, the story has been widely circulated that to bloom a bromeliad all you need do is seal a mature plant in a large plastic bag with a ripe apple for a few days. The theory is that ethylene gas—a natural ripening agent—given off by the apple will trigger bud formation in the bromeliad. This is more or less effective; but according to the writings of the late Victor Ries, who was a professor of horticulture at Ohio State University at the time he made the discovery in the early 1930s, it can't be just any old apple. It should be a ripe Jonathan. Leave the apple and the bromeliad sealed together for about a week; then return the plant to its usual growing spot. With luck, it will flower in a few weeks.

CONTAINERS: Standard plastic or clay pot, or hanging basket.

PROPAGATION: Remove offsets that form around mature plants; see Chapter 6 for specific instructions.

Bromeliad (broh-MEE-lee-ad). Bromeliad Family

LIVING WITH IT: The plant shown is in a 4-inch pot. While young, display on a sill, shelf, or in a fluorescent-light garden. Older plants make fine subjects for hanging baskets. Flowers are blue or white. The related orange browallia, *Streptosolen jamesonii,* requires the same culture; it has orange flowers. The browallias are fine indoor plants if you can give them a cool, sunny window in winter — they bloom months on end, and the blues are lovely. They are most popular as container plants outdoors in warm weather. Seedlings can be put out when the weather warms and

danger of frost is past. Browallias propagated in late summer from cuttings will live over the winter indoors and can be set out in spring.

Before frost, bring large browallias indoors; enjoy them as long as flowers last; then cut back to 4 inches, withhold fertilizer, and keep on the dry side until you set them out once more.

LIGHT: Sunny east, south, or west window from fall to spring. Less direct sun is needed in summer, especially outdoors.

TEMPERATURE: Ideally, 55 to 70 degrees during winter heating season. If over 70 degrees, fresh, circulating air is vital.

POTTING SOIL: All-purpose (see Chapter 3).

WATERING NEEDS: Water often enough to keep evenly moist. Avoid extreme dryness, but water less in fall and winter. Mist often.

FEEDING: Feed blooming type in spring, summer, and early fall. Do not feed in late fall or in winter.

PROBLEMS: Avoid hot, dry, stale air; it prevents healthy growth.

CONTAINERS: Standard clay or plastic pot, or hanging basket.

PROPAGATION: Sow seeds, in winter or spring; root tip cuttings, in the summer.

Browallia (broh-WALL-ee-uh). Nightshade Family • *Browallia* A-34.

CACTI

Cereus (left), in 11-inch tub; old-man cactus, *Cephalocereus senilis* (right), is planted in a 15-inch tub.

Mammillaria (left) and golden barrel (right), in 11-inch pots; *Notocactus ottonis* (center) is in a 4-inch pot.

LIVING WITH IT: The variety among cacti is not only amazing, it is mind-boggling. There are plants hardly bigger than a pebble and towering trees, typified by the giant saguaros of the Southwest deserts. Most, but not all, have the prickly thorns or spines we associate with cacti. Some grow in sunbaked deserts; others are leafy plants from the jungle. And finally, some grow wild where winter temperatures dip to zero and below, while others will die if subjected to freezing temperatures. All cacti are classified as succulents because they have thickened stems and sometimes a thickened, large taproot, with both types capable of storing quantities of water during a rainy season so they are able to survive periods of drought. As house plants, the desert cacti need full sun in order to grow into their natural shapes. They will live indefinitely in poor light, but growth will be pale and spindly and, generally speaking, unattractive. There will not be flowers unless the plants have abundant sun during most of the year. Small, young cacti of all types do fairly well in a fluorescent-light garden when placed 2 inches under the tubes. Desert cacti show new vigor when moved outdoors in warm weather, but you must take care not to let them sunburn in the beginning. Indoor sun is not as intense as that of outdoors on a warm day. Move cacti outdoors to a spot where they receive morning or afternoon sun, but some shade the rest of the day. After a few weeks, they will tolerate full sun without burning.

The chief misconception about growing desert cacti as house plants is that they hardly ever need to be watered. There is an old saying that goes like this: Subscribe to the Tucson, Arizona, newspaper. When it

Aporocactus flagelliformis (Rat-tail cactus) A-35; *Cephalocereus senilis* (Old-man cactus) A-36; *Cereus* A-37.

rains in Tucson, water your cactus plant; otherwise, let it alone. This is an amusing idea, but put into practice, it will result in shriveled, unhealthy cacti. For best long-term growth and flourishing, healthy cacti, study the watering needs described on page 85. On the same page are noted some cacti that bloom best if dry in winter.

In recent years, there has been a great deal of research, by both private and agricultural extension specialists, in the culture of cacti. It has been found that the old way of keeping cacti starved for food and water is not necessarily the best way. With a program of regular feeding and watering, very much the same as that used to grow geraniums, cacti grow much more rapidly and are healthier. If you grow yours this way, you must provide soil (cactus mixture) that drains rapidly, and the pots must never be left standing in water.

Although there are thousands of cacti, the kinds introduced here are among the best and most easily found in local shops and in specialists' mail-order catalogs. Small cacti purchased from non-specialist sources are often in too-small pots filled with soil drier than the Mojave Desert and as hard as cement. If you buy a plant in this condition, put it in the sink, wash off all the soil, and replant it in barely moist cactus soil; after a few weeks, let the roots reestablish themselves, and begin a regular watering program.

Aporocactus (uh-por-oh-CACK-tus) *flagelliformis* is called rat-tail cactus because it has long stems that trail down from the container. Display it on a shelf or pedestal or in a hanging basket, so the stems can cascade freely. In season, there are small red flowers.

Cephalocereus (suh-fal-oh-SEAR-ee-us) *senilis* is the old-man cactus. When young, display it on sill, shelf, or table. Old plants (like that shown on page 82) are expensive, but make handsome living sculptures to place on floor or low table. Spotlight at night for dramatic effect. The short spines of this amusing cactus are covered by long white hairs, which begin to develop even in seedlings. Children love to cut out and paste paper eyes, nose, and mouth on the "body." Some comb hair to stand out and call it the Phyllis Diller cactus. Sand, white marble chips, or black stones used as a covering for the soil surface accent the old man's appearance. He bears rose-colored flowers.

Cereus (SEAR-ee-us) species such as *peruvianus* and *tetragonus* grow into thick, tall columns, which are at present in great demand for use as living sculpture indoors. It takes many years to grow one 6 feet tall, so you must expect to pay a sizable price for such a specimen. Be sure you invest in a cereus that has been cultivated in a container by a knowledgeable plant person and not in a specimen that has been recently torn from its roots and stolen from the desert. Any cactus so treated may never recover from the shock it has suffered. Plants called night-blooming cereus are famed for their beautiful white flowers, which last only one evening. These include the trailing or semiupright *Hylocereus undatus* and *Selenicereus macdonaldiae;* the upright, slender-columned *Trichocereus pachanoi;* and the leafy, more

Aporocactus flagelliformis (Rat-tail cactus) A-35; *Cephalocereus senilis* (Old-man cactus) A-36; *Cereus A-37.*

CACTI

Prickly-pear opuntia in an 11-inch tub.

Rat-tail cactus in an 8-inch basket.

or less upright (with staking) *Epiphyllum oxypetalum,* which is a jungle cactus.

Echinocactus (eck-ee-no-CACK-tus) *grusonii* is the popular golden barrel. It has beautiful golden spines symmetrically arranged on a green body. It may eventually grow to 3 feet in diameter and produce yellow flowers around the top. Large golden barrels are very expensive; if you decide to buy one, be sure the plant you select is well rooted and nursery grown, not recently pulled up in the desert.

Echinocereus (eck-een-oh-SEAR-ee-us) *reichenbachii* is a small globe seldom more than 6 inches high when grown indoors. It is covered with stiff, flattened spines. In season it will be nearly covered by purple flowers. *E. rigidissimus* is of similar size and may also bear purple flowers. It is worth growing just to see the perfectly symmetrical arrangement of the flattened spines, which grow in rows.

Echinopsis (eck-in-OPP-sis) *multiplex* is the old-fashioned Easter-lily cactus. It is one of the best small (6 inches tall) barrel-type cacti to grow as a flowering house plant. The blooms have pretty rosy-red petals.

Lobivia (loh-BIV-ee-uh) is a popular cactus among amateur collectors because it grows small (it seldom needs a pot larger than 5 inches in diameter) and bears beautiful flowers. If these are to appear on schedule in spring or summer, it is necessary in winter to keep the plants nearly dry in a cold room (40 to 55 degrees) where there is plenty of fresh air.

Echinocactus grusonii (Golden barrel cactus) A-38; *Echinocereus reichenbachii* A-39; *E. rigidissimus* A-40; *Echinopsis multiplex* (Easter-lily cactus) A-41; *Lobivia* A-42.

Mammillaria (mam-mil-LAY-ree-uh) represents one of the most popular groupings of cacti for growing as house plants. Most develop short, round bodies or small columns, often with attractive spines arranged in eye-catching, symmetrical designs. The relatively small flowers, often encircling the top of the plant, are an added feature. The plant blooms most successfully if it is kept nearly dry in winter and at a temperature of 45 to 55 degrees.

Notocactus (noh-toh-CACK-tus) species such as *ottonis* (pictured on page 82), *rutilans,* and *haselbergii* are prized for beautiful flowers, which appear on plants that may be no more than 2 inches high. For best flowering, keep dry and cool (50 to 60 degrees) in the winter.

Opuntia (oh-PUNT-ee-uh) is the familiar prickly-pear cactus. Some grow tall, as the one shown opposite, while others are miniatures for small pots or desertscape plantings. Some are spineless, others wickedly thorny; be very careful in handling them.

Rebutia (ruh-BOOT-ee-uh) is similar in all respects to *Lobivia* —it is small, almost miniature, with wonderful flowers. Culture is the same.

Jungle cacti of the Christmas-cactus type, including *Rhipsalidopsis, Schlumbergera,* and *Zygocactus,* are discussed in Chapter 8. The leafy *Epiphyllum* (epp-ee-FILL-um), called orchid cactus, makes a handsome hanging-basket plant in a sunny east or west window. Grow it in a mixture of 2 parts all-purpose potting soil to 1 part perlite. Keep evenly moist in the spring and the summer; in the fall and the winter, water only enough to keep the leaves from shrinking. Mist the leaves frequently. *Rhipsalis* and *Hatiora* require similar care and make fascinating basket plants.

LIGHT: Ideal is a sunny south window; adapts to sunny east or west window. Young cacti grow well in fluorescent light; see page 82.

TEMPERATURE: Average house in winter, except as noted in individual descriptions for cacti that need a cold period in winter to set buds.

POTTING SOIL: Cactus mix (see Chapter 3).

WATERING NEEDS: Water well. Within an hour, pour off the water remaining in the saucer. Do not water again until the surface soil feels dry. But do not wait to water until the soil is bone-dry. Shower plant occasionally to clean away dust.

FEEDING: Feed with all-purpose plant food in spring and summer; little or no feeding is recommended in fall and winter.

PROBLEMS: Insufficient light causes spindly, malformed growth. Too much water, fertilizer, and warmth in winter will prevent flowering. Mealybugs and scale insects may attack; see Chapter 4 for treatment. If the skin of a cactus is broken by careless handling, tiny black thrips (an insect) or red spider mites may attack, causing a portion of the body to be sunken and discolored (see Chapter 4).

CONTAINERS: Standard plastic or clay pot, tub, or hanging basket.

PROPAGATION: Plant seeds, division, or root tip cuttings, ideally in spring or summer.

Pronunciations are given in text above. Cactus Family • *Mammillaria* A-43; *Notocactus* A-44; *Opuntia* (Prickly pear cactus) A-45; *Rebutia* A-46; *Epiphyllum* (Orchid cactus) A-47; *Rhipsalis* A-48; *Hatiora* A-49.

CALADIUM

Miniature caladium; 3-inch pot.   Hybrid caladium; 6-inch pot.

LIVING WITH IT: The big caladiums are grown in containers outdoors in summer for their colorful leaves, but they also make beautiful fancy-foliage plants indoors. They grow best during the long hours of summer daylight. As the shorter days of autumn approach, growth slows, the insignificant flowers appear, mostly hidden by the leaves, and a dormant season begins (see below and Chapter 4). Miniature caladium (*C. humboldtii*) and dwarf hybrids will grow well in a fluorescent-light garden where the lights burn 16 hours daily. If they also have warmth, their season will last longer, as much as 8 months.

LIGHT: Ideal is a sunny east or west window, or a bright north window; adapts to full sun if kept evenly moist. For best leaf growth, plant tubers in late winter or early spring; as days grow short in autumn, set away to rest in a dark but warm closet. A minimum 4-month resting period is needed once each year.
TEMPERATURE: Average house during the winter; suffers under 62 degrees while in active growth, under 50 degrees while resting.
POTTING SOIL: All-purpose (see Chapter 3).
WATERING NEEDS: Water often enough to keep evenly moist while in active growth. While dormant, keep soil barely damp. Mist caladium frequently while in active growth.
FEEDING: Feed all-purpose plant food while in active growth; follow container directions. Do not feed while dormant.
PROBLEMS: Insufficient light causes weak stems and pale leaves.
CONTAINERS: Standard plastic or clay pot, or hanging basket. Miniature caladium thrives in a terrarium.
PROPAGATION: Plant tuber divisions (see Chapter 6).

Caladium (kuh-LAY-dee-um). Calla Family • *Caladium hybrids* A-50; *C. humboldtii* (Miniature caladium) A-51.

LIVING WITH IT:
The plant shown is in an 8-inch pot. Display on table, pedestal, or floor. This dwarf citrus is well loved because of its shiny evergreen leaves and the fragrant white flowers that bloom intermittently most of the year. These are followed by small oranges. Flowers, immature lime-green fruit, and bright oranges may all be on the plant at the same time. The oranges are sour and are perfect for making marmalade. This citrus, like the smaller Meyer lemon and Otaheite orange, is easy to grow if certain conditions are met. As with other woody plants, severe drying causes most of the

leaves to fall, and the plant may die. Fresh, circulating air is needed during winter heating. Overwatering, especially in cloudy winter weather, may cause leaf drop. If leaves on a healthy citrus show yellow mottling, lack of soil acidity is probably the cause. Feed with an acid-type fertilizer or chelated iron. A summer outdoors in partial shade will give the plant renewed vigor.

LIGHT: Full sun in an east, south, or west window.
TEMPERATURE: Average house in winter, ideally a range of 60 to 70 degrees during the heating season.
POTTING SOIL: African-violet (see Chapter 3).
WATERING NEEDS: Keep soil evenly moist. Occasional slight drying is desirable. Avoid extremes of wetness or dryness; see above.
FEEDING: Feed blooming-type all year; also see above. Mist leaves regularly to ward off attacks of red spider mites.
CONTAINERS: Standard clay or plastic pot, or tub.
PROPAGATION: Root cuttings of half-ripened wood, in spring or summer.

Citrus (SIT-truss). Citrus Family • *Citrus mitis* (Calamondin) A-52.

CALATHEA

LIVING WITH IT:
The plant shown is in a
5-inch pot. Display
on table, shelf, sill, or
on the floor in an
arrangement with
other plants. Calathea
resembles the popular
prayer plant, or
maranta. The main
difference—other than
botanical—is that
calatheas are less
prone to brown leaf
tips. Calatheas are
sometimes hard to find;
if you come across
one, buy it, give it good
care, and soon there
will be enough offsets
to divide the plant into
two or more. These
plants are cultivated
for showy foliage.
In some varieties,
the reverse of the
leaves is maroon or
burgundy; this color
may carry onto the leaf surface in the form of spots, blotches, or veins.
Old plants in large pots–12-inch diameter– may spread as much as 24
inches, but a height over 18 inches is rare. All plants will thrive in
natural light strong enough to read or do needlework by. Young
calatheas are suited to growing in a fluorescent-light garden. Frequent
misting will help prevent brown leaf tips.

LIGHT: Ideal is a bright north window or about 2 feet from a sunny east
window, or similar brightness in a west window.
TEMPERATURE: Average house. Suffers if the temperature goes below
60 degrees.
POTTING SOIL: African-violet or terrarium soil (see Chapter 3).
WATERING NEEDS: Water about every 3 days, or often enough to keep
the soil evenly moist. Extended dryness causes dead leaf tips.
FEEDING: Feed all-purpose plant food all year round following con-
tainer directions for frequency of feeding.
PROBLEMS: Hot, dry atmosphere plus dry soil browns leaf tips.
CONTAINERS: Standard clay or plastic pot with drainage hole.
PROPAGATION: Plant root divisions, in spring or summer.

Calathea (kal-uh-THEE-uh). Arrowroot Family • *Calathea* A-53.

LIVING WITH IT:
The plants shown are in 6- and 8-inch pots; in two years they grow to about 18 inches tall and just as wide. Display on a table, sill, shelf, or floor. The evergreen foliage is always attractive; it may be plain green or green variegated with striking silver or white, or pale-yellow. From time to time, there are white flowers similar to a calla lily (to which it is related). These are followed by green berries, which turn bright orange-red and will remain attractive for months. This is a remarkable plant in that it never needs sun shining directly on the leaves. It will thrive, for example, as much as 20 feet from a bright window. A large Chinese evergreen makes a handsome accent when displayed on a tall wicker stool or other pedestal, especially in the down light of a ceiling-mounted floodlight. If this light is burned 6 to 8 hours every evening, no natural light is needed to sustain healthy growth. A cast-iron trouble-free plant.

LIGHT: No sun shining directly on the leaves. Otherwise, any light sufficiently bright to read or do needlework by.
TEMPERATURE: Average house; suffers below 55 degrees.
POTTING SOIL: Mix two parts all-purpose with one of vermiculite (see Chapter 3).
WATERING NEEDS: Water about every 3 days, or often enough to keep the soil in a range between wet and evenly moist. Occasional dryness causes little or no harmful effects.
FEEDING: Feed all-purpose all year; follow container directions.
PROBLEMS: Avoid cold drafts.
CONTAINERS: Standard clay or plastic pot, or a decorative container.
PROPAGATION: Root tip cuttings or plant seeds, in spring or summer.

Aglaonema (ag-loh-NEE-muh). Calla Family • *Aglaonema* (Chinese evergreen) A-54.

COFFEE TREE

LIVING WITH IT:
The plant shown is in an 11-inch pot. Display while young on sill, shelf, or table. Shrub or tree sizes may be placed on a low table or the floor. Seedlings and rooted cuttings produce beautiful foliage, each shiny, dark-green leaf waved along its edge. In time, the coffee plant matures enough to produce an annual crop of fragrant white flowers, followed by berries (the coffee beans), which change from green to bright red. Coffee is related to the gardenia. When without flowers or berries, the plants bear an amazing resemblance. Like other woody plants cultivated in containers, coffee resents drying out severely. If it dries enough to cause wilting, many old leaves will turn yellow and drop off even if the plant is watered immediately. A coffee plant does well in average house temperatures, but really prefers air that is pleasantly moist and fresh. In winter, mist the leaves daily; shower them monthly.

LIGHT: Two to 4 hours of sun in winter. With good culture, adapts to light of a north window. Young plants thrive in fluorescent light.
TEMPERATURE: Average house, but suffers under 55 degrees.
POTTING SOIL: African-violet, because it is acid (see Chapter 3).
WATERING NEEDS: Keep evenly moist; avoid extreme dryness, sogginess.
FEEDING: Feed all-purpose plant food all year, following container directions. Encourage mature plants to flower by feeding in spring and summer with blooming-type plant food.
PROBLEMS: Avoid drafts of hot, dry, stale air. Watch for mealybugs (see Chapter 4).
CONTAINERS: Standard clay or plastic pot, or tub, with drainage hole.
PROPAGATION: Sow seeds, root tip cuttings of new wood, in the winter or the spring.

Coffea (koff-EE-uh). Madder Family • *Coffea arabica* (Coffee tree) A-55.

COLEUS

LIVING WITH IT: Plants shown are in 6-, 5-, and 3-inch pots. All are varieties of one species; only leaf variegations differ. Display coleus, a medium-small plant, on sill, shelf, or table. Naturally tall-growing varieties may be trained into tree shapes (standards); see page 44. The trailing coleus, *C. rehneltianus,* and its varieties make fine hanging-basket plants. Of all the plants with variegated leaves, coleus offers the greatest range of colors, from brilliant to subdued, and it is one of the easiest of all house plants to grow. It has only one major flaw—it is the mealybug's favorite home. Coleus flowers are relatively insignificant. If allowed to bloom, they rob the plant of strength to put into foliage. So when you see tight clusters of flower buds at branch tips, pinch off. Young coleus, up to one year old, produce the best growth. It is a good idea to root cuttings once a year and discard the woody old plant.

LIGHT: Sunny east, south, or west window. Tolerates bright light of a north window. Grows perfectly in a fluorescent-light garden.
TEMPERATURE: Average house, but suffers under 55 degrees.
POTTING SOIL: All-purpose (see Chapter 3).
WATERING NEEDS: Water often enough to keep the soil evenly moist. When soil approaches dryness, coleus wilts immediately, but recovers quickly as soon as it is watered well.
FEEDING: Feed all-purpose all year; follow container directions.
PROBLEMS: Watch for mealybugs under the leaves and on the stems. If they appear, treat as described in Chapter 4.
CONTAINERS: Standard clay or plastic pot with drainage hole, or a hanging basket.
PROPAGATION: Sow seeds or root tip cuttings, in any season.

Coleus (KOH-lee-us). Mint Family • *Coleus* (Painted nettle) A-56; *C. rehneltianus* (Trailing coleus) A-57.

COLUMNEA

LIVING WITH IT:
The plant shown is in an 8-inch pot. Plant is attractive on sill, shelf, pedestal, or table or in a hanging basket. This relative of the African violet has only recently begun to be popular. Species like *Columnea arguta, C. gloriosa,* and *C. hirta* tend to flower seasonally. Recent hybrids created at Cornell University and by Michael Kartuz tend to be everblooming. Leaves vary from ½ to 2 inches long; some are medium green, others dark green to bronzy, reddish, or brownish. The tubular flowers with flared or reflexed (curving back) petals may be velvety red, orange, or yellow. Columneas will thrive and flower if given the same care as African violets. They seem to adapt to less than ideal conditions. Where there is not enough winter light and humidity for blooming, columneas still make fine foliage plants. Start new plants from cuttings every 2 years. Old growth tends to become woody and leafless at the base. Flowers appear on new growth.

LIGHT: Ideal is 2 or 3 hours of sun in an east, south, or west window. North light produces acceptable foliage, but flowering is not likely. Varieties that grow semiupright do well under fluorescent light.
TEMPERATURE: Average house; suffers below 55 degrees.
POTTING SOIL: African-violet (see Chapter 3).
WATERING NEEDS: Keep the soil evenly moist. Tolerates some soil dryness if the atmosphere has 50% or more humidity. Mist often.
FEEDING: Feed blooming all year; follow container directions.
PROBLEMS: Avoid chilly drafts, dry air, and soggy, wet soil.
CONTAINERS: Standard clay or plastic pot, or hanging basket.
PROPAGATION: Root tip cuttings, in any season.

Columnea (koh-LUM-nee-uh). Gesneriad Family • *Columnea* A-58.

COPPER-LEAF

LIVING WITH IT: The plant shown is in a 3-inch pot. When young, as this plant is, display on sill, shelf, table, or grow in a fluorescent-light garden. In a year or two, copper-leaf will grow to small shrub size and can be placed on a pedestal, a low table, or the floor. The flowers of copper-leaf (*Acalypha wilkesiana macafeana*) are insignificant, but the mature leaves are beautiful, an autumn red-brown with variegation of pinkish copper to rosy orange. The related chenille plant (*A. hispida*) requires the same culture, outlined below. This plant has plain green leaves and long, drooping flower spikes, as fuzzy as chenille, in colors that vary from off-white to muddy red-rose. There are also some fine pinks and rose-reds. Young chenille plants less than 12 inches tall may produce flower spikes long enough to droop lower than the base of the pot; these are most attractive displayed on pedestals or in hanging baskets.

LIGHT: Ideal is a sunny east, south, or west window in winter. In the summer months, place where less direct sun is received.

TEMPERATURE: Average house in winter; suffers below 55 or over 75.

POTTING SOIL: All-purpose (see Chapter 3).

WATERING NEEDS: Water about every 3 days, or often enough to keep the soil evenly moist at all times. Mist frequently.

FEEDING: Feed copper-leaf all-purpose plant food and chenille plant blooming plant food, all year; follow container directions.

PROBLEMS: Hot, dry, stale air may cause leaves to drop prematurely.

CONTAINERS: Standard plastic or clay pot, or tub, with drainage hole.

PROPAGATION: Root tip cuttings of half-ripened wood, in the spring or the summer.

Acalypha (ack-uh-LYE-fuh). Spurge Family • *Acalypha wilkesiana macafeana* (Copper-leaf) A-59; *A. hispida* (Chenille plant) A-60.

CORALBERRY

LIVING WITH IT:
The plant shown is in a 6-inch pot. This starts as a terrarium seedling or sill-size plant, grows large enough to display on a shelf, table, or floor, may grow to 4 feet tall, but seldom more than a foot wide. Its shiny, waxy, evergreen leaves have scalloped, crinkled edges. Clusters of fragrant white or pink flowers bloom in spring and summer. They are followed by a striking show of berries, which turn to polished red in fall and winter and often last until another crop appears. Plants of flowering size may be difficult to find, but an inexpensive seedling will reach this size in a few years and will live virtually forever. A mature coralberry is beautiful, but requires devoted care. It must never suffer from bone-dry soil or from blasts of dry, forced-air heat in winter.

LIGHT: Ideal is 2 or 3 hours of sunlight in winter, bright indirect light in summer; tolerates light of a north window all year.
TEMPERATURE: Average house in winter, preferably in a cool spot (not over 70 degrees). Suffers in artificial heat over 75.
POTTING SOIL: Half-and-half all-purpose and humus (see Chapter 3).
WATERING NEEDS: Water about every 3 days, or often enough to keep the soil evenly moist. Mist frequently.
FEEDING: Feed all-purpose plant food in fall and winter; feed blooming in spring and summer; follow container directions for frequency.
PROBLEMS: In hot, dry, stale air, red spider mites usually attack (see Chapter 4).
CONTAINERS: Standard clay or plastic pot with drainage hole.
PROPAGATION: Sow seeds, any time. Root cuttings of half-ripened wood, in spring or summer.

Ardisia (ar-DEE-zee-uh). Myrsine Family • *Ardisia* (Coralberry) A-61.

LIVING WITH IT:
The plant shown is in an 8-inch pot. Display, as a young plant, on sill, shelf, or table; older plants grow to shrub or tree size and make handsome accents set alone on the floor or a low table. The plants do produce flowers, but they are insignificant. It is for their colorful leaves that crotons are cultivated. These are shiny, leathery and have a variety of shapes. Outdoors in the tropics, crotons may reach heights of 15 or more feet and are often used in hedges in full sun. As a house plant, croton adapts amazingly well to low light, provided its other needs are met. It prefers fresh, circulating air with 30% or more humidity. Red spider mites are sure to attack the foliage in a hot, dry, stuffy atmosphere. Croton is a euphorbia; and like most members of this family, it thrives in soil that ranges from nicely moist to almost dry before watering. Growth is poor in heavy, badly drained soil.

LIGHT: Ideal is a sunny south window in winter. Tolerates east or west sun, and adapts to bright north light.

TEMPERATURE: Average house; suffers below 60 degrees.

POTTING SOIL: Cactus. Or you can mix two parts all-purpose to one part sand or perlite (see Chapter 3).

WATERING NEEDS: Water well. One hour later, drain off excess water in saucer. Repeat when surface begins to feel dry. Mist often.

FEEDING: Feed all-purpose plant food all year; follow container directions for frequency of feeding.

PROBLEMS: Hot, dry, stale air promotes red spider mites (see Chapter 4).

CONTAINERS: Standard clay or plastic pot, or tub, with drainage hole.

PROPAGATION: Root tip cuttings in soil, in spring or summer.

Codiaeum (koh-DEE-um). Spurge Family • *Codiaeum* (Croton) A-62.

DONKEY-TAIL

LIVING WITH IT:
The plant shown is in an 8-inch hanging basket. Display young plants on sill, shelf, or table. The "tails" grow to be several feet long on old and well-cared-for plants— and make the donkey-tail one of the most beautiful of foliage plants to display in a hanging basket or on a pedestal. Donkey-tail plants sell almost as quickly as they appear on the market, and it's a slow-growing plant, so there is no way to have a real specimen donkey-tail unless you grow it yourself. Though it is related to such cast-iron, hardy outdoor plants as *Sedum spectabile,* a donkey-tail (*S. morganianum*) cannot survive freezing. If yours is to be placed outdoors in summer, protect it from stormy winds; otherwise, the leaves will be blown from the stems. If you move it outdoors in warm weather, do not allow hot midday sun to shine on it until the leaves have time to adjust to outdoor light in a partly shaded place.

LIGHT: Ideal is a sunny east, south, or west window. Tolerates the light of a bright north window, but may grow spindly.
TEMPERATURE: Average house; suffers over 75 or under 55 degrees.
POTTING SOIL: All-purpose (see Chapter 3).
WATERING NEEDS: Water well, then not again until the surface soil begins to feel dry when you pinch some between your fingers.
FEEDING: Feed all-purpose plant food all year; follow container directions for frequency.
PROBLEMS: Soggy wet or extremely dry soil will cause leaf drop.
CONTAINERS: Standard plastic or clay pot, with a drainage hole, or a hanging basket.
PROPAGATION: Root leaf or tip cuttings, ideally in spring or summer.

Sedum (SEE-dum). Stonecrop Family • *Sedum morganianum* (Donkey-tail; Burro's tail) A-63.

Young plants of *Dracaena marginata* (left) and *D. fragrans massangeana* (right) grow here in 6-inch pots.

'Florida Beauty' (left), 4-inch pot; *D. deremensis* (center), 6-inch pot; *D. sanderiana* (right), 3-inch pot.

LIVING WITH IT: Dracaena is that tall plant with leathery leaves that look like corn leaves, which you often see in office gardens. Mature dracaenas vary in size from the 2-foot 'Florida Beauty' and *D. sanderiana* to indoor-tree size. Remarkably durable plants, they flourish in bright light with little or no direct sun. Young dracaenas will be stunted if not transplanted to a size-larger pot when roots fill the present one, but mature plants can be kept in the same container for years if fed regularly and top-dressed yearly (see Chapter 5).

'Florida Beauty,' a variety of *D. godseffiana*, is a small plant with twiggy stems and leaves like a large elm leaf with smooth edges.
In *D. godseffiana* the leaves are lightly spotted with yellow to creamy white on a dark-green background; 'Florida Beauty' has more of the creamy or yellow variegation than of green. Once in a while, one of these dracaenas blooms and develops showy red fruits, which can last for a year. Young plants of this species are great for terrariums and dish gardens. They also grow well in fluorescent light.

D. sanderiana, another small species, has slender cane stems with gray-green, white-striped leaves. It is sold by the millions in—or for— terrariums and dish gardens. Like other similar never-say-die house plants, such as heartleaf philodendron and Chinese evergreen, it is almost always neglected, taken for granted, and generally mistreated.

Dracaena godseffiana A-64; *D. g.* 'Florida Beauty' A-65; *D. sanderiana* A-66.

DRACAENA

A pity, because given more care and a shower now and then to clean the leaves, it can be a truly beautiful plant.

D. fragrans, old-fashioned corn plant, has plain-green leaves on sturdy, upright stems that will reach ceiling height in a few years. The leaves in this species, especially, resemble those of corn. Leaves of variety *massangeana* have chartreuse or golden-green stripes running down the center.

D. deremensis warneckei grows and looks much like *fragrans,* but the leaves are narrower and have thin white stripes. Both are especially good choices for locations where there is little light.

Madagascar dragon tree, *D. marginata,* has narrow, dark-green leaves, edged in burgundy; variety 'Tricolor' has green, pink, and white leaves. These droop gracefully in low light; but given a little sun, the leaves stand out stiffly in tufts on top of bare stems that may grow straight up or in fascinating angles and curves.

LIGHT: Ideal spot is a sunny east or west window, the light of a bright north window, or similar brightness a few feet from a south window. *D. fragrans* in particular will adapt perfectly to low light—for example, in an interior office where it receives only the illumination cast by overhead fluorescents burned approximately 9 hours daily.

TEMPERATURE: Average house in winter; suffers below 55 degrees or in hot, dry heat above 80 degrees. Daily misting helps, especially if the atmosphere is dry. Sponge or shower the leaves clean once a month.

POTTING SOIL: All-purpose (see Chapter 3).

WATERING NEEDS: Water often enough to keep the soil evenly moist, but don't keep it soggy. *D. marginata* is the least tolerant of overwatering. Soil allowed to become severely dry will cause many of the older leaves of *D. marginata* and *D. godseffiana* ('Florida Beauty') to turn yellow and fall from the stems. Other types of dracaena react to severe dryness with leaf tips that turn brown and die.

FEEDING: Feed with an all-purpose plant food all year; follow the container directions for frequency.

PROBLEMS: A cunning cat may chew off the tender leaf tips of *D. marginata* while you're not looking, but you'll recognize the telltale signs. A cat may also use the characteristically bare trunks of an older *marginata* as a scratching post. Otherwise, dracaenas are remarkably free from pests. *Marginata* is the exception; it is prone to red-spider-mite attack in a hot, dry, stale atmosphere. If the soil dries out severely, any dracaena growing in a hot, dry atmosphere will develop brown leaf tips; *sanderiana* is especially vulnerable. Any dracaena that grows too tall may be shortened by air-layering (see Chapter 6). After you have removed the top part rooted by the air-layering process, the bottom trunk, now bare, will usually sprout again and form a new plant.

CONTAINERS: Standard plastic or clay pot, or tub, with good drainage.

PROPAGATION: Root tip cuttings or air-layer, in any season.

Dracaena (druh-SEE-nuh). Lily Family • *Dracaena fragrans* A-67; *D. f. massangeana* A-68; *D. deremensis warneckei* A-69; *D. marginata* (Madagascar dragon tree) A-70.

LIVING WITH IT:
The plant shown is in an 8-inch pot. When a plant is young, as this one is, display on a sill, shelf, or table. Dumbcane is often planted in terrariums, but grows too quickly for this use. In time, older dumbcanes reach to the ceiling and may spread several feet across. Mature leaves can measure 18 by 12 inches. There are varieties with leaves mostly green with the white variegation (*Dieffenbachia amoena*), or the pale chartreuse with dark-green edges and veins, ('Rudolph Roehrs'). The stem juice is poisonous; if touched to tongue, it causes painful swelling and paralysis, A

mature plant from a greenhouse keeps well for months in dim light; but for healthy growth to continue, it needs bright light. A common complaint about dumbcane is that, as the trunks grow tall, older leaves tend to fall off. Sometimes the effect is to create an interesting indoor tree. If the results are ugly, however, air-layering is the answer. See Chapter 6 for details about the propagation method.

LIGHT: Ideal is a sunny east or west window in winter; less light is needed in summer. Adapts to bright north light.
TEMPERATURE: Average house in winter; suffers below 60 degrees.
POTTING SOIL: All-purpose (see Chapter 3).
WATERING NEEDS: Water often enough to keep evenly moist. Mist frequently. Severe dryness causes older leaves to yellow and die.
FEEDING: Feed all-purpose all year; follow container directions.
PROBLEMS: Red spider mites will attack in hot, dry, stale air; see Chapter 4 for treatment. Stake ungainly, tall branches.
CONTAINERS: Standard plastic or clay pot, or tub.
PROPAGATION: Root tip cuttings or air-layer, ideally in spring.

Dieffenbachia (deef-in-BOCK-ee-uh). Calla Family • *Dieffenbachia* (Dumbcane) A-71.

ECHEVERIA

LIVING WITH IT:
The plant shown is in an 8-inch pot. Display this little succulent on sill, shelf, table, in a desertscape, or grow in a fluorescent-light garden. Or plant several in a bonsai pot or tray. The first time you see the perfectly symmetrical rosette of this plant, the reaction is almost sure to be, "What is that beautiful green (or blue-green) rose?" The echeverias with hairless leaves (some are fuzzy) do indeed look like roses. They are among the best of succulents for growing as house plants. In time, offsets (see Chapter 6) that grow around the mother plant, hen-and-chickens style, will fill the pot with rosettes. Seasonal flowers that rise from these are showy in almost all varieties, but it is for the beautiful foliage year-in and year-out that echeverias are prized.

LIGHT: Ideal is a sunny east, south, or west window all year, or about 4 inches below the tubes of a fluorescent-light garden.
TEMPERATURE: Average house, ideally not over 70 degrees in winter.
POTTING SOIL: Cactus (see Chapter 3).
WATERING NEEDS: Water well, then not again until the surface soil begins to feel dry. If you let the plant become completely dry, the older leaves will die.
FEEDING: Feed all-purpose plant-food all year; follow container directions. If mature plants do not flower, feed with blooming-type plant food, especially in late winter and spring.
PROBLEMS: Insufficient light causes pale, spindly growth.
CONTAINERS: Standard plastic or clay pot; also see above.
PROPAGATION: Root leaf cuttings, or remove and root offsets, in spring or when offsets appear.

Echeveria (eck-uh-VEER-ee-uh). Stonecrop Family • *Echeveria* A-72.

LIVING WITH IT: The plant shown is in a 3-inch pot. Display on sill, shelf, table, pedestal, or as a hanging-basket plant. The episcia, which is related to the African violet, was once called flame violet because of the scarlet flowers of some species. This name is seldom used. Episcia grows well in conditions that suit African violets, but needs more winter warmth, more frequent watering, and 40% or more humidity. Young plants thrive in a terrarium, but unless the stolons (runners like those strawberry plants throw out) are kept pinched off, it will soon outgrow its space. In the right

conditions, episcias make strikingly beautiful basket plants. The veined and variegated foliage may be green, bronze, silver, or pink; flowers may be white, yellow, pink, orange, red, or blue. Episcias grow to perfection under fluorescent light. If stolons begin to crowd the space, remove and root in soil to create new plants.

LIGHT: Ideal is 2 or 3 hours of sun in winter; bright, indirect light is sufficient in summer. Thrives in fluorescent light.

TEMPERATURE: Average house, on warm side. Suffers under 60 degrees. Avoid cold drafts in winter, from air-conditioning in summer.

POTTING SOIL: African-violet (see Chapter 3).

WATERING NEEDS: Water enough to keep soil evenly moist. Mist often.

FEEDING: Feed all-purpose plant food all year; follow container directions for rapid foliage growth. Feed blooming plant food any time, but especially spring and summer.

PROBLEMS: Avoid dry air, cold drafts, poorly drained soil.

CONTAINERS: Standard clay or plastic pot, drainage hole; hanging basket.

PROPAGATION: Root stolons, in any season.

Episcia (ee-PISH-uh). Gesneriad Family • *Episcia* (Flame violet) A-73.

EUONYMUS

LIVING WITH IT:
The plant shown is in a 4-inch pot. Display on sill, shelf, table, or grow in terrarium or fluorescent-light garden. This small-leaved evergreen is the variety *Euonymus japonicus microphyllus variegatus.* Hardy out of doors in all but the coldest climates, it makes a fine house plant. Two other *E. japonicus* varieties, with larger leaves, grow into attractive foliage plants with little or no pruning. They are *medio-pictus* (dark-green edges with gold centers) and 'Silver Queen' (white edges, dark-green centers). They also are excellent subjects for growing indoors year round as bonsai. Bonsai is the Japanese word for woody shrubs or trees that are dwarfed by root and top pruning and kept for decades, sometimes centuries, in small pots or trays. The euonymus shown in the photograph also is useful in the creation of a miniature landscape in a large dish garden or open terrarium.

LIGHT: Ideal is a bright north window, a sunny east or west window, or similar brightness a few feet from a south window.
TEMPERATURE: Ideal is 60 to 70 degrees in winter; suffers over 75 degrees. Provide fresh, circulating air.
POTTING SOIL: All-purpose (see Chapter 3).
WATERING NEEDS: Water often enough to keep evenly moist. Never allow euonymus to dry out. Frequent misting helps.
FEEDING: Feed all-purpose all year; follow container directions.
PROBLEMS: Hot, dry, stale air invites red spider mites (see Chapter 4).
CONTAINERS: Standard plastic or clay pot; see also above.
PROPAGATION: Root cuttings of half-ripened wood, ideally in spring.

Euonymus (yew-ON-ee-muss). Bittersweet Family • *Euonymus japonicus microphyllus variegatus* A-74; *E. j. medio-pictus* A-75; *E. j.* 'Silver Queen' A-76.

Pencil euphorbia is in a 13-inch tub.

Hatrack (left), 13-inch tub; 'Bojeri' crown-of-thorns (right), 6-inch pot.

LIVING WITH IT:

A euphorbia may be as leafy and beautiful as a flowering poinsettia during the Christmas season (the poinsettia, which is *Euphorbia pulcherrima,* is discussed in Chapter 8), or as leafless and bizarre as the pencil euphorbia (*E. tirucallii*) shown here. There are also kinds with cactuslike thorns. The most common of these is the crown-of-thorns, *E. milii* whose dwarf variety, 'Bojeri,' is pictured here in flower. These and other succulent euphorbias are among the toughest of all house plants. They are able to survive, even thrive, in hot, dry air and in soil that is sometimes dry. Hatrack euphorbia (shown) is also called candelabra plant, for obvious reasons. It is *E. lactea.* While this plant is young, it can be accommodated on a sill, shelf, table, or even in a fluorescent-light garden. However, it grows with fair speed and will soon require display on a low table, pedestal, or on the floor. Hatrack is best treated as a piece of living sculpture, spotlighted at night to emphasize its shape and to set apart from other plants that might detract from it. Specimens 6 feet tall are not unusual. Crown-of-thorns is available in several forms, from the small 'Bojeri' to kinds with thorny stems almost as large as those of hatrack. New stem growth is accompanied by bright-green leaves and often by orange-red flowers. Stems of the smaller kinds can be trained to grow around a circle of wire anchored in the pot. *E. tirucallii* (pictured) is usually called

Euphorbia tirucallii (Pencil euphorbia; Milk bush) A-77; *E. milii* (Crown-of-thorns) A-78; *E. m. 'Bojeri'* (Dwarf crown-of-thorns) A-79; *E. lactea* (Hatrack) A-80; *E. lactea cristata* (Brain cactus) A-81; *E. obesa* A-82.

EUPHORBIA

milk-bush, an unfortunate name for a plant with poisonous, milky juice in the stems. Sometimes it is called pencil-cactus, also unfortunate since it is not a cactus. Pencil plant is a better name. Look closely, and if you have a sense of humor, you may want to call it "take me to your leader." In time, this euphorbia will grow to 6 feet or taller and may require staking. Like hatrack, older specimens will live for several months in low-light areas, but then they must have equal time in direct sun to maintain good health.

Large, upright species of *Euphorbia* that resemble hatrack include *coerulescens, hermentiana, ingens, lemaireana, neutra, trigona,* and *virosa.* Any one of these, but hatrack in particular, may be found in a crested form. Euphorbias, like cacti with crested tops, may seem fascinating or revolting, depending on how you feel about plant oddities. Crested hatrack is known as *E. lactea cristata.* Lots of growers call it brain cactus. Other crested kinds may have the word *monstrosa* added to their botanical names, and they are indeed monstrosities of the vegetable kingdom. All of these require the same care as other euphorbias. The oddities are most interesting if paired with a plant of normal shape. This contrast emphasizes the strangeness of the crested form. Spotlight the plants at night; the effect is eerie.

Typical of another interesting form of euphorbia is the globe-shaped *E. obesa.* It is rather like bishop's-cap cactus (see page 75). *E. bupleurifolia* displays yet another habit of growth. Leaves and flowers emerge from the top of a rough, pine-cone-like growth that emerges from the soil. When fitted to a bonsai container of suitable size, it is both strange and beautiful—as are most euphorbias.

LIGHT: Ideal is a sunny south window; acceptable is a sunny east or west window. Mature specimens can live for several months in bright north light or in similar brightness, but then they need time in a very sunny window to recuperate and resume growth. Dwarf 'Bojeri' can be cultivated in a fluorescent-light garden.
TEMPERATURE: Average house in winter; suffers below 55 degrees.
POTTING SOIL: Cactus mix (see Chapter 3).
WATERING NEEDS: Water well. Within an hour, pour off any excess moisture remaining in the saucer. Do not water again until the surface soil feels nearly dry when you rub it between your fingers.
FEEDING: Feed foliage-type euphorbias with all-purpose plant food all year, flowering types with blooming plant food all year. Follow directions on the container for quantity and frequency of the feedings.
PROBLEMS: Mealybugs occasionally attack euphorbias; see Chapter 4 for treatment. Otherwise, these plants are virtually indestructible. Insufficient light causes pale, spindly growth.
CONTAINERS: Standard plastic or clay pot, or tub, with drainage hole.
PROPAGATION: Root tip cuttings in any season. Let the cut stem dry overnight in open air before planting (see Chapter 6).

Euphorbia (yew-FOR-bee-uh). Spurge Family • *Euphorbia bupleurifolia* A-83.

LIVING WITH IT:
The plant shown is in a 5-inch pot. Display on sill, shelf, table, or fluorescent-light garden. This old-fashioned plant has always been popular with indoor gardeners who usually grow plants from seeds. Few suppliers sell plants. Exacum (a biennial) produces flowers on plants from seeds sown this year, then dies. Growing your own is easy; seeds grow as easily as do coleus seeds. One packet started in February or March will give all you want ready to bloom in fall and winter, with sturdy seedlings to share with friends. Summer-sown seeds bloom the following

winter, but the plants will be smaller than those started earlier. The starry lavender-blue flowers of exacum are fragrant and appear freely. If you clip off faded ones before the seed pods have time to develop, the amount of flowers and the flowering season will be increased. Seed catalogs sometimes list the variety *atropurpureum*, more purple.

LIGHT: Sunny east, south, or west window from fall to spring. Less direct sun is needed in summer. Thrives in fluorescent light.
TEMPERATURE: Ideally 55 to 70 degrees during winter heating season. If over 75 degrees, fresh, circulating air is vital.
POTTING SOIL: African-violet (see Chapter 3).
WATERING NEEDS: Water often enough to keep evenly moist. Mist often.
FEEDING: Feed all-purpose plant food in spring and summer, feed blooming type in fall and winter.
PROBLEMS: Dry soil and dry air will prevent flowering.
CONTAINERS: Standard clay or plastic pot with drainage hole.
PROPAGATION: Sow seeds, in winter, spring, or summer.

Exacum (EX-uh-kum). Gentian Family • *Exacum* A-84.

FATSHEDERA

LIVING WITH IT:
The plant shown is in a 6-inch pot. This grows to be a big plant best displayed at maturity on table or floor. Fatshedera is a horticultural "mule," developed by crossing English ivy (*Hedera*) with fatsia (*Aralia japonica*). Young plants that are cultivated in bright light stand without support. As the stems grow taller, staking is helpful. The five-lobed leaves are a refreshing bright green, and in a plant grouping their sturdy shape is a perfect foil for the delicate foliage of ferns. Like its parents, fatshedera during the winter heating season prefers a location with plenty of fresh, moist, circulating air. It is an excellent choice for an entryway, where fresh outdoor air will reach it frequently. Daily misting of the leaves will help keep the plant in good health through a long life and also prevent accumulation of dust. It is nearly trouble-free, except in hot, dry, stale air, when red spider mites are almost sure to attack (see Chapter 4). Do not let soil dry out severely.

LIGHT: Ideal is 2 or 3 hours of sun in winter; bright, indirect light is sufficient in summer. In a cool, but dark area such as an entryway, an incandescent floodlight may be used.
TEMPERATURE: Cool during winter season; suffers over 70 degrees.
POTTING SOIL: All-purpose (see Chapter 3).
WATERING NEEDS: Water often enough to keep soil evenly moist.
FEEDING: Feed all-purpose plant food year round.
PROBLEMS: Hot, dry, stale air encourages red spider mites.
CONTAINERS: Standard clay or plastic pot with drainage hole.
PROPAGATION: Root tip cuttings, in any season.

Fatshedera (fat-SHED-er-uh). Ginseng Family • *Fatshedera* A-85.

LIVING WITH IT:

Small, young ferns may be displayed on sill, shelf, table, or in a fluorescent-light garden or terrarium. In time, most grow large enough to display on a pedestal or in a hanging basket. A major appeal of ferns is that they thrive in bright light indoors, but need little or no direct sun. They also offer infinite variety, unusual growth habits, and foliage of a refreshing green. Ferns will not flourish on neglect —for example, in soil allowed to dry out frequently or in soil that drains poorly and becomes stagnant or sour-smelling. They wither quickly if placed in a draft of hot, dry air, yet thrive on common-sense, tender loving care (outlined in specifics at the end of this section, on page 110). And insect pests almost never attack these plants, even though the foliage of most ferns looks delicate. Because there are so many ferns in cultivation in such a variety of sizes and leaf shapes, indoor gardeners enjoy collecting them. Ten of the most popular and outstanding kinds of groups of ferns are discussed in the text that follows, beginning with the easiest to grow and proceeding to the most difficult. If you happen to have ideal conditions for a

Ferns, clockwise from top: bird's-nest, 11-inch pot; maidenhair, 6-inch pot; Fluffy Ruffles, 6-inch pot; and pteris, 6-inch pot.

Ferns, clockwise from top: Boston, 11-inch pot; bear's-paw, 8-inch pot; rabbit's-foot, 6-inch pot; and holly fern, 8-inch pot.

Staghorn fern mounted on 10-inch bark base.

FERNS

tree fern, ranked here as the most difficult kind of fern to grow, you may disagree; but under average indoor conditions, tree fern is hard to grow, while holly fern is easy.

Holly fern (species of *Cyrtomium;* sear-TOH-mee-um) has thick, leathery, relatively large leaves that are somewhat similar to those of the holly cultivated in outdoor gardens. *C. falcatum* is more delicate in appearance than its tougher, more compact, and more easily cultivated variety, *rochefordianum.* An established holly fern will survive as much neglect as will almost any house plant. If you treat it well, it will have so many fronds that you can afford to cut a few occasionally to use with flowers for a table centerpiece.

The rabbit's-foot ferns (species of *Davallia;* duh-VAL-ee-uh) have such finely cut and delicate-appearing fronds it is hard to believe they are among the most easily grown. The ferns' common names refer to their knobby, hairy rhizomes (equivalent of roots), which creep along the soil surface and from which the fronds grow. *D. fejeensis,* its variety *plumosa* (the fronds are more finely cut), *D. bullata mariesii,* and *D. trichomanioides* are similar in appearance, and all make incredibly beautiful hanging-basket plants. In time, the rhizomes will creep over the edges and down the sides of the container, completely surrounding it with "rabbit's feet" and fine greenery.

The bear's-paw ferns (species of *Polypodium;* polly-POH-dee-um), like the rabbit's-foot, have creeping rhizomes, but they are larger and have attractive cinnamon-colored "fur." Blue fern (because the fronds are bluish green), *P. aureum mandaianum,* is the most easily cultivated. It is not only one of the best large indoor ferns, but also one of the best of all large foliage plants to grow indoors on a pedestal or in a hanging basket. Place it where the light is bright but there is little or no direct sun. It is amazingly durable and a very good choice for indoor gardens in the trying conditions of commercial plantings such as those in office buildings and jetport lobbies.

Boston fern, while the most commonly cultivated, is not necessarily cast-iron in disposition. In practice, most kinds of *Nephrolepis* (neff-roh-LEEP-iss) are called Boston fern. Technically, this common name belongs to *N. exaltata bostoniensis.* There are many other variations of *N. exaltata,* including the frilly 'Fluffy Ruffles,' 'Norwoodii,' and 'Whitmanii,' plus the more delicate appearing 'Verona' and 'Smithii.' During the winter heating season, all prefer an atmosphere that is moist with fresh, circulating air on the cool side (ideally 60 to 70 degrees). They will survive some heat if they are misted frequently. Boston ferns in general seem to resent being handled, and they don't like changes in environment or transplanting. When healthy, all these ferns send out long, slender, yarnlike runners, which may be left to grow or clipped off. If one of these runners finds some moist soil, the tip will root and send up a baby fern.

Bird's-nest ferns (species of *Asplenium;* ass-PLEN-ee-um) are almost as easily grown as the holly fern; but if the soil dries out even

---

Cyrtomium (Holly fern) A-86; *Davallia* (Rabbit's foot fern) A-87; *Polypodium* (Bear's paw fern) A-88; *Nephrolepis exaltata bostoniensis* (Boston fern) A-89; *N. e.* 'Fluffy Ruffles' A-90; *Asplenium* (Bird's-nest fern) A-91.

once, the broad, leathery, shiny green fronds develop ugly tan or brown spots. The common name refers to the hairy, dark-brown cone that forms in the center of the plant and produces the leaves. The spores (equivalent of seeds) that develop on the reverse of mature fronds are a handsome cinnamon to dark-brown color and are clustered in neat rows. Individual fronds may grow to 2 feet long and as much as 10 inches wide on a plant that has a spread of 2 feet.

The Victorian table ferns (species of *Pteris;* pronounced "terrace") were, in fact, grown as table decorations in the cool parlors of Victorian homes. Some are plain green, others are green with silvery-white markings. The fronds on a single plant may vary considerably in size, shape, and height, as well as in color. These table ferns will grow to perfection in a large terrarium or in open air where African violets, rex begonias, prayer plants, or other ferns thrive.

Maidenhair ferns (species of *Adiantum;* add-ee-ANT-um) are prized for their thin, wiry stems, often nearly black when mature, and their delicate, pale-green fronds. Easiest to grow indoors is *A. hispidulum;* if this one thrives for you, try the showier but more delicate kinds such as *A. tenerum* and *A. raddianum.* They are lovely, but are sensitive to any kind of neglect, dryness, and hot drafts.

The one true miniature fern that is easy to find is *Polystichum tsus-simense* (polly-STITCH-um soos-suh-MEN-see). It grows in a tuftlike clump seldom more than 4 or 5 inches high. The miniature fronds are rather like those of the rabbit's-foot fern. This is one of the best of all plants for a terrarium kept in bright natural light with little or no direct sun, or in a fluorescent-light garden. It is especially beautiful in the company of miniature rex begonias, miniature gloxinias, creeping selaginella, and miniature sweet flag (*Acorus gramineus pusillus* or the variegated form). Another way to enjoy *P. tsus-simense* is to place it, pot and all, in a small bell jar kept in bright natural light (no direct sun) or in a fluorescent-light garden. It will thrive inside the bell jar, where humidity will be constantly high and there won't be any hot, dry drafts.

The staghorn ferns (species of *Platycerium;* plat-ee-SEAR-ee-um) are among the most fascinating of all plants. They have a curious leaf formation and flourish when attached to a plaquelike piece of tree-fern bark, but any piece of wood will do. Attach a generous thickness of unmilled sphagnum moss to the support; then gently tie the base of the staghorn in place. After a few years, the plant looks uncannily like a giant pair of antlers mounted on the wall, except that these are green and growing. Staghorn ferns need an atmosphere that is always moist (50% or more humidity during the winter heating season) and misting at least twice a day. Mist the bark or wood on which the plant is mounted and the entire staghorn fern. Baby staghorns will thrive planted in a small pot of osmunda fiber or unmilled sphagnum moss. Place the pot inside a terrarium where constantly high humidity is maintained. Once the baby outgrows this miniature greenhouse, more care

Pteris (Victorian table fern) A-92; *Adiantum* (Maidenhair fern) A-93; *Polystichum tsus-simense* (Miniature fern) A-94; *Platycerium* (Staghorn fern) A-95.

FERNS

is required. Staghorn ferns grow so slowly, and are therefore so expensive to purchase, it is fair neither to the fern nor to yourself to buy one unless you are already a dedicated and successful indoor gardener. If you are such a gardener, however, a well-grown, well-cared-for staghorn fern can be a living work of art and your crowning glory.

There are many tree ferns in cultivation. Those that grow best indoors are species of *Cibotium* (see-BOAT-ee-um). With age, these form a rough or furry, dark-brown trunk several feet tall, crowned by a head of long, broad, and beautifully cut fronds spreading several feet. *C. schiedei* is a good choice for house culture. It needs warmth, high humidity, fresh air, a little sun, and frequent misting.

LIGHT: Ideal is near a sunny east or west window, in a bright north window, or in similar light a few feet from a south window. Moved gradually closer to a fully sunny south window, many ferns, including Boston, holly, and rabbit's-foot fern, will thrive there — in winter, particularly. Any kind of fern, but especially maidenhair varieties, that is young or small enough to be accommodated in a fluorescent-light garden will flourish.

TEMPERATURE: Ideal is 60 to 70 degrees during winter heating; tolerates 75 degrees in moist, fresh air; suffers below 55. Daily misting benefits all ferns (misting is a necessity for staghorn and maidenhair), unless they are growing in a room where a humidifier is used in winter. Shower ferns with tepid water monthly.

POTTING SOIL: African-violet or terrarium (see Chapter 3). For the special requirements of staghorn fern, see above.

WATERING NEEDS: Water often enough to keep the soil evenly moist. Dry soil causes leaf tips of Boston fern to die back and in hours can kill entire fronds of maidenhair and rabbit's-foot ferns.

FEEDING: Feed with an all-purpose plant food all year; follow directions on the container for quantity and frequency. Be very careful not to overfeed any fern.

PROBLEMS: Ferns are remarkably free of insects. Occasionally, mealybugs attack a Boston fern, and brown scale is not unusual on the bird's-nest types; see Chapter 4 for treatment. The tricky thing about brown scale on a fern is that it may be mistaken for the dark-brown clusters of spores that form naturally on the undersides of mature fronds; to make sure, examine with a magnifying glass. Ferns seem resistant to attack by red spider mites. Other than insects, the main problems with these plants have to do with the environment. Drafts of hot, dry air wither old growth and prevent new.

CONTAINERS: Standard plastic or clay pot, with drainage hole; or hanging basket or terrarium.

PROPAGATION: Plant spores, divisions, or rhizome cuttings in any season (see Chapter 6).

Cibotium schiedei (Tree fern) A-96.

LIVING WITH IT:
The taller plant here is *Ficus elastica decora* in an 11-inch pot. The smaller is *F. benjamina,* the weeping fig, in an 8-inch pot. They are the most popular indoor trees and, when mature, are very costly. The ficus loses its leaves when it changes to less light, although it will adapt to less light within reason. Young plants are not only less costly but they suffer less in the adaptation process.

The common rubber tree, *F. elastica,* has plain dark-green leaves. *F. retusa nitida* has leaves similar to those of *F. benjamina* but has more compact, upright branches and is easy to prune to a formal, rounded shape. *F. diversifolia* has inch-wide triangular leaves and grows to 2 feet. In summer and fall, it covers itself with ½-inch figs (inedible). *F. triangularis,* with triangular leaves 2 inches or more across, grows to tree size. Other shrub and tree ficus are sometimes available. The creeping figs (*F. pumila, F. radicans*) may be used to carpet the ground around tree ficus or as basket plants.

LIGHT: Sunny east or west window, or a few feet from a fully sunny south window. Will adapt to bright north light. Also see above.

TEMPERATURE: Average house in winter; suffers in artificial heat over 80 degrees or in temperatures below 55.

POTTING SOIL: All-purpose (see Chapter 3).

WATERING NEEDS: Water well; then not until surface soil nears dryness. Mist leaves often.

FEEDING: Feed all-purpose all year; follow container directions.

PROBLEMS: Extreme wetness or dryness, lack of light, cause leaf drop.

CONTAINERS: Standard clay or plastic pot, or tub.

PROPAGATION: Root tip cuttings, in spring or summer; or air-layer.

Ficus (FYE-kuss). Fig Family • *Ficus elastica decora* (Rubber tree) A-97; *F. benjamina* (Weeping fig) A-98; *F. retusa nitida* A-99; *F. diversifolia* A-100; *F. triangularis* A-101; *F. pumila* (Creeping fig) A-102; *F. radicans* (Creeping fig) A-103.

FITTONIA

LIVING WITH IT: The plant shown is in a 6-inch pot. Display this relatively small plant in a terrarium or on a sill or shelf. Mature plants can be used as table plants or as hanging-basket plants. Fittonia is cultivated for its showy leaves, which may have silvery-white or rosy-pink veins on a ground of dark green. The flowers, which seldom occur, are not showy. This is one of the most desirable of plants cultivated for pretty foliage as it grows compactly without constant pinching. Also it is not prone to dying leaf tips and margins even under conditions less than ideal. However, to look its best, it needs humidity of 30% or more during the winter heating season. You can keep it in a terrarium or in a moist place, such as a bathroom. If fittonia is cultivated in open air (not in a terrarium), misting the leaves with water is highly beneficial. Ideally it needs an area 8 to 10 inches in diameter in which to spread its leaves. As the plant begins to outgrow the space allotted for it in a terrarium, simply cut back the stems and use them as tip cuttings. Fittonia grows beautifully under fluorescent light.

LIGHT: Ideal is 2 or 3 hours of sun in winter; adapts to light in a north window and thrives under fluorescent light.
TEMPERATURE: Average house in winter, preferably 30% or more humidity.
POTTING SOIL: African-violet or all-purpose (see Chapter 3).
WATERING NEEDS: Water often enough to keep soil evenly moist.
FEEDING: Feed all-purpose all year; follow container directions.
PROBLEMS: Avoid hot, dry air, cold drafts, poorly drained soil.
CONTAINERS: Standard clay or plastic pot, hanging basket.
PROPAGATION: Root tip cuttings, in any season.

Fittonia (fit-TOH-nee-uh). Acanthus Family • *Fittonia* (Nerve plant) A-104.

LIVING WITH IT:
The tallest plant here, honeysuckle fuchsia, is in a 5-inch-pot; it is more easily cultivated than most fuchsias. The smaller plants (in 4- and 3-inch pots) are typical of hundreds of colors in hybrids. Some fuchsias reach for the ceiling; some droop.

Tall types can be easily trained as trees; droopers, as basket plants. Fuchsias are good house plants only if the atmosphere is cool (50 to 70 degrees), moist (30% or more humidity), with fresh air circulating freely.

Moved from greenhouse into a room where air is hot, dry, and stale, plants lose leaves and flowers. Hybrids are best kept dryish fall and winter. Repot in spring; prune to shape attractively and to remove dead branches. Honeysuckle fuchsia ('Gartenmeister Bohnstedt') is an everbloomer in windows where geraniums bloom.

LIGHT: Sunny east or west window, or a few feet from a sunny south window, from fall to spring; less direct sun in summer.

TEMPERATURE: Preferably not over 70 degrees during the winter heating season; suffers above 75 or below 50.

POTTING SOIL: African-violet (see Chapter 3).

WATERING NEEDS: Water often enough to keep evenly moist, except hybrids, which need a rest, as noted above. Honeysuckle fuchsia can be kept in active growth all year. Mist often.

FEEDING: Feed blooming type spring to fall, following container directions; do not feed in winter, except honeysuckle fuchsia.

PROBLEMS: See above. White fly and red spider mites may attack.

CONTAINERS: Standard clay or plastic pot, tub or hanging basket.

PROPAGATION: Root tip cuttings, in spring or summer.

Fuchsia (FEW-shuh). Evening-Primrose Family • *Fuchsia* hybrids A-105; *F.* 'Gartenmeister Bohnstedt' (Honeysuckle fuchsia) A-106.

GARDENIA

LIVING WITH IT:
The plant shown is in an 11-inch pot. When young, display on a sill, shelf, table, or grow in a fluorescent-light garden. Older plants become sizable shrubs, eventually small trees, to display on a low table or floor. They have beautiful, shiny dark-green leaves and bear white flowers with a heady fragrance. If conditions are to its liking, it is easy to grow. If not, you may find it temperamental. The touchiest period is when a greenhouse plant is brought into hot, dry, stale air. If it survives, it adapts surprisingly well. Temperatures and soil acidity are critical. Night temperatures over 70 and under 60 discourage flowering. Soil must be in an acid pH range of 5.0 to 5.5 (see Chapter 3) or leaves turn yellow and drop. Fresh, moist air circulating freely is a necessity, especially in the winter heating season. Mealybugs are a problem.

LIGHT: Full sun in an east, south, or west window in winter; less is acceptable in summer. Young gardenias grow well in fluorescent light.
TEMPERATURE: Ideal is 70 to 72 degrees in the daytime, with a drop to 62 degrees at night. Avoid hot, dry, stale air.
POTTING SOIL: African-violet (see Chapter 3).
WATERING NEEDS: Often enough to keep the soil evenly moist. Extremes of wetness or dryness will cause leaf and bud drop. Mist often.
FEEDING: Feed blooming plant food all year, following container directions. If leaves begin to yellow, feed acid-type plant food.
PROBLEMS: Hot, dry air in combination with dry soil causes old leaves and flower buds to die prematurely; also see above.
CONTAINERS: Standard clay or plastic pot, or tub, with drainage hole.
PROPAGATION: Root tip cuttings, in spring or summer.

Gardenia (gar-DEE-nee-uh). Madder Family • *Gardenia* A-107.

Fancyleaf miniature (left), 3-inch pot;
miniature geranium (right), 3-inch pot.

Common geranium (left), 11-inch tub;
fancyleaf form (right), 8-inch pot.

LIVING WITH IT: To believe that all geraniums look like the popular red-flowered type shown above is to believe that the world ends at the horizon. The flowers come in all colors, single or double, many are feathered or spotted in a contrasting color. By categories, there are miniatures, dwarfs, ivyleafs, fancyleafs, scenteds, regals (sometimes called Lady or Martha Washington geraniums). A catchall classification called odd and rare includes types known as bird's-egg, climbing, evening-scented, poinsettia- and sweet-William-flowered, tuberous-rooted, and succulent (with spinelike growths along the stems). All of these grow indoors, as will the hundreds of named varieties known as the common or zonal geranium. Zonal refers to the zone of contrasting color prominent in the leaves of some varieties.

Unfortunately, most commercial growers propagate fewer than a dozen varieties, and this is responsible for the notion that only a few geranium types are available. Unusual kinds can be found in catalogs. Geraniums resent being enclosed in a box for shipping, but they almost always survive though some leaves turn yellow and drop off.

Common or zonal geraniums: These are the kinds you see in most indoor gardens. There are single- and semidouble-flowered varieties in white, salmon, pink, and various reds. They are selected and propagated primarily for growing and flowering outdoors in warm weather. They survive winter indoors but don't flower too well. Some kinds available from house plant specialists bloom better in winter on more compact plants. Some you might like to try include 'Battle of Gettysburg' (orange center, violet edge); 'Maxime Kovalevski' (orange); 'Double Dryden' (cherry-red, white eye); 'Montmart' (double violet); 'Prince

---

Pelargonium (Common geranium) A-108.

GERANIUM

of Orange' (double, bright orange); and 'Radiance' (bright pink, white center). Even more interesting are 'Apple Blossom' (pink-edged white flowers like clusters of miniature bicolor roses); 'Bird's Egg' (dark-pink spots on lavender-pink ground); 'Double New Life' (red-and-white-striped flowers; also called 'Stars and Stripes'); 'Formosa' (bright pink; petals deeply fringed); 'Mr. Wren' (white-edged bright pink); 'Poinsettia' (shaggy petals of scarlet; also available in pink); and 'Sweet William' (picotee-edged single pink). These make fine house plants and may also be grown in containers outdoors in the summer in the same way ordinary geraniums can be grown.

Miniature and dwarf geraniums: These are exactly the same as common or zonal geraniums except that the miniatures grow less than 6 inches tall, the dwarfs less than 10 inches. Stems and leaves of all tend to be miniature, but individual flowers are approximately the same size as regular geraniums—there are merely fewer florets in each cluster. These are perfectly suited in size to a fluorescent-light garden or for growing as a collection on shelves placed in the sunniest window possible. If you love geraniums and have limited sunny window space, the miniatures and dwarfs will give you maximum variety in minimum space. They come in all geranium colors, single and double. Foliage may be plain green or vividly zoned. Dozens of named varieties are available, with such charming labels as 'Doc,' 'Dopey,' 'Sneezy,' 'Tweedle Dee,' 'Tweedle Dum,' and 'Zip.' They grow best in 2- to 4-inch standard pots. Or you can make a project of finding 2- to 4-inch ornamental ceramic bonsai containers and matching each geranium's color and branch structure to the container with the most complimentary shape and color. Outdoor shrubs and trees usually trained as bonsai cannot spend winter indoors in heated houses, but miniature and dwarf geraniums make excellent all-year bonsai house plants.

Ivyleaf geraniums: These are hybrids of *Pelargonium peltatum* that have thick, waxy leaves shaped like those of English ivy. The two plants are in no way related; but during winter heating season, both prefer an indoor atmosphere that is on the cool (60 to 70 degrees) side, with an abundance of fresh, moist, circulating air. A major difference between the two is that, while English ivy will thrive in bright light with little or no direct sun, ivyleaf geraniums need as much sun as they can possibly get in the winter for best growth. The ivyleaf geraniums produce some of the prettiest of indoor flowers if you can provide the conditions they need.

Ivyleaf geraniums are at their best planted in hanging baskets or in pots placed on pedestals or shelves where stems can cascade freely. The smallest ivyleaf geranium is 'Gay Baby.' It has bright-green leaves, sometimes nearly hidden by an abundance of small pink blooms. 'Sugar Baby' is similar in size and even more free-flowering. Standard-size ivyleafs include the colors shown in the photograph on the opposite page, plus pale pink and white. 'L'Elegante,' or sunset ivy geranium, has beautiful foliage that combines green, gray-green, creamy-white, and

Pelargonium (Miniature and Dwarf geranium) A-109; *P. peltatum* (Ivyleaf geranium) A-110.

116

Ivyleaf geraniums in 8-inch pots. These geraniums make excellent basket plants and bloom all winter.

Scented geraniums, clockwise from top: rose, 8-inch pot; nutmeg, 6-inch pot; and variegated lemon, 4-inch pot.

rosy-pink variegation. 'Crocodile' has the typical leaf of an ivy geranium, but it has a network of prominent gold veins; the flowers are pink. 'White Mesh' is similar, with creamy to chartreuse veins and pale-pink double flowers.

Fancyleaf geraniums: Geraniums called fancyleaf include forms of common geranium that have leaves prominently variegated with a second—and sometimes a third—color. The flowers produced by fancyleaf geraniums are a bonus, because the foliage alone makes them worth growing. 'Wilhelm Langguth' is shown in left photograph on page 115. Other showy fancyleafs include 'Alpha' (small golden-green leaves, each with a distinct brown ring; and single red flowers produced in abundance); 'Lady Pollock' (leaves green, orange, red, and yellow); 'Miss Burdett Coutts' (leaves green, cream, pink, and purple); and 'Mrs. Cox' (leaves green, pink, red, and yellow). The fancyleafs grow well in a fluorescent-light garden. Plant short, rooted cuttings, which can be kept compact by frequent pinching of the tips.

Scented geraniums: When you lightly squeeze or brush against the leaves of these geraniums, they give off a pungent scent, which, depending on the variety, may be that of rose, lemon, apple, apricot, filbert, ginger, lime, nutmeg, orange, strawberry, coconut, peppermint, or pine. From time to time, all the scented geraniums bear flowers, but they are cultivated primarily for their fragrant foliage. For blooms,

Pelargonium 'Wilhelm Langguth' (Fancyleaf geranium) A-111; Scented geranium A-112.

GERANIUM

some of the best kinds are filbert, ginger, orange, and 'Brilliant.'

Regal, Lady or Martha Washington geraniums: Hybrids of *Pelargonium domesticum,* often combined with other parents, make up this group. In the full bloom of late winter and spring, they are breathtaking and similar in appearance to and as beautiful as a magnificent potted azalea. One of the oldest hybrids, 'Mrs. Layal,' also called pansy geranium, is perhaps the best for growing as a house plant. The showier, newer hybrids should be cut back to 8 inches after flowering and fed all-purpose until January, then switched to a blooming type.

Odd and rare geraniums: All make interesting and surprisingly satisfactory house plants. The tuberous-rooted, succulent types rest in summer. Keep them nearly dry, and do not feed. In autumn, repot, and gradually apply more water until they are in active growth. Then begin to feed with blooming-type fertilizer, to promote winter and spring flowering. These prefer sandy soil, like that for cactus.

LIGHT: Ideal is a sunny south window in winter. Geraniums adapt to a sunny east or west window; but stems may grow spindly during long periods of cloudy weather in winter, and there will be few flowers. Geraniums that are moved outdoors for warm weather usually do not continue to flower well when brought inside. Instead, cut the stems back to 8 inches, and give them a winter rest. Store the pots in a cool, but frost-free place. Keep the soil barely moist. Repot in spring; set in a sunny place, and resume routine care. Miniatures may be cultivated permanently in a fluorescent-light garden.

TEMPERATURE: Ideal is 60 to 70 degrees during the winter heating season; tolerates 75 degrees, suffers under 55. Fresh, circulating air is essential for healthy geraniums.

POTTING SOIL: Mix 3 parts all-purpose with 1 part perlite or sand (see Chapter 3).

WATERING NEEDS: Water well. Within an hour, pour off any moisture remaining in the saucer. Do not water again until a pinch of soil feels nearly dry. Be wary—if soil becomes so dry that leaves wilt, all the older ones will turn yellow and die, as will the flower buds.

FEEDING: Feed with blooming-type plant food all year; follow directions on the container for quantity and frequency. All-purpose plant food may be used to promote rapid growth of cuttings, but the relatively high nitrogen content discourages flowering.

PROBLEMS: Hot, dry, stale air causes geraniums to develop spindly, weak stems and few if any flowers. Overwatering and poorly drained soil kept soggy will cause stems to rot and turn black at the soil line. If this happens, make tip cuttings of healthy growth, and discard the old plant. Geraniums are virtually pest-free.

CONTAINERS: Standard plastic or clay pot, tub, or hanging basket. Geraniums bloom best when slightly pot bound.

PROPAGATION: Plant seeds or root tip cuttings, in any season (see Chapter 6). Cuttings root well in a fluorescent-light garden.

Pelargonium (pel-are-GO-nee-um). Geranium Family • *Pelargonium domesticum* hybrids (Regal, Lady or Martha Washington geraniums) A-113.

LIVING WITH IT:
Red-flowered florists' gloxinia is shown in an 11-inch pot; lavender-flowered sinningia 'Doll Baby' in a 4-inch pot; miniature sinningia 'White Sprite' in a 5-inch glass container.

Miniatures are commonly called sinningias; larger plants, gloxinias. Dwarfs and miniatures have slipper-shape flowers; larger plants have slipper- or trumpet-shape flowers. Dwarfs will grow in moderately moist air or in a mostly closed terrarium. Miniatures prefer a closed terrarium. Gloxinias require lots of fresh air. The fleshy tubers are planted so tops are barely covered. Gloxinias started from seed form a tuber and bloom in 6 to 8 months. After flowering, cut off old gloxinia growth; new will sprout. The tiny sinningias are grown from seed in a closed terrarium.

LIGHT: Sunny east, south, or west window from fall to spring; less direct sun in summer. Gloxinias thrive in fluorescent-light gardens.
TEMPERATURE: Ideally 70 to 75 degrees in the daytime, with a drop to 65 to 70 degrees at night. Humidity of 30% or more is vital. See above.
POTTING SOIL: African-violet (see Chapter 3).
WATERING NEEDS: Keep evenly moist. Once a year after flowering, let rest for 2 months.
FEEDING: Feed blooming type all year (except during rest period); follow container directions for frequency.
PROBLEMS: Hot, cold, or dry drafts cause flower buds to die. Tiny black thrips (an insect; see Chapter 4) sometimes damage growth.
CONTAINERS: Standard clay or plastic pot; terrarium for miniatures.
PROPAGATION: Seeds, leaf or tip cuttings, or tuber division, in any season.

Sinningia (sin-IN-jee-uh). Gesneriad Family • *Sinningia* (Gloxinia) A-114; *S.* 'Doll Baby' A-115; *S. pusilla* 'White Sprite' (Miniature sinningia) A-116.

GOLD-DUST PLANT

LIVING WITH IT:
The plant shown is in a 3-inch pot. When it is young, display in terrarium or on sill or shelf. At maturity it becomes a woody shrub with individual leaves that grow 8 or more inches long and 2 inches wide, each dusted and spotted with gold. Outdoors it grows over 10 feet tall. A good selection if you are looking for a house plant that can produce a mass of foliage. At a distance, the gold markings give the effect of dappled sunlight. The gold-dust plant grows year-round outdoors in the air-polluted heart of New York City. When gradually hardened to cold, it survives winter temperatures of 20 degrees and lower. Tip cuttings 12 inches or so long from outdoor shrubs can be used in flower arrangements indoors. They will root easily in the water and may then be transferred to pots of moist soil. The gold-dust plant suffers if soil is allowed to dry and if it is kept in drafts of hot, dry, stale, forced-air heat during long winter months.

LIGHT: Ideal is 2 or 3 hours of sun in winter; bright, indirect light in summer; tolerates light of a north window all year.
TEMPERATURE: Coolness in winter, preferably not over 70 degrees. Suffers in artificial heat over 75 degrees.
POTTING SOIL: Half-and-half all-purpose and humus (see Chapter 3).
WATERING NEEDS: Water about every 3 days, enough to keep the soil evenly moist. Mist frequently.
FEEDING: Feed all-purpose all year; follow container directions.
PROBLEMS: Red spider mites will attack in hot, dry, stale air (see Chapter 4).
CONTAINERS: Standard clay or plastic pot, or tub, with drainage hole.
PROPAGATION: Root tip cuttings, preferably in spring or summer.

Aucuba (aw-KEW-buh). Dogwood Family • *Aucuba* (Gold-dust plant) A-117.

LIVING WITH IT:
The plant shown is in an 8-inch pot. Display young plants on sill or shelf; show off the graceful and pendulous branches of mature plants on a small table, a pedestal, or in a hanging basket. Grape-ivy (*Cissus rhombifolia*) is thought to be a diehard. Actually it only tolerates and survives neglect. To become a truly beautiful plant, which it should be, it has preferences worth catering to. Avoid severely dry soil and drafts of hot, dry air on the leaves. If you use grape-ivy as a hanging-basket plant, do not hang it in a warm, heated room. Grape ivy will grow in a dry atmosphere if temperature is on the cool side. Mist the leaves daily if possible, and shower them with tepid water once a month to keep them clean. Kangaroo vine, a relative, is treated elsewhere in this book. Other cissus worth growing include *C. adenopoda* (fuzzy leaves, olive-green above, burgundy underneath), *C. discolor* (exquisite foliage; requires high humidity), and *C. striata* (miniature grape-ivy).

LIGHT: Ideal is 2 or 3 hours of sun in winter; adapts to light in a north window. Grows well under fluorescent light.
TEMPERATURE: Average house, but suffers in blasts of forced-air heat over 75 degrees.
POTTING SOIL: All-purpose (see Chapter 3).
WATERING NEEDS: Water often enough to keep soil evenly moist; avoid extremes of wetness and dryness. Mist often.
FEEDING: Feel all-purpose all year; follow container directions.
PROBLEMS: Hot, dry, stale air are its main enemies (see above).
CONTAINERS: Standard clay or plastic pot, hanging basket.
PROPAGATION: Root tip cuttings in any season.

Cissus (SISS-us). Grape Family • *Cissus rhombifolia* (Grape-ivy) A-118; *C. adenopoda* A-119; *C. discolor* A-120; *C. striata* (Miniature grape-ivy) A-121.

HAWAIIAN TI PLANT

LIVING WITH IT:
The plant shown is in a 3-inch pot. While small, display on sill, shelf, table, or in a terrarium. Eventually it grows to shrub or tree size, for display on table, pedestal, or floor. Mature stems of this dracaena relative are cut into pieces 4 to 6 inches long and sold as "logs." When a log is placed on moist, sterile soil and kept pleasantly warm in bright light, dormant eyes sprout upward along it, roots grow downward, and a beautiful foliage plant develops. Because of the combination of color in the foliage — white, pink, rose, and green — Hawaiian ti is as showy as a flowering plant. It is sensitive to drafts of hot, dry air and to cold drafts. Careless watering, too much or not enough, or a combination, causes leaf tips and edges to turn brown. In hot, dry, stale air, red spider mites are likely to attack. To maintain the leaves in good health, shower or sponge them at least once a month. Daily misting helps.

LIGHT: Sunny east or west window, or a few feet from a sunny south window. Adapts to bright north light.
TEMPERATURE: Average house in winter; suffers in artificial heat over 80 degrees or in temperatures below 55. Avoid drafts.
POTTING SOIL: Mix 3 parts all-purpose with 1 part peat moss (see Chapter 3).
WATERING NEEDS: Water well. Do not water again until the surface soil begins to feel dry.
FEEDING: Feed all-purpose all year; follow container directions.
PROBLEMS: Temperature and moisture extremes, spider mites.
CONTAINERS: Standard clay or plastic pot, or tub.
PROPAGATION: Root "log" cuttings (see above) or tip cuttings, or air-layer, in any season.

Cordyline (kor-duh-LYE-nee). Lily Family • *Cordyline* (Hawaiian ti plant) A-122.

LIVING WITH IT: The plant shown is in a 5-inch pot. Display on sill, shelf, table, or in a fluorescent-light garden. This zebra haworthia (*H. fasciata*), is the most widely cultivated. It is one of perhaps a hundred succulents that grow with ease as house plants. Some kinds—*H. cuspidata,* for example—have fleshier leaves, with almost transparent tips or surfaces that let you see into the leaf. Haworthias, like many members of the Lily Family, have amazing tolerance for various lights. While zebra haworthia prefers lots of sun, it will live almost indefinitely and maintain its compact shape in bright light without sun. It is one of the best succulents for fluorescent-light gardens and is excellent in a miniature desert scene with other succulents and cacti. Insects almost never attack it, and occasional soil dryness causes little or no harm.

LIGHT: Ideal is a sunny east, south, or west window. Tolerates bright north light. Thrives in a fluorescent-light garden.

TEMPERATURE: Average house all year; suffers below 55 degrees.

POTTING SOIL: Cactus (see Chapter 3).

WATERING NEEDS: Water well, then not again until the soil surface is nearly dry. Good drainage is essential.

FEEDING: Feed all-purpose plant food all year; follow directions on the container for frequency.

PROBLEMS: Constant wetness about the roots, caused by overwatering and lack of drainage, may cause root rot. If this happens, remove from soil; wash off roots; trim off rotted ones; reroot plant in fresh soil.

CONTAINERS: Standard clay or plastic pot, or dish garden.

PROPAGATION: Remove and plant offsets in any season.

Haworthia (ha-WORTH-ee-uh). Lily Family • *Haworthia fasciata* (Zebra haworthia) A-123; *H. cuspidata* A-124.

HIBISCUS, CHINESE

LIVING WITH IT:
The plant shown is in an 11-inch pot. Display on table or floor. Sometimes you can buy one trained to tree shape. A favorite flowering shrub of the tropics, it is as easily cultivated as a wax begonia. Although the flamboyant flowers last only a day, buds appear year-round on new growth. Colors are pink, red, yellow, orange, and white, in singles and doubles, and there are hybrids in subtle pastels. The main requirement for constant bloom is abundant sunlight. Moderate humidity (30% or more) and freely circulating air also help all buds mature into perfect flowers. It is the nature of hibiscus to grow into large shrubs. You can prune them to convenient size at any time. If the soil dries out severely, many leaves will turn yellow and fall, as will any developing flower buds. Drafts of hot, dry air and soil that have become soggy from lack of proper drainage will cause similar symptoms. Chinese hibiscus benefits from spending the warm months outdoors in a sunny spot in the garden or on the patio.

LIGHT: Sunny east, south, or west window. When young, small plants grow and bloom well in a fluorescent-light garden.
TEMPERATURE: Average cool house in winter, between 60 and 70 degrees. Fresh, circulating air with 30% or more humidity is desirable.
POTTING SOIL: All-purpose (see Chapter 3).
WATERING NEEDS: Water enough to keep evenly moist; see above.
FEEDING: Feed blooming all year; follow container directions.
PROBLEMS: In stale, hot, dry air, red spider mites will attack.
CONTAINERS: Standard clay or plastic pot, or tub.
PROPAGATION: Root cuttings of half-ripened wood, ideally spring, or summer.

Hibiscus (high-BISS-kuss). Mallow Family • *Hibiscus rosa-sinensis* (Chinese hibiscus) A-125.

LIVING WITH IT:
The plant shown is in a 6-inch pot. Display young plants on sill or shelf. Mature plants are graceful enough to be featured on a table or to be used as hanging basket plants. Outdoors, impatiens is one of the best flowering plants for container growing in shaded or semishaded corners. In climates that don't necessitate winter heating, it is a good house plant. Also, it grows well under fluorescent-light if the air is pleasantly moist and circulates freely.

In overheated, dry homes, plants brought indoors at summer's end often fall prey to red spider mite. It can survive severe wilting caused by dry soil, but many older leaves will die. Today's hybrids include types that grow mostly upright to about 12 inches and others that form mounds 6 to 8 inches high and 12 inches across. Flowers may be white, orange, red, pink, or red-and-white variegated. Foliage may be light green, olive-green, or reddish brown. Cyclone hybrids have strikingly variegated foliage, with intense markings of gold, orange, pink, red, cream with various greens.

LIGHT: Ideal is 2 or 3 hours of sun in winter. Survives north light, but will grow leggy and flower only in summer.
TEMPERATURE: Average house; suffers under 55 degrees. Fresh, circulating air, with 30% or more humidity, is a necessity.
POTTING SOIL: All-purpose or African-violet (see Chapter 3).
WATERING NEEDS: Keep evenly moist; avoid excess wetness or dryness. Mist often.
FEEDING: Feed blooming type all year; follow container directions.
PROBLEMS: Hot, dry, stale air invites red spider mite (see Chapter 4).
CONTAINERS: Standard clay or plastic pot with drainage hole.
PROPAGATION: Sow seeds or root tip cuttings, in any season.

Impatiens (im-PAY-shenz). Balsam Family • *Impatiens* (Busy Lizzie; Patient Lizzie) A-126.

English ivies 'Pin Oak' (left) and *denticulata* (right) in 3-inch pots; 'Merion Beauty' (center) in 4-inch pot.

'My Heart' (left) and 'Sylvanian' (right) grow in 3-inch pots; 'Glacier' (center) is growing in a 4-inch pot.

LIVING WITH IT: English ivy is a darling of indoor gardeners because of its good looks and versatility and because it is easy to grow. It can be anything from a small-leaved, free-form, fuzzy little drooper that graces a bare corner to a large, stylized topiary. Young rooted cuttings of the small-leaved ivies will flourish in a cool terrarium with good air circulation. Mature plants remain small enough to display on sill, shelf, table, pedestal, or in a hanging basket or a fluorescent-light garden. The fascination of ivies comes from their instability in leaf shape, size, and color. Collect several varieties of ivy; cultivate over a period of years; and in time you will probably discover that some branches have mutated, or sported, and produced leaves different in shape from the parent plant. Sometimes a plain-green plant grows a branch with variegated foliage.

The best ivies for indoors are those with a naturally compact growing habit and small leaves. Some of the most popular appear in the pictures here. Interesting ivies to look for are those with green leaves that have gold centers or are flecked with white or gold. Once in a while, you can find a miniature, each leaf barely ½ inch long—for instance, 'Needlepoint'—that is perfect for a bottle garden.

It is really interesting to train English ivies indoors as topiaries. In Chapter 10, one is shown trained as a living Christmas wreath. The topiary technique is fairly simple; but a finished, perfectly grown topiary takes constant care, time to mature—and patience. English-ivy topiaries are trained usually in one of two ways. The easier method is to make a form of galvanized wire and anchor it in the pot of a vigorous, dense, small-leaved ivy such as 'Merion Beauty' or 'Glacier.' Choose a plant that has long, leaf-filled branches. Tie branches up and along the frame to conform to its shape. Clip off wayward branches that cannot be worked into the design; you can use these pieces as tip cuttings to start new plants. This method works best for designs that are more or less two-dimensional, with height and width but very little depth. Besides a circle (or wreath shape) you might try a diamond, heart, spade, or club shape.

The first few days after tying, some ivy leaves will die. Remove them. Rest the plant for three days in a rather dim light, then place it in a bright north window, or a few feet away from a sunny east or west window. Mist immediately after tying, and every few days for three weeks, then mist once a week.

To make a Christmas-wreath topiary, like the one on page 223, choose a plant with branches about 36 inches long, and a wreath form that measures 14 inches across. Long-branched ivies, especially for topiaries, are sold in September by specialists.

LIGHT: Ideal is a bright north window or a sunny east or west exposure. A naturally bushy, compact English ivy such as 'Merion Beauty' or 'Glacier' will last as long as 2 years on a desk or table without any natural light, existing solely on the illumination from ceiling fluorescents (as in an interior office) or from a table lamp burned for a few hours each evening—provided it is faithfully tended as outlined below. English ivy will thrive in a fluorescent-light garden.
TEMPERATURE: Ideal is 60 to 70 degrees during winter heating, tolerates more if air is moist and fresh. Suffers in dry, stale air.
POTTING SOIL: All-purpose (see Chapter 3).
WATERING NEEDS: Water often enough to keep evenly moist. If the soil dries out to the point of wilting the ivy, all the older leaves will die, along with the growing tips. Severe dryness kills English ivy. If possible, mist daily in winter, and once a week rinse the entire plant in clean, tepid water.
FEEDING: Feed with an all-purpose plant food all year; follow the directions on the container.
PROBLEMS: Red spider mite is the greatest enemy of English ivy cultivated as a house plant. Mites almost always attack in air that is hot, dry, and stale; for treatment, see Chapter 4. Daily misting and weekly bathing in water discourage these pests.
CONTAINERS: Standard plastic or clay pot with drainage hole, or hanging basket or terrariums.
PROPAGATION: Root tip cuttings, in any season.

Hedera (HED-er-uh). Ginseng Family • *Hedera helix* (English ivy) A-127.

IVY, GERMAN

LIVING WITH IT:
The plant shown is in a 5-inch pot. Nice on sill, shelf, pedestal, table, or in a hanging basket. At a glance, a cascade of this beautiful medium-green foliage might easily be mistaken for English ivy. Culture is virtually the same for both ivies, but they are not related. German-ivy (*Senecio mikanoides*) reveals its affiliation with the Daisy Family when it blooms. In winter or spring, clusters of yellow daisy flowers appear. There is also a variegated form with leaves that are golden-yellow and green. German-ivy grows quickly, and stems remain soft and delicate. Like wandering Jew and Swedish-ivy, growing tips need frequent pinching out. This encourages branching and dense, full growth that will cover the container. German-ivy likes coolness and was popular in Victorian homes. Excessive dry winter heating will wither tender new growth; in every other way, it is a fine house plant.

LIGHT: Sunny east or west window in winter is ideal. Move back from the window in summer to avoid too much intense sunlight and heat. Tolerates bright light of a north window or similar brightness.
TEMPERATURE: Ideal is 55 to 70 degrees during the winter heating season. If over 70 degrees, fresh air is essential.
POTTING SOIL: All-purpose (see Chapter 3).
WATERING NEEDS: Keep evenly moist. Avoid extreme dryness. Mist often.
FEEDING: Feed all-purpose plant food all year; follow container directions for frequency.
PROBLEMS: Avoid hot, dry drafts, which will wither new growth.
CONTAINERS: Standard plastic or clay pot, or hanging basket.
PROPAGATION: Root tip cuttings, in any season.

Senecio (suh-NEE-see-oh). Daisy Family • *Senecio mikanoides* (German-ivy; Parlor-ivy)
A-128.

LIVING WITH IT: The plant shown is in a 5-inch pot. Young plants will thrive in a fluorescent-light garden. Display older specimens on sill, shelf, table, pedestal, or in hanging baskets. Except for the fact that mature red-ivy plants form dangling or trailing stems of foliage, this plant bears no resemblance to true English ivy and is in no way related. It is called red because when light, temperature, and soil moisture are right, leaf undersides become maroon or burgundy. Leaf surfaces are usually dull metallic or silver-green. To be fully appreciated, especially during the night, red-ivy needs to be well lighted to dramatize

the silvery leaf surfaces and the maroon-blushed leaf reverses. Red-ivy is more than an attractive trailing plant; it is easy to grow and unusually tolerant of light, temperature, and moisture conditions. Primarily a foliage plant, from time to time it bears clusters of small white flowers.

LIGHT: Ideal is a bright north window or similar brightness a few feet from a sunny window. Tolerates direct east or west sun in winter.

TEMPERATURE: Suffers over 75 or below 55 degrees in winter, but tolerates higher temperatures in summer.

POTTING SOIL: All-purpose (see Chapter 3).

WATERING NEEDS: Keep evenly moist. Avoid soggy, wet, poorly drained soil. Tolerates a little dryness occasionally. Mist often.

FEEDING: Feed all-purpose all year; follow container directions.

PROBLEMS: Red spider mites attack in hot, dry, stale air (see Chapter 4 for remedies for these pests).

CONTAINERS: Standard plastic or clay pot, or hanging basket.

PROPAGATION: Root tip cuttings, in any season.

Hemigraphis (hem-ee-GRAF-iss). Acanthus Family • *Hemigraphis* (Red-ivy, Flame-ivy)
A-129.

JADE PLANT

LIVING WITH IT:
The plant shown is in an 11-inch pot. When young; display on sill, shelf, table, or in a fluorescent-light garden or dish-garden desertscape. Place older plants on floor, table, or pedestal, and light them at night to reveal the sculptural qualities of mature growth. Jade plant (*Crassula argentea*) is a magnificent addition to container gardens, indoors and out. It will not tolerate frost, but you can grow it indoors in winter and outdoors in warm weather. When you move it outdoors in spring, be careful to expose it gradually to more sun until it "tans," as you do. Too much direct sun all at once will burn unsightly spots in the leaves. In either location, it tolerates various kinds of light. Plain dark- or pale-green, thinly spaced leaves indicate insufficient light. In ample sun, the leaves vary from light to golden green, with coppery-red edges. A jade with this kind of coloration will likely have clusters of starry white flowers in winter or spring.

LIGHT: Ideal is a sunny east, south, or west window. Tolerates the light of a bright north window. Fluorescent-light garden acceptable.
TEMPERATURE: Average house in winter. Suffers over 80 degrees in extremely dry soil; suffers below 50, especially in soggy, wet soil.
POTTING SOIL: Cactus (see Chapter 3).
WATERING NEEDS: Water well, then not again until soil surface is dry.
FEEDING: Feed all-purpose plant food all year, following container directions. If the jade plant is kept cool and on the dry side in the winter in poor light, do not fertilize.
PROBLEMS: See above. Also, mealybugs may attack (see Chapter 4).
CONTAINERS: Standard plastic or clay pot, or tub.
PROPAGATION: Root leaf or tip cuttings, preferably during the spring or the summer.

Crassula (KRASS-yew-luh). Stonecrop Family • *Crassula argentea* (Jade plant) A-130.

LIVING WITH IT:
The plant shown is in a 3-inch pot. Display on sill, shelf, table when young. Older plants grow into small shrubs. These may be trained to upright form, for display on table or floor. Or tops may be pruned to encourage side growth, for display on a pedestal or in a hanging basket. Like its outdoor relative lilac, jasmine is famed for wonderfully fragrant blossoms. *Jasminum sambac* (shown) has reddish-brown, tapered buds that furl open into lovely, white flowers. Of the many jasmines, this one is the most tolerant of average house temperature in winter.

It is most likely to flower in summer, but if given the right light, temperature, and humidity, may flower in almost any season. If you follow the culture outlined below and never let jasmine dry out; it will grow bushier, better, and more flowery year after year. The related sweet-olive (*Osmanthus fragrans*) grows similarly, requires the same care, and tends to be everblooming; intensely fragrant flowers.

LIGHT: Full sun in east, south, or west window in winter; less is acceptable in summer. Small jasmines grow well in fluorescent light.

TEMPERATURE: Ideal is 70 to 72 degrees in the daytime, with a drop to 62 to 65 degrees at night. Avoid hot, dry, stale air.

POTTING SOIL: African-violet (see Chapter 3).

WATERING NEEDS: Keep the soil evenly moist. Mist often. Extremes of wetness or dryness will cause leaf and bud drop.

FEEDING: Feed blooming all year; follow container directions.

PROBLEMS: Aphids may attack tip growth (see Chapter 4).

CONTAINERS: Standard plastic or clay pot, tub, or hanging basket.

PROPAGATION: Root cuttings or half-ripened wood, spring or summer.

Jasminum (JAZZ-min-um). Olive Family • *Jasminum sambac* (Jasmine) A-131; *Osmanthus fragrans* (Sweet-olive) A-132.

KALANCHOE

LIVING WITH IT:
The plant shown is in a 6-inch pot. While young, display on sill, shelf, table, or in a fluorescent-light garden. Older plants become handsome pieces of living sculpture to display on table, pedestal, or floor. When they are lighted at night, the effect is dramatic. *Kalanchoe beharensis* (shown) is the largest and the boldest of kinds commonly cultivated as house plants. For care of small *K. blossfeldiana* varieties for seasonal flowers see Poinsettias, Chapter 8. Kinds to cultivate primarily for foliage include *K. pinnata,* which has large, red-edged, and scalloped green leaves. When a leaf is removed and placed on moist soil, or even pinned to a curtain in midair, baby plants will sprout at every leaf scallop. The smaller *K. tomentosa* has reddish, brown-tipped blue-green leaves covered with dense, short white hairs. *K. tubiflora* has purplish, brown-spotted, tubular leaves, at the ends of which baby plants form. Kalanchoes survive all kinds of neglect but are never truly attractive unless they have enough sun.

LIGHT: Ideal is a sunny south window. Tolerates a sunny east or west window, as well as fluorescent-light culture while young.
TEMPERATURE: Average house in winter. Suffers below 55 degrees.
POTTING SOIL: Cactus (see Chapter 3).
WATERING NEEDS: Water well, then not again until surface is dry.
FEEDING: Feed all-purpose all year; follow container directions. Encourage older plants to flower by feeding with blooming-type.
PROBLEMS: Insufficient sun causes spindly, misshaped leaves.
CONTAINERS: Standard plastic or clay pot, or tub; drainage hole.
PROPAGATION: Root leaf or stem cuttings, in any season.

Kalanchoe (kal-an-KOH-ee). Stonecrop Family • *Kalanchoe beharensis* A-133; *K. blossfeldiana* A-134; *K. pinnata* A-135; *K. tomentosa* A-136; *K. tubiflora* A-137.

LIVING WITH IT:
The plant shown is in an 8-inch pot. Display on sill, shelf, pedestal, or in hanging basket. Older plants may be placed on the floor or a low table and trained to climb a string or a wooden trellis. Set the support against a wall with bright sun at least 2 hours each day. Kangaroo vine (*Cissus antarctica*) is related to grape-ivy (and true grape). It is easy to grow—or anyway fairly easy to keep alive. For it to show its ability to grow by leaps and bounds, as the name implies, it needs the conditions and care outlined below. While it can survive dim light, new growth will be spindly and

leaves unnaturally small and thinly spaced. Do not hang basket high, where air is hot and dry. Air should be relatively moist, cool, and freely circulating. This plant grows so easily and quickly it is propagated by the millions and is available from most dealers.

LIGHT: Ideal is a sunny east or west window or near a sunny south window. See above. Tolerates a bright north window. Thrives in fluorescent light.
TEMPERATURE: Ideally 55 to 70 degrees during winter. If over 70, fresh circulating air is essential.
POTTING SOIL: All-purpose (see Chapter 3).
WATERING NEEDS: Keep evenly moist. Avoid extreme dryness, which causes leaf drop. Good drainage is essential. Mist often.
FEEDING: Feed all-purpose all year; follow container directions.
PROBLEMS: Hot, dry, stale air invites red spider mites (see Chapter 4).
CONTAINERS: Standard plastic or clay pot, or hanging basket.
PROPAGATION: Root cuttings or half-ripened wood, any time (see Chapter 6).

Cissus (SISS-us). Grape Family • *Cissus antarctica* (Kangaroo vine) A-138.

LANTANA

LIVING WITH IT:
The plant shown is in a 5-inch pot. Display young plants on sill or shelf; as the plant matures, its graceful cascade of branches and pretty pink, rose, yellow, orange, or creamy-white flowers make it a good hanging-basket plant. Lantana is sometimes trained to a tree form (see Chapter 5). One of the best of flowering container plants for outdoors; indoors it is tricky to grow in hot, dry, stale air. Before bringing one into your home, look for white-fly eggs under the leaves, and shake the plant. If white flies fly up, spray plant with a forceful stream of water to wash away flies and eggs. Isolate the plant, and repeat the washing every few days until there are no more insects. Examine new tender foliage for egg deposits. If there are any, pinch off and destroy these leaves. Select *L. montevidensis* and varieties for hanging-baskets, the woodier upright *L. camara* and varieties as small shrubs or to train as trees.

LIGHT: Full sun in a south window; sunny east or west windows.
TEMPERATURE: Average house, on the cool side in winter; suffers in winter temperatures over 70 degrees or below 55 degrees.
POTTING SOIL: All-purpose (see Chapter 3).
WATERING NEEDS: Water often enough to keep evenly moist in spring and summer; let surface approach dryness before watering in the fall and winter.
FEEDING: Feed a blooming plant food from late winter to early fall, following container directions for frequency. Do not feed from October to February.
PROBLEMS: White flies (see Chapter 4). Hot, dry, stale air in winter.
CONTAINERS: Standard clay or plastic pot, or hanging basket.
PROPAGATION: Root tip cuttings, in spring or summer.

Lantana (lan-TAN-uh). Verbena Family • *Lantana montevidensis* A-139; *L. camara* A-140.

LIVING WITH IT:
The plant shown is in a 5-inch pot. Display on sill, shelf, or table. Young plants may be cultivated in a fluorescent-light garden, but in time grow too tall and should be moved to natural sunlight. Although this lavender produces spikes of small flowers in season, it is cultivated primarily for the foliage, which gives off a delicious scent when brushed or squeezed lightly. It is related to English lavender, the fragrant garden herb used in perfume. Fernleaf lavender is winter-hardy outdoors only in warm, southern gardens, and it is

therefore best cultivated as a house plant in climates where severe winter freezing occurs. Other fragrant but tender lavenders that will scent your indoor garden include *Lavandula multifida* and *L. stoechas,* which produces lovely purple flowers in winter. To grow all of these, follow culture as outlined below. Herbs used for cooking are illustrated and discussed in Chapter 9.

LIGHT: Ideal is a sunny south window in winter; tolerates sunny east or west window. Fluorescent-light garden while small enough.

TEMPERATURE: Ideally 55 to 70 degrees during winter heating season. If over 70, fresh circulating air is essential.

POTTING SOIL: All-purpose (see Chapter 3).

WATERING NEEDS: Keep the soil evenly moist. Avoid extreme dryness; occasional near-dryness is acceptable. Mist often.

FEEDING: Feed all-purpose plant food all year.

PROBLEMS: Avoid hot, dry, stale air; it discourages healthy growth.

CONTAINERS: Standard plastic or clay pot with drainage hole.

PROPAGATION: Root cuttings of half-ripened wood, any time (see Chapter 6).

Lavandula dentata (lav-AN-dew-luh den-TAY-tuh). Mint Family • *Lavandula dentata* (Fernleaf lavender) A-141; *L. multifida* A-142; *L. stoechas* A-143.

LEOPARD PLANT

LIVING WITH IT:
The plant shown is in a 6-inch pot, for display on sill, shelf, or table. Also, if kept cool, grows well in a large terrarium. Some forms of this plant have plain green leaves; others have leaves variegated with golden-yellow to cream spots. When grown according to its needs, a plant has seasonal flowers — yellow daisies — which reveal the plant's relationship to all members of the Daisy Family. If you live in an apartment that is fairly hot and dry in winter, this plant is not likely to feel welcome. However, in a bright spot that receives 2 or 3 hours of sun in winter, with temperatures of 50 to 70 degrees and 30% humidity, it will grow into an attractive, unusual specimen. Its size can be controlled by pot size. For example, a small division removed from a full-size plant and rooted in soil can be dwarfed by keeping it in a 2- or 3-inch pot and giving it half-strength feedings. Take care to keep soil always evenly moist. Insects seldom attack the leopard plant. ·

LIGHT: Two or 3 hours of sun in winter; bright light but little or no direct sun in summer; does well in fluorescent light.
TEMPERATURE: Cool, preferably a range of 50 to 70 degrees in winter.
POTTING SOIL: All-purpose (see Chapter 3).
WATERING NEEDS: Keep evenly moist. Avoid extreme wetness, dryness. Frequent misting of the foliage is beneficial, especially in winter.
FEEDING: Feed all-purpose plant food all year; follow container directions for frequency.
PROBLEMS: Avoid hot, dry air during the winter heating season.
CONTAINERS: Standard clay or plastic pot with drainage hole.
PROPAGATION: Plant root divisions, preferably in spring or summer.

Ligularia (Lig-yew-LAY-ree-uh). Daisy Family • *Ligularia* (Leopard plant) A-144.

LIVING WITH IT:
The plant shown is in a 6-inch pot. Display young plants on sill, or shelf; hanging basket or a small pedestal shows off mature plants' grace. This grassy plant may have plain or green-and-white-striped leaves. In the South, it is a popular ground cover in areas of filtered shade. Plants called lily-turf are *Ophiopogon (O. intermedius argenteo-marginatus* is shown) or *Liriope*. Seldom sold as houseplants, they can be found in nurseries that sell ground covers. A miniature type is also grown. In spring or summer, the plants send up spikes of lav-

ender or purple flowers, followed by long-lasting berries about ⅜ inch in diameter; and varying from indigo-blue to purplish black. Red spider mites are a threat; otherwise, lily-turf is trouble-free. old leaves die naturally; gently pull or cut them from the base. Dead leaf tips on healthy leaves indicate too much heat and not enough soil moisture.

LIGHT: Ideal is 2 or 3 hours of sun in winter, but plants adapt to the light of a north window. They thrive in fluorescent-light gardens.
TEMPERATURE: Average house in winter, ideally on the cool side; suffers above 75 degrees and below 40 degrees in winter.
POTTING SOIL: All-purpose (see Chapter 3).
WATERING NEEDS: Keep evenly moist. Avoid over wetness or dryness. Mist frequently.
FEEDING: Feed all-purpose plant food all year; follow container directions for frequency.
PROBLEMS: Hot, dry, stale air during the winter heating season encourages red spider mites (see Chapter 4).
CONTAINERS: Standard clay or plastic pot with drainage hole.
PROPAGATION: Plant divisions or seeds, in any season.

Ophiopogon (oh-fee-oh-PHO-gon) or *Liriope* (luh-RYE-oh-pee). Lily Family • *Ophiopogon intermedius argenteo-marginatus* (Lily-turf) A-145; *Liriope* (Lily-turf) A-146.

LIPSTICK VINE

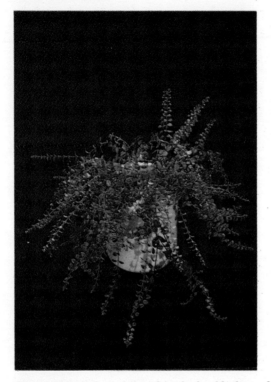

LIVING WITH IT:
The plant shown is in
an 8-inch pot. This
is a durable basket,
shelf, or pedestal plant
with thick, waxy
leaves on stems that
may grow 2 feet long.
The leaves are more
like those of the wax-
plant (*Hoya*) than
African violets and
gloxinias, to which this
vine is related. Inter-
mittently through the
year, clusters of flower
buds appear at the
ends of the stems, each
a burgundy-brown
tube holding a velvety,
orange-red flower bud.
The resemblance of
these clusters to a
group of lipsticks
suggested the plant's
popular name. They
make a showy, even
spectacular display.

Flowering can be inhibited by lack of light and humidity; however,
lipstick vine is as easily cultivated for foliage as Swedish-ivy and
wandering Jew. It has the habit of constantly sending up new growth
from the base of the stems, to form a dense, full cascade of foliage. Little
or no pinching back is necessary. It appreciates some misting.

LIGHT: Ideal is 2 or 3 hours of sunlight in winter, bright indirect light in
summer; tolerates the light of a north window all year.
TEMPERATURE Average house in winter; suffers below 55 degrees.
POTTING SOIL: African-violet or terrarium (see Chapter 3).
WATERING NEEDS: Water about every 3 days, or often enough to keep
soil evenly moist.
FEEDING: Feed blooming plant food all year; follow container direc-
tions. To encourage their' stem and leaf growth, switch to all-purpose
plant food.
PROBLEMS: Hot, dry stale air may wither tip growth and flower buds.
CONTAINERS: Standard hanging basket, or standard clay or plastic pot.
PROPAGATION: Root tip cuttings, any time of year.

Aeschynanthus (esk-uh-NANTH-us). Gesneriad Family • *Aeschynanthus* (Lipstick vine)
A-147.

LIVING STONES; STONEFACE

LIVING WITH IT: The plants shown are in 5-inch pots. This is a small plant, to display on sill, shelf, or table. Of all nature's curiosity plants, living stones are among the most fascinating and most easily cultivated in the house. The joined pairs of succulent leaves spread apart at the top. From this fissure single white, yellow, or orange daisy-shaped flowers appear in summer or fall. The plant bodies differ in color according to species, of which there are many. Mostly they are sand or stone color— beige, brown, gray, and blue-green. Plant several kinds in a

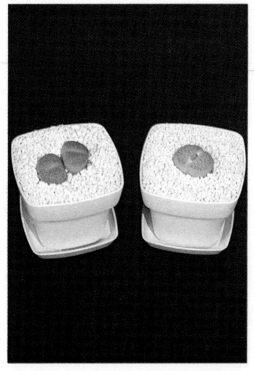

shallow clay pot or saucer; mulch around them with sand, place real rocks among them, matching plant and mineral stones as closely as possible. Living stones need as much direct winter sun as possible. They do well 2 or 3 inches below fluorescent light. If you are growing them in natural light in fall and winter, do not overwater during cloudy weather.

LIGHT: Full sun in east, south, or west window; fluorescent light.
TEMPERATURE: Average house in winter, ideally not over 70 degrees; suffers below 55 degrees, especially if the soil is wet.
POTTING SOIL: Cactus (see Chapter 3).
WATERING NEEDS: Water well. An hour later, pour off any excess in the saucer. Water again only when the surface soil is dry.
FEEDING: Feed blooming plant food in spring and summer; follow container directions. Do not feed in fall and winter.
PROBLEMS: Avoid overmoist soil, especially in fall and winter.
CONTAINERS: Standard clay or plastic pot, or well-drained dish garden (see Chapter 10).
PROPAGATION: Sow seeds, in spring or summer.

Lithops (LITH-ops). Carpetweed Family • *Lithops* (Living stones, Stoneface) A-148.

MAPLE, FLOWERING

LIVING WITH IT:
The plant shown is in a 6-inch pot. While young, display on sill, shelf, or table. Older plants become small shrubs or trees, to display on a low table, pedestal, or the floor. The leaves, which are shaped like those of the maple tree, may be green or green-and-white. Gracefully drooping flowers bloom most of the year and may be white, yellow, apricot, orange, pink, or red. One species, *Abutilon megapotamicum,* has plain-green or gold-and-green leaves, and produces dangling yellow flowers that bloom from a showy Chinese-red calyx. It has wiry, cascading stems and is remarkably handsome on a pedestal or in a hanging basket. Flowering-maples are not true maples. They are related to hollyhock and to Chinese hibiscus, which grows outdoors in the tropics and is a popular house plant in the North. If you provide the conditions outlined below, flowering-maple is an easy and rewarding indoor plant.

LIGHT: Full sun in an east, south, or west window in winter; less is acceptable in summer.
TEMPERATURE: Ideal is 70 to 72 degrees in the daytime, with a drop of 62 to 65 at night. Avoid hot, dry, stale air.
POTTING SOIL: All-purpose (see Chapter 3). For best growth, move to a size-larger pot as soon as roots fill the present one.
WATERING NEEDS: Water often enough to keep the soil evenly moist. Avoid extreme dryness; it causes leaf and flower-bud drop. Mist often.
FEEDING: Feed blooming all year; follow container directions.
PROBLEMS: Hot, dry, stale air invites red spider mites (see Chapter 4).
CONTAINERS: Standard plastic or clay pot, tub, or hanging basket.
PROPAGATION: Root tip cuttings, at any season.

Abutilon (abb-YEW-til-on). Mallow Family • *Abutilon* (Flowering-maple) A-149; *A. megapotamicum* (Flowering-maple) A-150.

MEXICAN FOXGLOVE

LIVING WITH IT:
The plant shown is in a 5-inch pot. Display on sill, shelf, table, in a fluorescent-light garden or terrarium.

This cold-sensitive, miniature relative of the snapdragon that grows outdoors looks a little similar to a miniature gloxinia. It is from Mexico, and the maroon-spotted, white, deep-throated flowers recall the markings of foxgloves, hence its popular name. When the plant is contented, the markings appear all year, especially if you clip off the old flowers before seed pods begin to develop. As Mexican foxglove is by nature a tidy, miniature plant, it is choice for a terrarium landscape, in the company of miniature ferns like *Polystichum tsus-simense,* small English ivies, and selaginellas.

Mexican foxglove is also one of the best everblooming plants for a fluorescent-light garden. The plant does have a healthy thirst. If you grow it in an individual pot that stands alone, be sure to keep the soil always moist; otherwise, growth will suffer.

LIGHT: Ideal is a bright north window or similar brightness a few feet from a sunny window, or in a fluorescent-light garden.
TEMPERATURE: Average house in winter; suffers below 55, above 80.
POTTING SOIL: African-violet or all-purpose (see Chapter 3).
WATERING NEEDS: Water often enough to keep the soil evenly moist. Repeated dryness that causes severe wilt will eventually destroy the root system of this plant.
FEEDING: Feed blooming all year; follow container directions.
PROBLEMS: Aphids and mealybugs may attack (see Chapter 4).
CONTAINERS: Standard plastic or clay pot, or a terrarium.
PROPAGATION: Plant seeds or root offsets, in any season.

Allophyton (al-oh-FYE-ton). Figwort Family • *Allophyton* (Mexican foxglove) A-151.

MOSES IN THE CRADLE

LIVING WITH IT:
The plant shown is in
an 11-inch pot. When
small, display on sill,
shelf, or table. Older
plants show off well in
hanging baskets
and are dramatically
beautiful in the glow
of a lighted pedestal.
The name comes from
the beguiling way
the plant blooms. It
bears its small white
flowers in boat-
shape maroon-and-
olive-green bracts.
A well-grown, well-
displayed plant is
a handsome specimen.
To keep it at its
best, remove dead
leaves and bracts.
Feed and water
it regularly, so the
green-and-maroon
leaves grow uniformly
well. Display the
plant with respect for its color and form. Study it from above, below, and
the side, in different lights. In its variegated form, Moses in the cradle
is even more striking: Each leaf is striped vertically with white or
a golden color that stands out distinctly from the olive-green base. Both
plain and variegated types are well worth growing.

LIGHT: Sunny east, west, or south window is ideal in winter; less sun is
needed in summer. Adapts to bright north light. Grows to perfection in a
fluorescent-light garden.
TEMPERATURE: Average house in winter; suffers below 55 degrees.
POTTING SOIL: All-purpose (see Chapter 3).
WATERING NEEDS: Water often enough to keep evenly moist. Careless
over- or underwatering results in dead leaf tips.
FEEDING: Feed all-purpose all year; follow container directions.
PROBLEMS: Avoid insufficient light, which causes pale, weak growth
and results in failure to bloom.
CONTAINERS: Standard plastic or clay pot, or hanging basket.
PROPAGATION: Root offsets or tip cuttings, at any season.

Rhoeo (ROH-ee-oh). Spiderwort Family • *Rhoeo* (Moses in the cradle) A-152.

LIVING WITH IT:
Both plants shown are in 3-inch pots. They are plain green *Myrtus communis* (common myrtle) and the variegated *M. c. variegata*. Display on sill, shelf, or table. If kept cool, myrtle is an easy and attractive plant. It also makes a handsome topiary, in ball, cube, fantasy tree, or animal shape. Once your myrtle is well established, buy or make a wire topiary silhouette on which to train it. Set the form in the pot; with short-bladed pruning shears, prune away all growth, old and new, that fails to fit the shape you are training the myrtle to be. You must be ruthless about removing any growth that falls outside the form. However, cut intelligently. Remove growth just inside the topiary form, so the cut tip can grow new twigs and leaves that will hide the dead tip end. Cut close to a pair of leaves so as little as possible of leafless tip will show. Culture for topiary myrtles is the same as for untrained ones.

LIGHT: Ideal is a sunny east, south, or west window in winter; less sun needed in summer. If small enough, fluorescent-light garden.
TEMPERATURE: Average house in winter, but preferably on the cool side (60 to 70 degrees), with fresh, circulating air.
POTTING SOIL: African-violet (Chapter 3).
WATERING NEEDS: Water often enough to keep evenly moist. Severe dryness may cause the entire plant to die. Do not let plant stand in water. Mist frequently.
FEEDING: Feed all-purpose all year; follow container directions.
PROBLEMS: Hot, dry, stale air invites red spider mite (see Chapter 4).
CONTAINERS: Standard plastic or clay pot.
PROPAGATION: Root half-ripened cuttings (see Chapter 6).

Myrtus (MERT-us). Myrtle Family • *Myrtus communis* (Myrtle) A-153; *M. c. variegata* (Variegated myrtle) A-154.

NEPHTHYTIS; ARROWHEAD PLANT

LIVING WITH IT:
The plant shown is in an 11-inch pot. When it is young, display on sill, shelf, or table. Older plants may be trained upright on a moss or bark totem pole (as shown) or around a moss-lined wire hanging basket. This plant, though commonly referred to as nephthytis and related to the true—and rare—*Nephthytis*, is really a *Syngonium*. Syngoniums are often mixed with other foliage plants in commercial dish gardens; they quickly outgrow the other plants and dangle awkwardly. Grown alone in the right container, syngonium can be handsome and as trouble-free as any plant. A young syngonium forms a bushy clump of arrowhead-shape leaves, any shade of green, from pale chartreuse to dark green, often with marks or veins of silver, cream, white, or yellow. In time, air roots form on stems, and search for a moist, rough climbing surface. You can provide one with a moss or bark totem; or set plant in a moss-lined wire basket and train stems all around.

LIGHT: Ideal is a few feet from a sunny east, south, or west window in winter, with little or no direct sun. Thrives in a bright north window or fluorescent light. The brighter the light, the brighter the leaf color.
TEMPERATURE: Average house in winter; suffers below 55.
POTTING SOIL: All-purpose (see Chapter 3).
WATERING NEEDS: Keep soil evenly most. Mist often.
FEEDING: Feed all-purpose all year; follow container directions.
PROBLEMS: Hot, dry, stale air encourages red spider mites. Watch for mealybugs. Treat both pests as described in Chapter 4.
CONTAINERS: Standard clay or plastic pot; moss-lined wire hanging basket.
PROPAGATION: Root cuttings, in any season.

Syngonium (sin-GO-nee-um). Calla Family • *Syngonium* (Nephthytis; Arrowhead plant) A-155.

NIGHT-JESSAMINE

LIVING WITH IT:
The plant shown is in a 4-inch pot. When young, display on sill, shelf, table, or grow in a fluorescent-light garden. Older plants form upright shrubs, or they may be allowed to grow outward for hanging baskets. Cestrum stems are so pliable you can train and tie them to a wooden or wire trellis in the pot. The plant will become two-dimensional, having height and width but little depth. Although the bright-green foliage is always attractive, it is the intensely fragrant white flowers that are its treasure.

These appear on young plants, even on small, well-rooted cuttings, and the buds are so insignificant that a whiff of the enticing scent is often the first hint of bloom. The plant shown, *Cestrum nocturnum,* blooms at night; the similar *C. diurnum* blooms in the daytime.

Another species, *C. purpureum,* has reddish-maroon flowers and is everblooming. All three are available from specialists and are appearing more frequently in local shops as the fragrance becomes known.

LIGHT: Full sun in an east, south, or west window in winter; less is acceptable in summer. Small cestrums grow well in fluorescent light.
TEMPERATURE: Ideal is 70 to 72 degrees in the daytime, with a drop to 62 to 65 degrees at night. Avoid hot, dry, stale air.
POTTING SOIL: All-purpose (see Chapter 3).
WATERING NEEDS: Keep the soil evenly moist. Mist often. Extreme dryness will cause leaves and flower buds to die.
FEEDING: Feed blooming all year; follow container directions.
PROBLEMS: Aphids on tip growth; mealybugs (see Chapter 4).
CONTAINERS: Standard plastic or clay pot, or hanging basket.
PROPAGATION: Root the tip cuttings of half-ripened wood, ideally in the summer.

Cestrum (SEST-rum). Nightshade Family • *Cestrum nocturnum* (Night-jessamine) A-156; *C. diurnum* A-157; *C. purpureum* A-158.

NORFOLK ISLAND PINE

LIVING WITH IT:
The plant shown is
in a 13-inch pot.
Araucaria excelsa is
tree-size; to display
on a table when it is
young, on the floor
as it grows larger.
On its native Pacific
island it grows over
200 feet tall. As a
house plant it is
slow-growing; old
plants will stay at
ceiling height.
Seedlings under 6
inches tall are often
sold for terrariums.
If you use one this
way, bury the pot in
the soil, and hide the
rim with sheet moss
or small stones. The
plant can then be
moved to a larger pot
without disturbing
the other plants
or, perhaps more
important, without digging up its roots. This needled evergreen, like
others, should never suffer for lack of water. Severe drying, even once,
kills many needles and branches; they will never grow back. Keep cool
in winter. Mist frequently. It will not tolerate drafts of hot, dry heat.

LIGHT: Ideal is 2 or 3 hours of sun in winter, bright indirect light in
summer; tolerates light of a north window all year.
TEMPERATURE: Cool spot in winter, not over 70 degrees. Suffers over 75.
POTTING SOIL: Half-and-half all-purpose and humus (see Chapter 3).
WATERING NEEDS: Water about every 3 days, or often enough to keep
the soil evenly moist.
FEEDING: Feed all-purpose all year; follow container directions.
PROBLEMS: In hot, dry, stale air, red spider mites usually attack (see
Chapter 4).
CONTAINERS: Standard clay or plastic pot, or tub, with drainage hole.
PROPAGATION: Sow seeds, any time. You can root the terminal (top of
main stem) shoot when pine grows too tall or if it has lost many lower
branches. Rooted tip cuttings of side branches do not make good plants.

Araucaria (are-oh-KAY-ree-uh). Pine Family • *Araucaria excelsa* (Norfolk Island pine) A-159.

LIVING WITH IT: The plant shown is in a 5-inch pot. This plant, like the onion we eat, is a member of the Lily Family, but not a true onion. Its common name makes sense, however, when you see the green bulb that grows partly above-ground and forms baby bulbs just under the surface. Eventually these bulblets break through the skin. To multiply your plants, remove the bulblets, and pot individually, with base snuggled into the surface of moist soil. Mature plants send up stems to 3 feet tall, tipped by a spike of 100 or more white flowers. The pregnant onion *(Ornithogalum caudatum)* is one of those old-fashioned folk plants that people enjoy growing, but is not often found in commercial nurseries. Since it is grown for its oddities, display it by itself so that its unusual form and strange way of producing babies can be seen to advantage. This is an ideal plant for the classroom: It fascinates children and really doesn't mind some neglect, as during holidays.

LIGHT: Full sun in an east, south, or west window. Babies do well in a fluorescent-light garden; don't let the leaves touch the tubes.

TEMPERATURE: Average house in winter; suffers over 75, below 55.

POTTING SOIL: All-purpose (see Chapter 3).

WATERING NEEDS: Water well. An hour later, pour off excess water in the saucer. Water again when surface soil nears dryness.

FEEDING: Feed all-purpose plant food all year; follow container directions for frequency. If a mature plant fails to flower, feed with blooming plant food for several months.

PROBLEMS: Avoid soggy, wet, poorly drained soil.

CONTAINERS: Standard clay or plastic pot with drainage hole.

PROPAGATION: Remove bulblets on old bulb's surface; plant as above.

Ornithogalum (or-nith-OGG-uh-lum). Lily Family • *Ornithogalum caudatum* (Pregnant onion, False sea-onion) A-160.

ORCHID

Miniature laelia (left), 4-inch pot; *Cattleya fulvescens* (right), 8-inch pot.

This species of *Epidendrum* orchid is displayed in a 6-inch pot.

LIVING WITH IT: Some 30,000 different orchids grow wild around the world, in both cold and tropical climates. The lady-slipper orchids (species of *Cypripedium*) we cultivate outdoors all year in shady gardens are fine examples of cold-hardy varieties. Among tropicals, countless types make good house plants. Four of the best are shown here and on page 150. Orchids are not strictly shade plants; they need fresh, moist air that circulates freely. If you can grow thriving African violets, begonias, or bromeliads, you'll likely be successful with orchids. Buy established, flowering-size plants from an orchid specialist. The small varieties listed as "botanicals" grow well in fluorescent-light gardens.

Orchids of the *Cattleya* (CAT-lee-uh) type are best known. These may be labeled as *Cattleya, Brassocattleya, Laelia, Laeliocattleya,* and *Brassavola* (the "brass" of *Brassocattleya*). Although we think of these as lavender-pink or "orchid" colored, and sometimes white, they can be a lovely yellow, orange, scarlet, apricot, or green, often with two or more colors combined. One of the easiest orchids for beginners , *Brassavola nodosa,* which has small greenish-white flowers, is wonderfully fragrant at night. Orchid specialists offer many small-growing hybrids that are less than 10 inches high when mature. These are ideal growing on a sunny sill or in a fluorescent-light garden. Species of older hybrids are inexpensive, but exciting new varieties command stiff prices.

Cypripedium (Lady-slipper orchid) A-161; *Cattleya* A-162; *Brassocattleya* A-163; *Laelia* A-164; *Laeliocattleya* A-165; *Brassavola* A-166; *B. nodosa* A-167.

LIGHT: Ideal is a sunny east, west, or south window. The miniatures will grow well in a fluorescent-light garden.

TEMPERATURE: Average house temperatures during the winter heating season. Needs fresh, moist air that circulates freely.

POTTING SOIL: Osmunda fiber, redwood bark, shredded fir bark, or chunks of tree-fern bark. All are available from orchid specialists.

WATERING NEEDS: Drench growing medium; allow slight drying before watering again. Do not leave pot standing in water. Mist often.

FEEDING: Feed alternately all year with all-purpose and blooming-type plant foods; follow container directions for frequency.

PROBLEMS: Insufficient light causes unnaturally dark-green foliage and results in little or no flowering. In proper light, cattleya leaves are pale to yellowish green. Too much sun causes burned spots.

CONTAINERS: Special clay pot with side openings for perfect drainage (available from orchid specialists). If special care is taken not to overwater, standard plastic or clay pot may be used.

PROPAGATION: Plant root divisions, following the flowering season.

Epidendrum (epp-ee-DEN-drum) orchids are fairly closely related to the cattleyas. Some have pseudobulbs, from which the leaves grow; others have tall, reedlike stems. One of the easiest to grow is the reed-stemmed *E. o'brienanum,* which has clusters of small flowers that are orange-red and yellow. A mature plant of this epidendrum may be almost always in bloom. It will thrive potted in unmilled sphagnum moss that is kept between moist and nearly dry.

LIGHT: Ideal is a sunny east, west, or south window. The miniatures will grow well in a fluorescent-light garden.

TEMPERATURE: Average house temperatures during the winter heating season. Needs fresh, moist air that circulates freely.

POTTING SOIL: If the variety is epiphytic (label tells), grow it in osmunda fiber, redwood bark, shredded fir bark, or chunks of tree-fern bark; all are available from orchid specialists. If terrestrial (a ground orchid), grow in a mixture of equal parts shredded fir bark, peat moss, and perlite.

WATERING NEEDS: Drench growing medium; allow slight drying before watering again. Do not leave pot standing in water. Mist often.

FEEDING: Feed alternately all year with all-purpose and blooming-type plant foods; follow container directions for frequency.

PROBLEMS: Insufficient light and dry, stale air prevent flowering.

CONTAINERS: If epiphytic, special clay pot with side openings for perfect drainage (available from orchid specialists). Standard plastic or clay pot may be used for the terrestrials, and for the epiphytic types as well, if special care is taken not to overwater.

PROPAGATION: Plant root divisions, following the flowering season.

Epidendrum A-168; *E. o'brienanum* A-169.

ORCHID

Oncidium orchid in an 8-inch pot.

Lady-slipper orchid in a 5-inch pot.

Oncidium (on-SID-ee-um) orchids are called dancing girl because of the flower shape and the way they move in the slightest breeze. The flowers vary from tiny to 3 or 4 inches across, blooming in quantity on long, gracefully arching stems. Variegata and equitant types have fans of short leaves 1 to 4 inches long and spikes of small flowers in pink, brown, white, or yellow. They grow well on cork-bark slabs or attached to a bromeliad tree (see page 78).

LIGHT: Ideal is a sunny east or west window, or near a sunny south window. Miniatures grow well in a fluorescent-light garden.
TEMPERATURE: Average house in winter. Suffers in hot, dry heat. Provide humidity in fresh air that circulates freely.
POTTING SOIL: Osmunda fiber, redwood bark, shredded fir bark, or chunks of tree-fern bark. All are available from orchid specialists.
WATERING NEEDS: Drench growing medium; allow to dry out before watering again. Do not leave pot standing in water. Mist often.
FEEDING: Feed alternately all year with all-purpose and blooming-type plant foods; follow container directions for frequency.
PROBLEMS: Insufficient light and dry, stale air prevent flowering.
CONTAINERS: Clay pot with side openings for perfect drainage, or standard plastic or clay pot if careful not to overwater.
PROPAGATION: Plant root divisions, following the flowering season.

Oncidium A-170.

ORCHID

Paphiopedilum (paff-ee-oh-PEED-ill-um) orchids are tropical versions of cold-hardy, northern lady-slipper orchids (species of *Cypripedium*). In practice, they are almost always called lady-slippers, "cyps" (for cypripedium), or "paffs" (for paphiopedilum). Lady-slippers are among the best of all orchids for growing as house plants. The short, compact leaves, plain green or mottled, are attractive all year. The flowers rise up on short, straight stems, and unless subjected to a hot, dry atmosphere, each lasts several weeks. Some are shiny and waxy or leathery; others softer, with hairs along petal edges. The colors and the color combinations and arrangements are extraordinary; there are pencil-thin lines, tiny dots, and larger spots in white, green, brown, pink, rose, purple, red, and yellow. The green-and-white *P. maudiae* is a good one for the neophyte to learn on.

Recently, *Phalaenopsis* (fay-luh-NOP-siss) orchids have become increasingly popular as house plants. Best known is the large white called moth orchid, a favorite in bridal bouquets. There are also varieties with similar or smaller flowers in pink, red, yellow, bronze, and lavender, often striped, spotted, or otherwise marked in a contrasting color. The compact, small plants look like paphiopedilums, plain green or attractively variegated in contrasting color. Culture for the phalaenopsis is the same as for paphiopedilums, with minor variations. They thrive in fluorescent-light gardens. One difference is that phalaenopsis are best planted in osmunda fiber, redwood bark, shredded fir bark, or chunks of tree-fern bark kept constantly moist. Do not leave pots standing in water. To flower well, phalaenopsis need four weeks in autumn or winter at around 55 degrees. After this period of coolness, return to house warmth. If you grow African violets or gloxinias successfully and can arrange to provide phalaenopsis with a month of coolness, you will find them easy and beautiful house plants.

LIGHT: Ideal location is near a sunny east or west window, or in a fluorescent-light garden. Too much hot sun will cause burned spots or yellowing.
TEMPERATURE: Average house during the winter heating season. High humidity with fresh, circulating air is desirable.
POTTING SOIL: Grow in a mixture of equal parts sphagnum peat moss, perlite, river gravel, and milled sphagnum moss.
WATERING NEEDS: Drench growing medium; allow to dry slightly before watering again. Do not leave pot standing in water. Mist often.
FEEDING: Feed alternately all year with all-purpose and blooming-type plant foods; follow container directions for frequency.
PROBLEMS: In temperatures below 60 degrees, take special care not to overwater. Hot, dry, stale air prevents flowering.
CONTAINERS: Standard plastic or clay pot.
PROPAGATION: Plant root divisions, ideally in the spring months.

Orchid Family ● *Paphiopedilum* A-171; *P. maudiae* A-172; *Phalaenopsis* A-173.

OXALIS; SHAMROCK; FOUR-LEAF CLOVER; FIREFERN

LIVING WITH IT:
The plant shown is in a 6-inch pot. Display on sill, shelf, table, in hanging basket, or grow in a fluorescent-light garden. *Oxalis siliquosa* (shown) has become more popular than older favorites because it grows so easily. Other oxalis worth collecting are *O. hedysaroides rubra* (firefern), similar but taller, excellent for terrariums; *O. rubra,* common pink with shamrocklike leaves; *O. regnellii,* which has unusual square-cut leaves, olive-green above, flushed maroon below, and white flowers; *O. martiana aureo-maculata,* whose leaves are similar in shape to those of *O. rubra* but strikingly gold-veined. Although *O. hedysaroides rubra* needs high humidity and will thrive in a terrarium, all the others will grow in the average dwelling if there is fresh air; otherwise, red spider mites are likely to attack. *O. hedysaroides rubra* and *O. regnellii* adapt best to low light.

LIGHT: Ideal in winter is a sunny east or west window, or 2 hours daily of sun in a south window. Do not let direct summer sun touch plants more than 2 hours daily. Excellent for fluorescent-light garden.
TEMPERATURE: Ideal is 70 to 72 degrees in the daytime, with a drop to 62 to 65 degrees at night. Avoid hot, dry, stale air.
POTTING SOIL: All-purpose (see Chapter 3).
WATERING NEEDS: Keep soil evenly moist. Extreme dryness causes leaves to die early. If species has a tuberous root, rest 2 months yearly, as for gloxinia, page 119. Mist often.
FEEDING: Feed blooming all year; follow container directions.
PROBLEMS: Mealybugs, red spider mites, and aphids (see Chapter 4).
CONTAINERS: Standard plastic or clay pot, or hanging basket.
PROPAGATION: Plant divisions, root tip cuttings of some species.

Oxalis (OX-uh-liss). Wood-Sorrel Family ● *Oxalis siliquosa* (Shamrock; Four-leaf clover) A-174; *O. hedysaroides rubra* (Firefern) A-175; *O. rubra* A-176; *O. regnellii* A-177; *O. martiana aureo-maculata* A-178.

Dwarf date palm (left), 15-inch tub. Young kentia palm (right), 11-inch tub.

Bamboo palm (back) grows in a 13-inch tub. Fan palm, a species of *Livistona* (front), also grows in a 13-inch tub.

LIVING WITH IT:

Palms, like puppies, look more or less the same when very young and, once trained to live indoors, are wonderful house pets. However, mature heights vary in their natural tropical homelands from 30 inches to 60 feet. Indoors, the potential giants seldom exceed ceiling height, but only the miniature Neanthe bella palm fits on a sill, a shelf, a table, or in a terrarium. Display the others on a pedestal, a table, or on the floor. Species to try include: Bamboo palm (species of *Chamaedorea;* kam-ee-DOH-ree-uh), with slender cane- or bamboolike stems and graceful fronds that grow up more than out. Chinese fan palm (species of *Livistona;* liv-iss-TOH-nuh), with rounded, fan-shaped fronds. Dwarf date palm (species of *Phoenix;* FEE-nix), low rosette when young, but eventually forms

Chamaedorea elegans bella (Neanthe bella; Miniature palm) A-179; Bamboo palm A-180; *Livistona* (Chinese fan palm) A-181; *Phoenix* (Dwarf date palm) A-182.

PALM

a trunk especially nice for a pedestal. Fishtail palm (species of *Caryota* (kay-ree-OH-tuh), with leaf tips cut fishtail fashion. Kentia (species of *Howeia* HOW-ee-uh), old-fashioned parlor palm, the best all-around large house-plant palm. Lady palm (species of *Rhapis;* RAY-pis), almost as tough as kentia, but more graceful, with fronds that grow up more than out. Neanthe bella (species of *Chamaedorea;* kam-ee-DOH-ree-uh), miniature and easy to grow. And last, the areca or butterfly palm (species of *Chrysalidocarpus;* kriss-al-id-oh-KARP-us), most widely distributed large palm, but also the most difficult to maintain in good health indoors.

LIGHT: Ideal is a sunny east or west window, or a few feet from a sunny south window. Most will adapt to the light of a bright north-facing window or similar brightness. Once they get used to life indoors, older palms are good keepers in fairly low light. To maintain at their best, palms grown in low light, every few months give them an equal amount of time in some direct sun, especially during the winter.

TEMPERATURE: Average house during the winter heating season. Suffer in artificial heat over 80 degrees, also in temperatures below 50. The more moisture in the house, the better. Fresh, circulating air helps.

POTTING SOIL: All-purpose (see Chapter 3).

WATERING NEEDS: Water often enough to maintain a range between wet and nicely moist. Perfect drainage is essential; palms do not like to stand for several days or more in water. However, frond after frond will die if the soil is allowed to dry out between waterings. A palm 6 feet tall growing in a 12-inch clay pot is likely to need a quart of water twice each week. Mist frequently.

FEEDING: Feed all-purpose plant food all year; follow directions on the container for frequency.

PROBLEMS: Palms suffer in drafts of hot, dry air or if chilly breezes blow on them in the winter. If the air around a palm is hot, dry, and stale, red spider mites are almost sure to attack; see Chapter 4 for treatment. To grow well and look their best, palms need to have the fronds sponged or showered clean several times a year. Leaf tips die back if you let the soil dry out too much between waterings; this affects both old leaves and emerging fronds. It is not necessary, however, to remove an entire frond just because some of the tips have turned brown; just use a pair of sharp scissors to trim off the dead part. Reshape the end; don't cut it off bluntly. When an entire frond turns yellow or brown, remove it by cutting, not by pulling, from the main stem. Outdoors, the wind assists tightly closed fronds to open; indoors, you may have to help nature by gently separating individual leaves so they stand free along the frond.

CONTAINERS: Standard plastic or clay pot, or tub, with drainage.

PROPAGATION: Plant seeds or root divisions, in any season.

Caryota (Fishtail palm) A-183; *Howeia* (Kentia palm) A-184; *Rhapis* (Lady palm) A-185; *Chrysalidocarpus* (Butterfly palm -areca) A-186.

LIVING WITH IT: The plants shown are in 5- and 3-inch pots. *Pellionia daveauana* has brownish, purple-edged, silvery leaves; those of *P. pulchra* are gray-green with dark-brown veins. Display on sill, shelf, table, in a hanging basket, or grow in a terrarium landscape or fluorescent-light garden. Either kind may be planted as a ground cover for the soil around a large indoor tree. Since the trailing stems of these plants root wherever they touch moist soil, their leaves will soon form a solid mat. Well-grown pellionias are beautiful plants, especially in light that reveals the subtle variegation of the dark colors. Pellionias are easy to grow, but a perfect specimen is usually seen only in a professional collection. Travel damage between greenhouse and sales outlet and neglect in care cause some leaves to die, while others show unsightly brown spots. Pellionias benefit from frequent misting unless they are growing in a terrarium.

LIGHT: Ideal is a bright north window or similar brightness a few feet from a sunny window or in a fluorescent-light garden.
TEMPERATURE: Average house in winter; suffers below 55 degrees.
POTTING SOIL: African-violet or all-purpose (see Chapter 3).
WATERING NEEDS: Water often enough to keep evenly moist.
FEEDING: Feed all-purpose all year; follow container directions.
PROBLEMS: Avoid hot or dry drafts, which brown leaf tips.
CONTAINERS: Standard plastic or clay pot, hanging basket, or terrarium.
PROPAGATION: Root tip cuttings, in any season.

Pellionia (pell-ee-OH-nee-uh). Nettle Family • *Pellionia daveauana* A-187; *P. pulchra* A-188.

PEPEROMIA

LIVING WITH IT:
The plants shown are in 3-inch pots. They include *P. obtusifolia* (upper) and *P. caperata*. Display on sill, shelf, table, in a floor grouping, or in a hanging basket. Not long ago, the only peperomias commonly to be seen were the watermelon-begonia, *P. sandersii,* and *P. obtusifolia,* which have probably graced more commercial dish gardens than any other plants. Available today are many rosette-forming plants with straight stems and heart-shape leaves of any shade of green, with silver and near-black markings. Other species, such as *P. scandens,* make good hanging-basket plants. Watering is the key to success. Most have watery stems and are touchy about overwatering. But, if dry to wilting point, many leaves are lost as the stems seem unable to revive. Otherwise, plants are remarkably carefree. The minute flowers cluster in dense, pale-green spikes.

LIGHT: Ideal is full sun in an east or west window, or part sun in a south-facing window. Peperomias thrive in fluorescent light.
TEMPERATURE: Average house in winter; suffers below 60 degrees.
POTTING SOIL: All-purpose (see Chapter 3).
WATERING NEEDS: Water well. An hour later, pour off any excess water in the saucer. Water again when the surface soil is approaching dryness. Avoid extremes of wetness and dryness.
FEEDING: Feed all-purpose plant food all year; follow container directions for frequency.
PROBLEMS: Soggy, wet, poorly drained soil; very dry soil (see above).
CONTAINERS: Standard clay or plastic pot with drainage hole.
PROPAGATION: Leaf cuttings, division, or tip cuttings will produce baby plants (see Chapter 6).

Peperomia (pep-er-OH-mee-uh). Pepper Family • *Peperomia obtusifolia* A-189; *P. caperata* A-190; *P. sandersii* (Watermelon begonia) A-191; *P. scandens* A-192.

LIVING WITH IT:
The plant shown is in a 5-inch pot. It stays small enough to display on sill, shelf, table, or to grow in a fluorescent-light garden. Plants may be grouped in a shallow pot or a hanging basket. *Capsicum annuum* (shown) bears edible, extremely hot peppers. Do not confuse it with the Jerusalem cherry (see Chapter 8), whose round, red fruits are not edible. Growers start pepper seeds in spring to have flowering and fruiting plants in August and through fall and winter. If it has everything it needs, a Christmas pepper can be kept from year to year. As peppers turn dark red and wither, clip them off (use to start new plants). In spring, shear back a third to a half of old growth. Repot in fresh soil after working away most of the old soil from the roots. Plants kept outdoors in warm weather where insects can pollinate them freely will bear the largest crop of fruit. Bring in Christmas pepper plants before the first frost of the year.

LIGHT: Full sun in an east, south, or west window in winter; less sun is acceptable in summer. Also grows well in fluorescent light.

TEMPERATURE: Average house temperatures in winter; suffers above 75 and below 55 degrees.

POTTING SOIL: All-purpose (see Chapter 3).

WATERING NEEDS: Keep soil evenly moist. Extreme dryness or wetness will cause leaf and flower-bud drop. Mist often.

FEEDING: Feed blooming all year; follow container directions.

PROBLEMS: Aphids may attack tip growth; in hot, dry, stale air, red spider mites may attack. See Chapter 4 for treatment.

CONTAINERS: Standard plastic or clay pot, or hanging basket.

PROPAGATION: Sow seeds, in spring or early summer.

Capsicum (KAP-sick-um). Nightshade Family • *Capsicum annuum* (Christmas pepper) A-193.

PHILODENDRON

Philodendrons: fiddleleaf (left), 13-inch tub; heartleaf (right), 11-inch tub.

Monstera deliciosa, called Philodendron pertusum when young; in an 11-inch tub.

LIVING WITH IT: Philodendrons have two virtues that make them among the most popular indoor plants. They also have potential for greatness many growers don't know about. Ease of culture and willingness to grow in dim light, torrid heat, and despite neglect are the virtues. What gardeners fail to capitalize on is that many philodendrons, though they remain small-leaved and insignificant when grown in little pots with no support, can become big giant-leaved plants when staked to bark poles. All that's needed is some care, a large pot, a stake, and a knowledge of which philodendrons stay small and which grow big when staked. Some remain small always. One of these is probably the most widely grown house plant: heartleaf philodendron (*P. oxycardium,* sometimes sold as *P. cordatum*). Its trailing stems will form a neat mound of greenery for a desk or tabletop, or you can grow it in a hanging basket or provide a moist totem pole and train the stems upward (see Chapter 5).

Young plants of silver-leaved *P. sodiroi* grow similarly; but given good care and a support to climb, this variety will eventually grow much larger leaves. Confined to a terrarium or a bottle garden, *P. sodiroi* will remain small, almost miniature, indefinitely.

If you would like a philodendron that will produce big leaves and grows large on a stake, look for 'Burgundy,' with dark-green leaves suffused with maroon; fiddleleaf or horsehead (*P. panduraeforme,*

Philodendron oxycardium (Heartleaf philodendron) A-194; *P. sodiroi* A-195.

sometimes called *P. mandaianum*); and elephant's-ear (*P. domesticum*, sometimes called *P. hastatum*). Indoors, the leaves of these plants usually grow up to 10 inches long and about 6 inches wide. For best growth, all need a rough, moist surface on which to climb, such as a bark or moss totem pole.

This type of philodendron climbs by means of aerial roots. Others, called self-heading, grow by means of a trunk or column, almost like a shrub. Among these are the cut- or split-leaved philodendrons. It is in this group that the greatest confusion as to what plant is which type exists. The main complication is a philodendron relative, *Monstera deliciosa,* known as *P. pertusum* while it is young and small. There are true philodendrons that look like monstera: *P. bipinnatifidum* and *P. selloum.* One way to tell which is which is by growth pattern: monstera is a climber by nature and needs a totem pole. The other two are self-heading plants, and although a trunk may eventually form and raise the crown of leaves to indoor-tree height and a spread of 6 feet or more, they are essentially not climbers when cultivated as house plants. These large philodendrons may send long, thick roots across the soil surface and over the container's rim. Left to their own devices, the roots may simply dangle or find a nearby pot of moist soil to burrow into.

LIGHT: Ideal is a bright north or sunny east window, or similar brightness near a south or west window. Young plants grow well under fluorescent lights. Mature philodendrons keep well for several months in dim light, but then they need several months of bright light or some sun in order to recuperate.

TEMPERATURE: Average house in winter; suffers below 60 degrees. Survives dry heat at 80 degrees; with 50% or more humidity, warmth speeds growth.

POTTING SOIL: All-purpose (see Chapter 3).

WATERING NEEDS: Keep evenly moist; use water at room temperature. Can stand neglect, but repeated periods of soggy wetness or extreme dryness destroy the root system. Frequent misting benefits all philodendrons, but especially those in a hot, dry atmosphere.

FEEDING: Feed all-purpose all year; follow container directions.

PROBLEMS: Not insect prone; but if red spider mites or mealybugs attack, see Chapter 4 for treatment. The most common problem with philodendrons concerns cut- or split-leaved types whose new leaves grow smaller than the old ones and are plain, without splits. This is usually caused by one or a combination of three conditions: (1) temperatures are cold) (2) air is dry, (3) the main stem has grown taller than the totem pole and the aerial roots have no moist, rough surface to attach to. Correct by supplying a taller totem; for details, see Chapter 5.

CONTAINERS: Standard plastic or clay pot, tub, or hanging basket.

PROPAGATION: Root tip or stem cuttings, or air-layer, at any season when warmth and high humidity can be provided.

Philodendron (fill-oh-DEN-dron). Calla Family • *Philodendron panduraeforme* (Fiddle-leaf or Horsehead philodendron) A-196; *P. domesticum* (Elephant's ear philodendron) A-197; *Monstera deliciosa* (*P. pertusum*) A-198; *P. bipinnatifidum* A-199; *P. selloum* A-200.

PIGGYBACK PLANT

LIVING WITH IT:
The plant shown is in a 6-inch pot. Display this leafy green plant on sill, shelf, table, pedestal, in hanging basket. Piggyback, or pickaback, produces baby plants on the surface of old leaves at the point where leaf joins stem. If you understand the piggyback's likes and dislikes, it can be an outstanding house plant. It grows wild along the Pacific Coast from Alaska to northern California and therefore prefers fresh, cool, moist air. This is a short-lived plant, yet if you repot often to be sure it never is potbound and never let it dry out sufficiently to cause severe wilting, piggyback may live several years. Drafts of hot, dry air cause leaves to develop burned spots. Stale air that does not circulate encourages red spider mites. Piggyback is an especially fine office plant: It adapts to low-light situations and responds to lowered temperatures at night and on weekends. It is a favorite of children.

LIGHT: Best is a bright north window, or a few feet from an east, south, or west window where little or no sun shines directly on the leaves.
TEMPERATURES: Ideal is 55 to 70 degrees during winter heating season. Tolerates average house warmth if soil is always moist.
POTTING SOIL: All-purpose (see Chapter 3).
WATERING NEEDS: Water enough to maintain a range between wet and moist. Drying out will cause wilting and leaf loss. Mist frequently.
FEEDING: Feed all-purpose plant food all year; follow container directions for frequency.
PROBLEMS: Dry soil and drafts of hot, dry air (see above).
CONTAINERS: Standard clay or plastic pot, or hanging basket.
PROPAGATION: Root baby plants that form on old leaves; see Chapter 6.

Tolmiea (toll-MEE-uh). Saxifrage Family • *Tolmiea* (Piggyback plant) A-201.

'Silver Tree' (left) and 'Moon Valley' (right) in 5-inch pots; blackleaf *Pilea repens* (center) in 4-inch pot.

Creeping Charlie pilea (left) in 5-inch pot; artillery-fern (right) *Pilea serpillacea,* in 6-inch pot.

LIVING WITH IT: Display any pilea on sill, shelf, table, or in a dish garden, terrarium, or fluorescent-light garden. Besides varieties shown, others that make excellent house plants are: aluminum plant (*Pilea cadierei*); *Pilea depressa;* panamiga or Pan-American friendship plant (*P. involucrata*); *P. microphylla* (similar to *P. serpillacea* and also called artillery-fern); silver panamiga (*P. pubescens argentea*); and 'Black Magic.' Creepers are beautiful in small hanging basket or on a pedestal where stems can cascade freely; these include *P. depressa, P. nummularifolia* (creeping Charlie), and 'Black Magic.' Some bear a resemblance to their unpleasant relatives the stinging nettles, but all named here are harmless, beautiful, nearly pest-free.

LIGHT: Ideal is a sunny east or west window, the light of a bright north window, or similar brightness. Too much sun fades the leaves. Thrives in a fluorescent-light garden.
TEMPERATURE: Average house in winter; suffers below 60 degrees.
POTTING SOIL: All-purpose or terrarium (see Chapter 3).
WATERING NEEDS: Water often enough to keep evenly moist. Mist often.
FEEDING: Feed all-purpose all year; follow container directions.
PROBLEMS: Either severely dry or soggy, poorly drained soil may cause stems to die near the soil surface.
CONTAINERS: Standard plastic or clay pot, hanging basket, terrarium or dish garden.
PROPAGATION: Root tip cuttings, in any season.

Pilea (pie-LEE-uh). Nettle Family • *Pilea* 'Silver Tree' A-202; *P.* 'Moon Valley' A-203; *P. repens* (Blackleaf pilea) A-204; *P. nummularifolia* (Creeping Charlie pilea) A-205; *P. serpillacea* (Artillery-fern) A-206.

PINK POLKADOT PLANT; FRECKLEFACE

LIVING WITH IT:
The plant shown is in a 6-inch pot. A small plant, to display on sill, shelf, table, or to cultivate in a fluorescent-light garden. It's charming in a terrarium, but as it matures, it tends to overgrow its neighbors. Older plants may be grown in hanging baskets. This plant is perhaps more a curiosity than a truly worthwhile house plant. However, when it is grown in sufficient light, the pink spots intensify and give the olive-green leaves a rosy-pink suffusion that is lovely. As with coleus and Swedish ivy, growing tips must be pinched out.
In season, the plant produces spikes of lavender flowers. After these fade, cut back a third to a half of old growth, and repot in fresh soil. Keep soil barely moist, and do not feed until new growth begins. Then resume watering and feeding.

LIGHT: Ideal is a sunny east, south, or west window in winter; less light is needed in summer. Grows well in fluorescent light. Survives north light, but spots will be paler than desirable.
TEMPERATURE: Suffers over 75 or below 55 degrees in winter, but can bear higher heat in summer.
POTTING SOIL: All-purpose (see Chapter 3).
WATERING NEEDS: Water often enough to keep evenly moist. Dryness that causes wilting will wither older leaves (see above). Mist often.
FEEDING: Feed all-purpose plant food all year, except as noted above. Follow container directions.
PROBLEMS: Hot, dry, stale air invites red spider mites (see Chapter 4).
CONTAINERS: Standard plastic or clay pot, or hanging basket.
PROPAGATION: Root tip cuttings, in any season.

Hypoestes (high-poh-EST-eez). Acanthus Family • *Hypoestes* (Pink polkadot plant; Freckleface) A-207.

PITTOSPORUM

LIVING WITH IT: The plant shown is in a 5-inch pot. This grows to be a large plant for display on table, pedestal, or floor. A broadleaf-evergreen shrub popular outdoors in mild climates, it also makes a handsome house plant in a place where temperature is cool in winter. The leaves—which may be plain green or gray-green with white edges—grow in whorls (circles of leaves originating at the same spot on the stem) at stem ends. The stems spread out, then up to form a unique silhouette. Spotlighting at night will emphasize the dramatic branch

structure. For an even more exotic appearance, prune extraneous branches—in effect creating a bonsai. Pittosporum is especially attractive in an oriental jardiniere. Healthy plants bear clusters of sweet-scented white flowers in late winter or spring. This shrub, though a poor choice for a warm apartment, will, given the right conditions, make a showy, long-lived specimen house plant.

LIGHT: Ideal is a sunny east or west window in winter, or a few feet from a sunny south window. Less direct sun is needed in summer.
TEMPERATURE: Ideal is 55 to 70 degrees during winter heating season. Tolerates more heat in fresh, circulating, moist air.
POTTING SOIL: All-purpose (see Chapter 3).
WATERING NEEDS: Water enough to keep soil moist almost all the time, but allow slight drying between waterings. Mist frequently.
FEEDING: Feed all-purpose plant food in summer and autumn; blooming plant food in winter and spring; follow container directions.
PROBLEMS: Hot, dry, stale air shrivels leaves, encourages red spider.
CONTAINERS: Standard clay or plastic pot, or tub, with drainage hole.
PROPAGATION: Root tip cuttings of half-ripened wood, preferably in summer.

Pittosporum (pit-TOS-por-um). Pittosporum Family • *Pittosporum* A-208.

PLEOMELE

LIVING WITH IT:
The plant shown is in a 19-inch tub and is large enough to serve as an indoor tree. Young pleomeles may be displayed on a table or pedestal. Like the dracaenas to which it is related, this is one of the best of all the foliage house plants, and virtually pest-free. Besides *Pleomele reflexa* (shown), there is a form with creamy-yellow-striped leaves. Pleomele will survive neglect—soil allowed to become extremely dry and drafts of hot, dry, or cold air. However, careless culture causes the leaf tips to die. Since the leaves have a long life, permanent damage to the tips spoils the plant's appearance. You can correct this to some extent by trimming away the dead tips, cutting the leaves to retain their original shape. A large pleomele is as striking as sculpture if it is given the right place in a room and floodlighted at night to dramatize shape and color.

LIGHT: Ideal is a sunny east or west window in winter, or a few feet from a south window. Tolerates bright north light.
TEMPERATURE: Average house in winter; suffers below 55 degrees. Sponge or shower leaves often to clean.
POTTING SOIL: All-purpose (see Chapter 3).
WATERING NEEDS: Keep moist. Occasional slight drying out of the surface soil is not harmful (see above). Mist often.
FEEDING: Feed all-purpose plant food all year, following container directions for frequency.
PROBLEMS: Too much hot, direct sun will burn yellow spots in leaves.
CONTAINERS: Standard plastic or clay pot, or tub.
PROPAGATION: Root tip cuttings or air-layer, in any season (for instructions see Chapter 6).

Pleomele (plee-OH-may-lee). Lily Family • *Pleomele reflexa* A-209.

PODOCARPUS

LIVING WITH IT:
The plant shown is in an 8-inch pot. When young, display on sill, shelf, or table. Popular in outdoor gardens where severe winter freezing does not occur, older plants of this Japanese evergreen are among the finest of indoor trees. To create a tree effect with a plant only 3 to 5 feet tall, place it on a low table, pedestal, or stool so that the branches will be elevated. Provided it has everything else it needs, podocarpus tolerates a wide range of light indoors, from the light of a sunny window to that of a bright north window.

Individual leaves are durable, almost leatherlike. Drafts of hot, dry air will turn tips brown. Stale air that does not circulate may invite an attack of red spider mite, but podocarpus is less susceptible to this pest than many other indoor plants. Frequent showering of the leaves with tepid water will help keep them healthy for a maximum life span. Older podocarpus almost always benefit from being staked upright.

LIGHT: Ideal is a sunny east or west window or near a sunny south window. Tolerates light of a bright north window.
TEMPERATURE: Ideally 55 to 70 degrees during the winter heating season. If over 70, fresh circulating air is essential.
POTTING SOIL: All-purpose (see Chapter 3).
WATERING NEEDS: Water often enough to keep evenly moist. Avoid extreme dryness, which causes leaf tips to die. Mist often.
FEEDING: Feed all-purpose all year; follow container directions.
PROBLEMS: Hot, dry, stale air stunts growth and shrivels leaf tips.
CONTAINERS: Standard plastic or clay pot, or tub, with drainage.
PROPAGATION: Root cuttings of half-ripened wood, in any season.

Podocarpus (poh-doh-KARP-us). Podocarpus Family • *Podocarpus* A-210.

POLYSCIAS

Variegated *Polyscias paniculata* (left), 13-inch tub; *P. fruticosa,* 11-inch tub.

Polyscias balfouriana (left), 13-inch tub; its variety *pennockii,* 11-inch tub.

LIVING WITH IT: When plant is small, display on sill, shelf, table, or in a fluorescent-light garden. All the varieties shown can grow large enough to be treated as indoor trees. From the time a polyscias is 2 or 3 feet tall, it should be displayed on a pedestal, as a piece of living sculpture, and lighted at night to dramatize the beautiful foliage and strange, twisted, corky branches.

When you look at a polyscias, it is hard to imagine that it is closely related to English ivy, aralia (*Fatsia japonica*), fatshedera, false aralia (*Dizygotheca elegantissima*), and schefflera. All are members of the Ginseng Family; their chief resemblance lies in the flowers. Since they rarely flower indoors, the family ties are difficult to visualize. The polyscias, false aralia, and schefflera are better suited to warm indoor winter temperatures than are other members of the family.

The individual leaflets that form the leaves of *P. balfouriana* grow to 3 inches across. It is the most striking of the varieties grown indoors. The type called *P. b. marginata* has edges that are creamy white to pale chartreuse. In the variety *pennockii* the variegation spreads out from the leaf center to an irregular edging of shiny, dark green. *P. fruticosa* is the most popular species.

Plant shops offer sizes from inexpensive young plants less than 12 inches tall to aged specimens 6 feet or more in height and nearly as wide. These cost several hundred dollars. The variety *P. elegans* is more delicate in appearance. Because individual leaves look like parsley, it is often called parsley aralia. Either of the polyscias, when young, may be trained as bonsai; in cramped quarters they stay small indefinitely. Never let soil dry out. The branch structure can be pruned to an artistic bonsai design. The main trunk will grow yearly, but pruning can keep plants at 18 inches high or less if you are faithful about it.

Polyscias guilfoylei victoriae resembles *P. fruticosa,* but it is not as fine textured. The leaves have cream-white edges. *P. paniculata* (plain green) and its variegated form (pale chartreuse and creamy-white on a dark-green base) is still bolder in appearance, midway between *P. fruticosa* and *P. balfouriana.*

LIGHT: Ideal is a sunny east or west window, or a few feet from a sunny south window. Adapts to the light of a bright north window or to similar brightness. When polyscias is moved away from an abundance of light (for example, from outdoors where it receives early-morning or late-afternoon sun to the indoors), it will immediately drop many older leaves, and some corky stems may fall; given good care, it will adapt and in time resume growth. Don't be discouraged if the plant seems to fail; continue to care for it and it probably will come back.

TEMPERATURE: Average house in winter; suffers in artificial heat over 80 degrees (unless accompanied by fresh, moist, circulating air) and in temperatures below 55 degrees. Prefers high humidity and fresh air, especially if temperatures are high.

POTTING SOIL: All-purpose (see Chapter 3).

WATERING NEEDS: Water often enough to keep evenly moist. Polyscias survives occasional short periods of dryness, but older leaves will drop off and the plant will lose its beauty. Frequent misting is beneficial.

FEEDING: Feed all-purpose plant food all year; follow container directions for frequency.

PROBLEMS: In hot, dry, stale air, red spider mites are likely to attack; see Chapter 4 for treatment. Leaf drop is the most common complaint; it is usually caused by a change in environment. Polyscias adapts well to a variety of conditions if it is given the treatment it needs. Let it alone; if you move it to a new location every few days, it will never have time to adapt and may eventually die.

CONTAINERS: Standard plastic or clay pot, or tub, with drainage hole.

PROPAGATION: Root tip cuttings, ideally in spring or summer.

Polyscias (poh-liss-EE-us). Ginseng Family • *Polyscias balfouriana* A-211; *P. b. marginata* A-212; *P. b. pennockii* A-213; *P. fruticosa* A-214; *P. elegans* (Parsley aralia) A-215; *P. guilfoylei victoriae* A-216; *P. paniculata* A-217.

PONYTAIL; ELEPHANT FOOT

LIVING WITH IT:
The plant shown is in a 13-inch pot. This is a big plant, to set on a table, large shelf, or the floor. It looks best when the leaves have room to spread in a symmetrical rosette. Cats love it. If you are a cat fancier, grow it as a hanging-basket plant until it becomes too large; then move it to a tall, catproof pedestal. Year-old seedlings display the unusual swollen base characteristic of the plant. It grows partly above the soil. This base (it stores water) continues to grow, eventually to as much as 2 feet across on specimen plants in large tubs. By this time, the bare stem will rise 6 to 8 feet, crowned by the rosette of leaves that twist and curve down. Older plants are often called elephant-foot plant (or tree) because of the bulbous base. Ponytail's water-storing ability (up to several months in a mature plant) makes it one of the toughest house plants. Great choice for someone who travels frequently, owns a weekend house, or is forgetful about watering.

LIGHT: Ideal is full sun in an east, south, or west window; tolerates light of a north window all year, especially when older.
TEMPERATURE: Average house in winter, preferably not over 75 degrees for long period. Suffers below 50 degrees.
POTTING SOIL: All-purpose (see Chapter 3).
WATERING NEEDS: Water well, then not again until surface soil is dry.
FEEDING: Feed all-purpose all year; follow container directions.
PROBLEMS: Avoid heavy, poorly drained soil in a pot left standing for long periods in a saucer of water, especially in cold temperatures. Handle leaves gently when cleaning, as they split easily.
CONTAINERS: Standard clay or plastic pot, or tub, with drainage hole.
PROPAGATION: Root offsets or plant seeds, spring, or summer.

Beaucarnea (boh-KAR-nee-uh). Lily Family • *Beaucarnea recurvata* (Ponytail, Elephant foot) A-218.

LIVING WITH IT: The plant shown is in a 5-inch pot. When young, display on sill, shelf, table, or in a hanging basket or a fluorescent-light garden. The species shown (*Scindapsus aureus*), given a moist, rough surface, climbs by means of aerial roots and grows larger leaves, which are cut or perforated like those of the related plant monstera. Suitable support is a moss or bark totem pole (see Chapter 5). Pothos is one of the most widely distributed of all house plants. A less common species, *S. pictus argyraeus,* has satiny, olive-green, heart-shaped leaves spotted silver.

Although both pothos seem to prefer soil that dries out slightly between waterings, tip cuttings will grow nicely almost indefinitely in a glass or vase. They also grow amazingly well in locations where there is little light. This makes them ideal table- and desk-top plants. With light a few hours each day from a lamp, they live happily. Plentiful light encourages better variegation of the foliage and makes prettier plants.

LIGHT: Ideal is that of a bright north window, or similar brightness a few feet from a sunny window. Thrives in fluorescent light.

TEMPERATURE: Average house in the winter; suffers below 60 degrees. Sponge or shower occasionally to keep leaves clean.

POTTING SOIL: African-violet (see Chapter 3).

WATERING NEEDS: Water often enough to keep evenly moist; occasional slight dryness is beneficial. Mist often.

FEEDING: Feed all-purpose all year; follow container directions.

PROBLEMS: Roots may rot and die if soil is soggy wet and poorly drained.

CONTAINERS: Standard plastic or clay pot, or hanging basket.

PROPAGATION: Root tip cuttings, in any season.

Scindapsus (sin-DAP-suss). Calla Family • *Scindapsus aureus* (Pothos; Devil's ivy) A-219; *S. pictus argyraeus* (Pothos) A-220.

PRAYER PLANT; RABBIT-TRACK PLANT; CATHEDRAL WINDOWS

LIVING WITH IT:
Both plants shown are in 4-inch pots. This is a handsomely marked foliage plant to display on sill, shelf, table, in a hanging basket or fluorescent-light garden. Young prayer plants are excellent in a medium-to-large terrarium landscape but, unless cut back often, they quickly grow over smaller plants. *Maranta leuconeura kerchoveana* (lower plant) is often called rabbit-track plant because of the leaf markings. *M. l. massangeana* (upper) is sometimes called cathedral windows. Hold a leaf in front of a strong light and you will see why. The name prayer plant, applied to both, refers to the leaves' habit of folding together at night like praying hands. Marantas are easy to grow. Hot, dry, stale air and soil allowed to dry out severely will cause leaf tips to turn brown. About once a month, cut off shriveled brown leaves. Modest spikes of white flowers bloom now and then. If your plant dies back after drying out, keep watering; it may grow again.

LIGHT: Ideal is light of bright north window or similar brightness a few feet from a sunny window. Thrives in fluorescent light.
TEMPERATURE: Average house in winter; suffers below 55 degrees.
POTTING SOIL: African-violet or all-purpose (see Chapter 3).
WATERING NEEDS: Keep evenly moist. Extreme dryness curls leaves inward and will result in dead leaf tips. Mist leaves daily if possible. Shower monthly to keep clean.
FEEDING: Feed all-purpose all year; follow container directions.
PROBLEMS: Hot, dry, stale air invites red spider mites (see Chapter 4).
CONTAINERS: Standard plastic or clay pot, or hanging basket.
PROPAGATION: Plant root divisions or root stem cuttings, any season.

Maranta (muh-RANT-uh). Arrowroot Family • *Maranta leuconeura kerchoveana* (Prayer plant; Rabbit track plant) A-221; *M. l. massangeana* (Prayer plant; Cathedral windows) A-222.

170

LIVING WITH IT: The plant shown, *Primula kewensis,* is in a 5-inch pot. Display on sill, shelf, table, or grow in a fluorescent-light garden. This yellow-flowered species is the best to grow indoors. Also grown indoors for winter-spring bloom are Chinese primrose (*Primula sinensis*), fairy primrose (*P. malacoides*), and poison primrose (*P. obconica*). Contact with its leaves may cause a painful skin rash. Any of them, if kept in a cool, moist, airy atmosphere in summer, may live from one year to the next and bloom indoors. Sow seeds indoors in late winter or spring. When 4 to 6 true

leaves show, transplant seedlings to individual small pots. Just before they become root bound (Chapter 5), move to larger pots. Never let dry out severely. Avoid drafts of hot, dry air or wind. If possible, summer outdoors in a cool, moist shaded place.

LIGHT: Ideal is a sunny east or west window, or in a fluorescent-light garden. Little direct sun is needed in hot summer weather.
TEMPERATURE: Ideal is 60 to 70 degrees in daytime in winter, with a drop to 50 to 60 at night. If temperatures are warmer, fresh, circulating air becomes essential.
POTTING SOIL: All-purpose (see Chapter 3).
WATERING NEEDS: Keep soil evenly moist at all times. Mist frequently.
FEEDING: Feed all-purpose plant food in summer and fall, a blooming type in winter and spring; follow container directions.
PROBLEMS: Hot, dry, stale air withers leaves and flower buds.
CONTAINERS: Standard plastic or clay pot with drainage hole.
PROPAGATION: Plant seeds (see above). Root division is usual method for primroses growing outdoors, but more difficult with indoor plants.

Primula (PRIM-yew-luh). Primrose Family • *Primula kewensis* (Primrose) A-223; *P. sinensis* (Chinese primrose) A-224; *P. malacoides* (Fairy primrose) A-225; *P. obconica* (Poison primrose) A-226.

PRIMROSE, CAPE

LIVING WITH IT:
Plant shown is in a
4-inch pot. Display on
a table, shelf, or sill.
This primrose-like
plant is from the Cape
of Good Hope, Africa,
hence the popular
name. The plant is
closely related to the
African violet and
shares its good traits:
easy to grow, almost
ever-blooming,
attractive foliage, and
compact habit. Nymph
hybrids like the one
shown also come with
flowers of purple, plus
light, medium, and
dark blue. In average
house warmth with
40% or more humidity,
combined with sun
in an east or west
window, or in a
fluorescent-light
garden, the Cape
primrose has no dormant season. Unless you want the long, twisted seed
pods (the plant's Latin name, Streptocarpus, means seed pod) to develop
and ripen, clip them off as soon as the flowers fade. Repot when
offsets crowd the pot. Two-year-old Cape primroses make beautiful
hanging-basket plants, but take care not to hang them in drafts that are
either hot or cold.

LIGHT: Ideal is a sunny east or west window, or set in a fluorescent-
light garden about 6 inches beneath the tubes. Does well in a sunny
south window in fall and winter, but needs some shade in spring and
summer.
TEMPERATURE: Average house. Suffers below 55 degrees.
POTTING SOIL: African violet mix, Chapter 3.
WATERING NEEDS: About every three days, or often enough to keep the
soil always evenly moist. Dryness causes dead leaf tips and bud drop.
FEEDING: Blooming type every two weeks all year around.
PROBLEMS: Hot, dry air stunts growth and causes flower buds to die.
CONTAINERS: Standard clay or plastic pot with drainage hole.
PROPAGATION: Root leaf cutting, offset, or plant seeds spring or sum-
mer.

Streptocarpus (strep-toh-KARP-us). Gesneriad Family • *Streptocarpus* (Cape primrose)
A-227.

PURPLE PASSION PLANT; PURPLE VELVET

LIVING WITH IT:
The plant shown is in a 3-inch pot. Display on sill, shelf, table, as a hanging-basket plant, or grow in a fluorescent-light garden. This is a member of the Daisy Family, and it bears orange daisy flowers occasionally. However, it is grown for its colorful foliage, olive-green leaves so thickly covered with purple hairs the entire plant looks reddish-purple. Purple passion plant will exist in the bright, sunless light of a north window; but if you want a brilliant display of color, give it as many hours as possible of direct sunlight. It also grows

well under fluorescent light. This is a plant that needs shaping. Left to itself, it grows up and out as if by whim and seldom becomes a fine, well-shaped specimen. Frequent pinching back of the stem tips encourages more compact, bushy growth. After a year or two, the old stems at the base become woody and unproductive. Start new plants from tip cuttings. Fresh, circulating air is essential.

LIGHT: Ideal is a sunny south, east, or west window, or in a fluorescent-light garden. Tolerates the light of a bright north window.
TEMPERATURE: Average house in winter; suffers below 55 degrees. Hot, dry drafts are not particularly harmful if soil is kept moist.
POTTING SOIL: All-purpose (see Chapter 3).
WATERING NEEDS: Water enough to keep soil evenly moist. Occasional slight dryness is not harmful. Mist often.
FEEDING: Feed all-purpose all year; follow container directions.
PROBLEMS: White flies may attack, also thrips (see Chapter 4).
CONTAINERS: Standard plastic or clay pot, or hanging basket.
PROPAGATION: Root tip cuttings, at any season.

Gynura (jye-NEW-ruh). Daisy Family • *Gynura* (Purple passion plant; Purple velvet) A-228.

REDBIRD CACTUS; DEVIL'S BACKBONE

LIVING WITH IT:
The plant shown is in an 8-inch pot. When young, display on sill, shelf, table, or grow in a fluorescent-light garden. Older plants become small shrubs, to place on a low table, the floor, in a basket, pedestal. Redbird cactus is not a cactus, but a succulent member of the Spurge Family. It is related to crown-of-thorns and the Christmas poinsettia. Redbird refers to the shape of the inch-long, red, birdlike flowers, which appear in the winter on plants growing outdoors in the tropics, but seldom on those cultivated indoors. Devil's backbone refers to the zigzag growth habit of the stems. The leaves are attractively variegated light, dark, and gray-green with white and rose markings. Placing a redbird cactus that is several years old in a cold room (40 to 50 degrees) for two months in winter, withholding fertilizer and water sometimes induces flowering.

LIGHT: Ideal is a sunny south window; tolerates the light of a sunny east or west window.
TEMPERATURE: Average house in winter, unless you want to try forcing bloom, in which case see directions above.
POTTING SOIL: Cactus (see Chapter 3).
WATERING NEEDS: Water in a pattern from nicely moist to nearly dry. Avoid soggy wetness and severe drying.
FEEDING: Feed all-purpose plant food in summer and autumn; none in winter; blooming-type in spring.
PROBLEMS: Poor light produces weak growth; otherwise trouble-free.
CONTAINERS: Standard plastic or clay pot with drainage hole.
PROPAGATION: Root tip cuttings, ideally in spring or summer.

Pedilanthus (ped-uh-LANTH-us). Spurge Family • *Pedilanthus* (Redbird cactus; Devil's backbone) A-229.

ROSARY VINE

LIVING WITH IT:
The plant shown is in an 8-inch pot. Display on sill, shelf, table, pedestal, or in a hanging basket. Stems allowed to dangle freely may grow to 4 or 5 feet in a year's time. They are wiry, almost stringlike. The plant was given its name because of the fleshy, round bulblets that form at intervals, like beads on a rosary. The inch-long flowers look rather like unopened parachutes in midair. The plant shown here, *Ceropegia woodii,* is the most attractive of the varieties available, but all ceropegias make fascinating house plants and are easily cultivated indoors. Ideal light is full sun, especially in the winter months; but ceropegias adapt well to less sun and even to the light of a bright north window. Planted in sandy soil that drains excess water quickly, ceropegias will survive considerable neglect. Repeated severe dryness of the soil may cause stems near the soil to shrivel so much they cannot accept moisture. If this happens, remove dead growth, root tip cuttings to make new plants.

LIGHT: Ideal is a sunny east, south, or west window. Rosary vine tolerates the light of a bright north window.
TEMPERATURE: Average house in winter; suffers below 55 degrees.
POTTING SOIL: Cactus or all-purpose (see Chapter 3).
WATERING NEEDS: Water in a pattern ranging from nicely moist to nearly dry. Avoid soggy wetness and severe drying (see above).
FEEDING: Feed all-purpose all year; follow container directions.
PROBLEMS: Mealybugs may attack; see Chapter 4 for treatment.
CONTAINERS: Standard plastic or clay pot, or hanging basket.
PROPAGATION: Plant bulblets, or root tip cuttings, in any season.

Ceropegia (sear-oh-PEE-jee-uh). Milkweed Family • *Ceropegia woodii* (Rosary vine) A-230.

ROSE, MINIATURE

LIVING WITH IT:
The plant shown is in a 4-inch pot. Display on a sunny sill, shelf, table, in a hanging basket, or grow in a fluorescent-light garden. Plants in bush or tree form are available in white, yellow, pink, red, and bicolors. Others look lovely in hanging baskets. Some even have "mossed" buds like the old-fashioned moss roses of Victorian gardens. Miniature roses will succeed indoors during the winter heating season only if they have at least 4 hours of direct sun and lots of fresh, moist air. They grow and flower well under fluorescent light. Indoors they fall prey to powdery mildew, black spot (fostered by stale air), and aphids. Treat diseases with a-rose fungicide, following directions on the container; for aphids, see Chapter 4. After each period of bloom, prune back, and let the plant rest 6 weeks in a cool, sunny room.

LIGHT: Four hours daily of sun in a sunny east, south, or west window are necessary for blooming. Or try a fluorescent light garden. Will live in north light, but is not likely to flower.
TEMPERATURE: Ideal is 65 to 70 degrees in the daytime, 55 to 65 degrees at night during the winter heating months. Shower frequently.
POTTING SOIL: All-purpose (see Chapter 3).
WATERING NEEDS: Keep in a range between nicely moist and slightly dry. Severe dryness or soggy wetness will cause leaf and bud drop. Shower often.
FEEDING: Feed blooming all year; follow container directions.
PROBLEMS: See above. Hot, dry, stale air invites red spider mites.
CONTAINERS: Standard plastic or clay pot, or hanging basket.
PROPAGATION: Plant seeds or root tip cuttings of half-ripened wood, in any season.

Rosa (ROH-zuh). Rose Family. ● *Rosa* (Miniature rose) A-231.

ROUGE BERRY; BLOODBERRY

LIVING WITH IT: The plant shown is in a 4-inch pot. Display on sill, shelf, table, as a hanging-basket plant, or cultivate in a fluorescent-light garden. The plants grow easily and quickly from seeds, reaching a height of 12 inches in six months' time. While the plant is quite young, clusters of tiny pink flowers appear. followed by little berries that soon change from green to lipstick-red and then fall all around the plant. It's an exasperating habit that probably keeps this old-fashioned plant from becoming a contemporary favorite. These berries are not edible. In fact, they are considered poisonous; the plant is closely related to garden pokeweed, whose berries are poisonous. Rouge berry (*Rivina humilis*) is short-lived as a plant and is best started fresh from seeds about once a year. Though your local garden center may not carry rouge berry, specialists who sell plants by mail usually stock it. Seeds are sometimes available.

LIGHT: Ideal is a sunny east, south, or west window. May also be grown in a fluorescent-light garden. Tolerates bright north light.
TEMPERATURE: Ideal is average house during the winter heating season; suffers below 55 degrees.
POTTING SOIL: All-purpose (see Chapter 3).
WATERING NEEDS: Keep nicely moist. Severe dryness or soggy wetness will cause leaf and bud drop. Misting helps, but is not vital.
FEEDING: Feed blooming all year; follow container directions.
PROBLEMS: Aphids often appear on new growth (see Chapter 4).
CONTAINERS: Standard plastic or clay pot with drainage hole.
PROPAGATION: Plant seeds, in any season.

Rivina (ruh-VEE-nuh). Pokeweed Family • *Rivina humilis* (Rouge berry; Bloodberry) A-232.

SAGO PALM

LIVING WITH IT:
The plant shown is in a 13-inch pot. A big plant, descended from prehistoric times, it has a pine-cone-like base from which it unfurls stiff, dark-green fronds almost like plastic. It is among the most durable of all foliage plants. Provided the winter atmosphere is not stuffy, hot, and dry, it probably will live as long as you do. Sago palm is slow-growing, so large specimens are fairly expensive. The leaves form a handsome, symmetrical rosette, which shows to best advantage when viewed from above or from the side. Since the leaves are so stiff, it is important not to place this plant where someone might bump into it, especially at eye level. Sago palm is closely related to *Dioon,* which requires similar culture but tolerates a little more warmth. Both might be mistaken for a palm or a fern, but they are neither.

LIGHT: Ideal is 2 or 3 hours of sun in a window facing east, south, or west. Tolerates light of a north window.
TEMPERATURE: 55 to 75 degrees in winter; suffers in hot, dry heat.
POTTING SOIL: All-purpose (see Chapter 3).
WATERING NEEDS: Water well; an hour later, drain off excess in saucer. Don't let sit in water. Water again when surface begins to dry. In winter, mist foliage daily.
FEEDING: Feed all-purpose plant food in spring and summer; follow container directions. Feed little or not at all in fall and winter.
PROBLEMS: Avoid hot, dry, stale air, poorly drained soil.
CONTAINERS: Standard clay or plastic pot, or tub, with drainage hole.
PROPAGATION: Offsets, if they occur, can be removed and rooted, in spring, but this is difficult.

Cycas revoluta (SIGH-kus rev-oh-LOO-tuh). Cycad Family • *Cycas revoluta* (Sago palm) A-233; *Dioon* A-234.

ST. AUGUSTINEGRASS, VARIEGATED

LIVING WITH IT:
The plant shown is in a 3-inch pot. Display on sill, shelf, table, pedestal, or in a hanging basket. This graceful grass with round-tipped, white-striped leaves spreads by creeping stolons, as do many lawn grasses.

A young plant (as shown) will grow into a beautiful hanging-basket plant in a year. Although this grass does prefer some coolness in the winter and plenty of fresh, circulating moist air, it is reasonably adaptable. Do not hang where hot, dry air will blow on it. With 30% or more humidity and temperature generally between 60 and 70 degrees in the winter,

it will thrive. Abundant sun also to its liking, but it tolerates north light, especially if it is placed outdoors in summer. Although you may be tempted to plant a small one in a terrarium, this is not a good idea. The creeping stolons would quickly crowd out everything else.

LIGHT: Ideal is a sunny east, south, or west window. Tolerates the light of a bright north window.
TEMPERATURE: Average house in winter, ideally not over 70 degrees. Suffers above 75 degrees in artificial heat.
POTTING SOIL: All-purpose (see Chapter 3).
WATERING NEEDS: Keep soil evenly moist. If winter light is poor and temperatures cool, be careful not to overwater. Misting appreciated.
FEEDING: Feed all-purpose plant food in spring and summer; follow container directions. Do not feed in fall and winter unless conditions are ideal for growth.
PROBLEMS: Avoid drafts of hot, dry air. Suffers without fresh air.
CONTAINERS: Standard clay or plastic pot, or hanging basket.
PROPAGATION: Plant root divisions, ideally in spring or summer.

Stenotaphrum (sten-oh-TAFF-rum). Grass Family • *Stenotaphrum* (Variegated St. Augustinegrass) A-235.

SCHEFFLERA; QUEENSLAND UMBRELLA TREE

LIVING WITH IT:
The plant shown is in a 13-inch pot. A large plant, to display on table or floor. All nurserymen love this plant because it is so easily propagated, grows so quickly in tropical nurseries, and stands up well to shipping. It presents no problems until a new owner takes it home. Schefflera may —as we are promised —adapt to life in a dark corner, but it really prefers bright light and some direct sunlight, especially in fall and winter. It does not like soil that is constantly wet; but ignore advice to "let it dry out completely between waterings." That doesn't work.

Schefflera likes *tropical* warmth; heat plus humidity is the key to success here—not dry furnace heat. Keep foliage clean. Seedling scheffleras are sometimes sold as terrarium plants, but they grow too quickly for this. When buying a sizable schefflera, avoid any with blackened, shriveled, or dead leaf tips—a sure sign of overwatering. It is normal for the plant to lose some older leaves after you take it home.

LIGHT: Ideal is bright light and some direct sun near an east, south, or west window. Tolerates north light if other conditions are right.

TEMPERATURE: Average house in winter, with humidity of 30% or more if possible; suffers below 60 degrees. Doesn't stand up to cold drafts.

POTTING SOIL: All-purpose (Chapter 3).

WATERING NEEDS: Water well, not again until surface nears dryness.

FEEDING: Feed all-purpose all year; follow container directions.

PROBLEMS: Wet soil and cold temperatures causes blackened leaf tips; hot, dry, stale air encourages red spider mites.

CONTAINERS: Standard clay or plastic pot, or tub, with drainage hole.

PROPAGATION: Plant seeds or root tip cuttings, in spring or summer.

Brassaia (brass-SAY-ee-uh). Ginseng Family • *Brassaia actinophylla* (Schefflera; Queensland umbrella tree) A-236.

SCILLA VIOLACEA

LIVING WITH IT:
The plant shown is in a 4-inch pot. Display on sill, shelf, table, in a terrarium or as a desertscape, or cultivate in a fluorescent-light garden. It is one of the best house plants and has an amazing tolerance to varying amounts of light, heat, humidity, and soil moisture. This succulent member of the Lily Family has become fairly common in recent years. So attractive is it, both as a plant and in disposition, that the common name, silver squill, is hardly known. It is almost always referred to by its full, formal name, *Scilla violacea*. Like

the garden scillas to which it is related, this bulb plant sends up slender spikes of graceful, reflexed bells. However, its main attraction is the silver-spotted, olive-green foliage with leaf reverses and stems blushed maroon. The bulbs tend to rise to the surface of the soil, so they appear to be vases holding the leaves and flowers. In a year's time, one healthy bulb will multiply into several.

LIGHT: Ideal is an east, west, or north window, or a few feet from a sunny south window; also, a fluorescent-light garden.
TEMPERATURE: Ideal is average house in winter; suffers below 55 degrees.
POTTING SOIL: All-purpose (see Chapter 3).
WATERING NEEDS: Keep between nicely moist and nearly dry. Soggy wetness or complete dryness will cause leaf tips to die back and may kill them. Misting beneficial but not essential.
FEEDING: All-purpose all year; follow container directions.
PROBLEMS: Heavy watering in cold, cloudy weather may cause root rot.
CONTAINERS: Standard plastic or clay pot, basket, or terrarium.
PROPAGATION: Plant divisions, in any season.

Scilla (SILL-uh). Lily Family • *Scilla violacea* (Silver squill) A-237.

SCREW-PINE

LIVING WITH IT:
The plant shown is a large specimen in a 13-inch pot. Display on table, pedestal, or floor, or in a hanging basket. Leaf edges have sharp teeth, so place the plant where you aren't likely to touch it absent-mindedly; when sponging the leaves, work cautiously. With leaves so tough, you would think no insect could attack them. Unfortunately, though, mealybugs do not agree; for treatment, see Chapter 4. Screw-pine is not a true pine, but the leaves spiral up and remind you of a corkscrew or a pine cone. A large, old, well-grown screw-pine makes such a handsome plant that it assumes the role of an important piece of sculpture. Display it on a pedestal or hang it in a basket, so the form can be appreciated. Improper growing conditions in general, but especially insufficient light, reduce the amount of white in the shiny green leaves — a pity, since the variegation adds to the plant's beauty.

LIGHT: Ideal is a sunny east or west window, or a few feet from a sunny south window. Tolerates bright north light.
TEMPERATURE: Average house in winter; suffers over 75 degrees, and below 55.
POTTING SOIL: All-purpose (see Chapter 3).
WATERING NEEDS: Water often enough to keep evenly moist; avoid excessive moisture that does not drain away, also extreme dryness. Mist as often as possible, especially in winter and spring.
FEEDING: Feed all-purpose plant food all year except autumn; in autumn, feed half as much; follow container directions for frequency.
PROBLEMS: Hot, dry, stale air invites red spider mite (see Chapter 4).
CONTAINERS: Standard plastic or clay pot, tub, or hanging basket.
PROPAGATION: Remove and root offsets, in any season.

Pandanus (pan-DAY-nus). Screw-Pine Family • *Pandanus* (Screw-pine) A-238.

SELAGINELLA; SWEAT PLANT; SPREADING CLUBMOSS

LIVING WITH IT: The plants shown are in 5- and 3-inch pots. These are cultivated best in terrariums or bottle gardens, where moist, draft-free air is constant. Plants shown are *Selaginella kraussiana* (top), *S. emmeliana* (left), and *S. kraussiana brownii* (right). *S. kraussiana* is called spreading clubmoss because the plant sends down stiltlike roots and spreads over other plants. This kind of growth occurs only in constant warmth and high humidity. You can have a fascinating terrarium or bottle garden by planting only selaginellas, either the same or different varieties. Except for *S. kraussiana,* most of the other kinds combine well in a miniature landscape with miniature ferns, begonias, gloxinias, and episcias. In a home where many plants are cultivated and relative humidity of 50% or more is maintained, selaginellas will do fairly well in the open atmosphere, provided they never dry out and are misted daily.

LIGHT: Ideal is a bright north window or similar brightness a few feet from a sunny window; thrives in fluorescent light.

TEMPERATURE: Average house in winter, but suffers over 75 degrees and under 55 degrees.

POTTING SOIL: Terrarium (see Chapter 3).

WATERING NEEDS: Water enough to keep evenly moist; avoid dryness. Mist daily.

FEEDING: Feed all-purpose plant food all year; follow container directions for frequency.

PROBLEMS: Hot, dry air shrivels leaves almost immediately.

CONTAINERS: Terrarium or bottle garden; standard plastic or clay pot (if open air of room is moist, as described above).

PROPAGATION: Plant divisions or root cuttings, in any season.

Selaginella (suh-lajh-ih-NELL-uh). Selaginella Family • *Sellaginella kraussiana* (Spreading clubmoss) A-239; *S. k. brownii* (Spreading clubmoss) A-240; *S. emmeliana* (Sweat plant) A-241.

SHRIMP PLANT

LIVING WITH IT:
The plant shown is in a 5-inch pot. This is a medium-size plant, for display on sill, shelf, table, or in a hanging basket. Small, soft-haired, light-green leaves grow on arching, slender stems. The true flowers are small and white, but they tip what appear to be the flowers: spikes of long-lasting bracts. These are usually pinkish or coppery-brown (chartreuse-yellow in the form called 'Yellow Queen'). The bracts' shape and color give the shrimp plant its name. A well-grown plant will branch freely, displaying a showy bract at every branch tip. As the bracts' color fades, clip them off, with 1 or 2 inches of stem. This encourages new bushy growth and more flowering. A native of Mexico, the plant will not thrive in winter in the average warm, stuffy dwelling. However, it will survive a winter indoors and quickly revive if set outdoors when frost-free weather arrives. Place on a porch where it will receive a few hours of direct sun every day.

LIGHT: Ideal is full sun in an east, south, or west window; tolerates less light in summer.
TEMPERATURE: During the winter, it does best in a cool window where temperatures stay within a range of 60 to 70 degrees.
POTTING SOIL: All-purpose (see Chapter 3).
WATERING NEEDS: Water about every 3 days, or often enough to keep the soil evenly moist. Mist frequently.
FEEDING: Feed blooming plant food; follow container directions.
PROBLEMS: Suffers in poor light and a hot, dry atmosphere.
CONTAINERS: Standard clay or plastic pot, or hanging basket.
PROPAGATION: Root tip cuttings, preferably during the spring or the early summer.

Beloperone (bel-oh-per-OH-nee). Acanthus Family • *Beloperone guttata* (Shrimp plant) A-242.

SNAKE PLANT; MOTHER-IN-LAW'S TONGUE

LIVING WITH IT: The tallest plant shown, *Sansevieria trifasciata,* is in a 13-inch pot; smaller plants, both *S. grandis,* are in 11- and 8-inch pots. Display on sill, shelf, table, or on the floor. "Snake plant" refers to the snakelike markings on the foliage of some kinds. "Mother-in-law's tongue" refers to the sturdy, if not indestructible, nature of the plant. Sansevieria will succeed whether it is hot or chilly and drafty (but not below 40 degrees), in full sun or in near darkness. The victim of its own cast-iron disposition, it is mostly taken for granted. Neglected, sansevierias are unattractive; but healthy plants grouped in interesting containers have beautiful form and color. Occasionally they produce sprays of small, greenish-white, fragrant flowers, like those of the spider plant, its relative. Sansevierias are now gaining sufficient popularity to create a demand for less common kinds.

LIGHT: Any window with any amount of light.
TEMPERATURE: Ideal is average house during winter heating season.
POTTING SOIL: All-purpose (see Chapter 3).
WATERING NEEDS: Ideal is to water well, then not again until the soil surface feels dry. Tolerates dryness, but dislikes soggy wetness.
FEEDING: Feed all-purpose plant food all year, following the container directions.
PROBLEMS: Nearly indestructible, but it pays to keep foliage clean.
CONTAINERS: Standard plastic or clay pot, or tub.
PROPAGATION: Plant divisions or offsets, in any season. This is one of few plants, the cuttings of which may not follow parent's coloring.

Sansevieria (sanz-uh-VEER-ee-uh). Lily Family • *Sansevieria trifasciata* (Snake plant; Mother-in-law's tongue) A-243; *S. grandis* A-244.

SONERILA

LIVING WITH IT:
The plant shown is in a 3-inch pot. The sonerila is newly popular because it is a perfect plant for growing in a bottle garden or terrarium where there are constant high humidity and warmth. It is also naturally small and compact. A single specimen like the one shown will thrive alone in a bell jar or in a similar glass or clear-plastic enclosure. Although the plant is grown primarily for the showy silver leaves on reddish stems, the occasional clusters of rosy-lavender flowers are quite beautiful. When kept in constant warmth and high humidity, the sonerila is surprisingly trouble-free. Like many other plants with somewhat watery stems—wax begonia and peperomia, for example—it resents too much wetness in the soil. Drafts of dry air, whether cold or hot, will wither the sonerila. Dead leaf tips are a sure sign that the plant is asking you for more humidity around it.

LIGHT: An hour or 2 of sun daily, preferably morning or afternoon. Sonerila grows to perfection in a fluorescent-light garden.
TEMPERATURE: Average house or slightly warmer; suffers below 60 degrees.
POTTING SOIL: All-purpose (see Chapter 3).
WATERING NEEDS: Soak the soil; then do not water again until the surface feels almost dry.
FEEDING: Feed all-purpose all year; follow container directions.
PROBLEMS: Lack of humidity, cold temperature, and drafts of any kind.
CONTAINERS: Standard clay or plastic pot, or plant directly in the soil of a terrarium or bottle garden.
PROPAGATION: Root tip cuttings, in any season; provide warmth and humidity as they grow.

Sonerila (soh-ner-ILL-uh). Meadow-Beauty Family • *Sonerila* A-245.

SPATHIPHYLLUM; PEACE-LILY; WHITE FLAG

LIVING WITH IT:
The plant shown is in a 13-inch pot. Display on table, floor, or pedestal. Almost always referred to by its botanical name rather than either of its common names, spathiphyllum is one of the best of all medium-size indoor foliage plants and produces graceful white flowers similar to a calla lily. *S. cannaefolium* is one of the most desirable because it has such fragrant flowers; but it is difficult to find. Several kinds of spathiphyllum are available, however; the plants may be classified according to height: small (18 to 24 inches tall), medium

(24 to 30 inches), and tall (30 to 48 inches). The flower sizes vary accordingly. A great asset of this peace-lily is that it is virtually pest-free. However, it is sensitive about quantity of light; too much quickly causes yellow, black, and brown burn spots; too little results in spindly, pale, undersize new growth and a rapid decline of the plant.

LIGHT: Bright light in a north window, or a few feet from a sunny east, south, or west window. Mature plants tolerate low light for up to six months, but should then be moved to adequate light.
TEMPERATURE: Average house in winter; suffers below 55 degrees.
POTTING SOIL: All-purpose (see Chapter 3).
WATERING NEEDS: Water enough to maintain a range between wet and moist. Dryness to the point of wilting causes the leaf tips to die back.
FEEDING: Feed all-purpose all year; follow container directions.
PROBLEMS: Too much direct sun, not enough light (see above), dry soil.
CONTAINERS: Standard clay or plastic pot.
PROPAGATION: Plant root divisions, in any season.

Spathiphyllum (spath-if-FILL-um). Calla Family • *Spathiphyllum* (Peace-lily; White flag) A-246.

SPIDER PLANT; AIRPLANE PLANT

LIVING WITH IT:
The plant shown is in an 8-inch pot. Display plant on sill, shelf, pedestal or in hanging basket. It is easy to grow; its plain or green-and-white-striped leaves have a refreshing appearance; and its habit of sprouting babies in midair is endlessly fascinating. (Cats love to play with the dangling plantlets; they also eat the leaves.) The plant adapts to various kinds of light and is virtually pestfree. Leaf tips die back when soil dries out severely. If new growth shows blackened or rotted areas, the soil is likely too acid; correct this by working a tablespoonful of horticultural limestone into the soil's surface. Spider plant has thick roots, almost like white radishes, and does best moved to a size-larger pot when the old one is filled with roots. It also needs drainage. A species that differs from ordinary spider plant is miniature *C. bichetii*. This forms clumps of grassy-green, white-edged leaves about 8 inches tall, but without plantlets.

LIGHT: Ideal is 2 or 3 hours of sun in winter; adapts to the light of a north window. Young plants do well under fluorescent light.
TEMPERATURE: Average house; suffers below 55 degrees or if hung in drafts of hot, dry winter heat.
POTTING SOIL: All-purpose (see Chapter 3).
WATERING NEEDS: Keep soil evenly moist. A large hanging basket may need as much as 1 quart of water twice a week. Misting appreciated.
FEEDING: Feed all-purpose all year; follow container directions.
PROBLEMS: Avoid severely dry soil and acid soil (see above).
CONTAINERS: Standard clay or plastic pot, or hanging basket.
PROPAGATION: Root airborne offsets or plant root divisions.

Chlorophytum (kloh-roh-FYE-tum). Lily Family • *Chlorophytum vittatum* (Spider plant; Airplane plant) A-247; *C. bichetii* (Miniature spider plant) A-248.

STAR OF BETHLEHEM; ITALIAN BELLFLOWER

LIVING WITH IT:
The plants shown are in 5-inch pots. Display on sill, shelf, table, pedestal, or in hanging basket. A relative of Canterbury bells and other campanulas in outdoor gardens, this plant has been cherished for its blue or white, single or double star-shape flowers. Unless you have a cool window in winter, it will be difficult to maintain. Its main growing season is in spring; flowers follow in summer. In autumn, trim stems to 4 or 5 inches, and until spring, keep the soil less moist than usual and do not feed. At the beginning of spring, water more freely and

resume fertilizing. While star of Bethlehem can be cultivated all year as a house plant, in summer it ideally should be outdoors where it receives early-morning or late-afternoon sun for an hour or two and shade the rest of the day. It is a perfect companion for tuberous begonias, fuchsias, impatiens, and caladiums. Protect from hot, dry air and wind.

LIGHT: A little morning or afternoon sun in spring and summer; bright light but no sun is acceptable in fall and winter.
TEMPERATURE: Average house heat spring and summer; not over 65 degrees other seasons.
POTTING SOIL: African-violet (see Chapter 3).
WATERING NEEDS: Water enough to keep evenly moist in spring and summer; let approach dryness before watering in fall and winter.
FEEDING: Apply blooming plant food in spring and summer; follow container directions. Do not feed in fall and winter.
PROBLEMS: Avoid excessive dry heat and soggy, poorly drained soil.
CONTAINERS: Standard clay or plastic pot, or hanging basket.
PROPAGATION: Root tip cuttings, in spring or early summer.

Campanula (kam-PAN-yew-luh). Bellflower Family • *Campanula* (Star of Bethlehem; Italian Bellflower) A-249.

STRAWBERRY, ALPINE

LIVING WITH IT:
The plant shown is in a 6-inch pot. Grow on sill, shelf, table, or in a fluorescent-light garden. Alpine strawberry is a *Fragaria,* a variety of the cultivated strawberry. It produces good berries of the prized *fraises des bois* type. The plants do not form runners as do the varieties grown only outdoors, but they quickly multiply into dense clumps, which are easy to divide into new plants. They grow from seed to fruit-bearing size in about 6 months. One variety sold as seed produces golden-yellow berries. Grow these plants indoors in winter months in a sunny window or a fluorescent-light garden. Provide temperatures between 60 and 72 degrees and plenty of fresh, moist air. Such conditions are possible in a home where an unused room is kept cool and in a basement fluorescent-light garden. Hot, dry, stale air will prevent flowering. So will lack of light and soil that is allowed to dry out severely.

LIGHT: Sunny east, south, or west window, or fluorescent-light garden.
TEMPERATURE: Ideal is 60 to 72 degrees during winter heating season; suffers over 75 degrees except in fresh, moist air.
POTTING SOIL: All-purpose (see Chapter 3).
WATERING NEEDS: Water often enough to keep evenly moist. Mist often.
FEEDING: Alternate feeding with an all-purpose and a blooming-type plant food all year; follow container directions.
PROBLEMS: Hot, dry, stale air encourages red spider mites; for treatment see Chapter 4.
CONTAINERS: Standard plastic or clay pot, or strawberry jar.
PROPAGATION: Plant seeds or divisions preferably in winter or spring.

Fragaria (fruh-GAY-ree-uh). Rose Family • *Fragaria* (Alpine strawberry) A-250.

STRAWBERRY-GERANIUM; STRAWBERRY-BEGONIA

LIVING WITH IT:
The plant shown is in a 5-inch pot. This is a rather small plant, to display on sill, shelf, table, pedestal, in a little hanging basket, or in a terrarium. The popular names refer to the leaves, which are shaped and scalloped like a geranium's, and to the stolons or runners, which bear baby plants in the same manner as strawberries. The plant, though winter-hardy outdoors to 10 degrees below zero, is amazingly tolerant of the average house conditions. A low-growing creeper, with leaves seldom more than 4 inches tall, it bears clusters of graceful, small, white

flowers on stems that may reach to 18 inches. After the flowers fade, cut off at the base. The more common *S. stolonifera* (sometimes called S. sarmentosa) has silver-veined, olive-green leaves with maroon on the back. Its variety 'Tricolor' is much showier, with leaves variegated green, olive, white, gray, and pink. For best color it needs a cool, moist atmosphere and soil kept on the dry side.

LIGHT: Ideal is a sunny east or west window in winter, or part shade in a south window. Adapts to north light. Thrives in fluorescent light.
TEMPERATURE: Ideal is 50 to 70 degrees during the winter heating season.
POTTING SOIL: All-purpose (see Chapter 3).
WATERING NEEDS: Water often enough to keep the soil evenly moist, although slight drying occasionally is desirable. Mist frequently.
FEEDING: Feed all-purpose all year; follow container directions.
PROBLEMS: Avoid drafts of hot, dry air, or leaf edges will die.
CONTAINERS: Standard clay or plastic pot, hanging basket, terrarium.
PROPAGATION: Root offsets, in any season.

Saxifraga (sax-IF-ruh-juh). Saxifrage Family • *Saxifraga stolonifera* (Strawberry-geranium; Strawberry-begonia) A-251; *S. s.* 'Tricolor' A-252.

SWEDISH-IVY

LIVING WITH IT: The plant shown is in an 8-inch pot. When mature, it makes a handsome, large hanging-basket plant; young plants may be grown on sill, shelf, or pedestal. This obliging plant has enjoyed a meteoric rise to fame since it began to be widely cultivated, in the 1950s. It is not Swedish, however, but Australian; not ivy but a member of the Mint Family (square stems are an obvious clue). An unusually good house plant, it will survive neglect and inexperience. The scalloped, plain-green leaf of the species *Plectranthus australis* (shown) is also available in a form with white-variegated green leaves. The leaves of *P. oertendahlii* are silver and olive above, burgundy below. Other species available from time to time are also fine for hanging baskets. The key to success with any plectranthus is to pinch out the growing tips frequently, to encourage dense, much-branched growth. It is also a good idea to start new plants from cuttings every 1 or 2 years, as old Swedish-ivy plants grow woody at the base and lose their vigor.

LIGHT: Up to half a day of sun in an east, south, or west window; tolerates north light. Rotate plant a quarter to half turn weekly, so that all parts receive an equal amount of light.
TEMPERATURE: Average house; suffers below 55 degrees.
POTTING SOIL: All-purpose (see Chapter 3).
WATERING NEEDS: Keep soil evenly moist. Avoid extremes of wetness, and dryness.
FEEDING: Feed all-purpose all year; follow container directions.
PROBLEMS: Insufficient light causes spindly growth.
CONTAINERS: Standard clay or plastic pot, or hanging basket.
PROPAGATION: Root tip cuttings, in any season.

Plectranthus (pleck-TRANTH-us). Mint Family • *Plectranthus australis* (Swedish-ivy) A-253; *P. oertendahlii* A-254.

192

LIVING WITH IT: The plant shown is in a 3-inch pot. A small plant, *Acorus calamus variegatus* is displayed best on a sill, shelf, or table, or in a terrarium. Though it is related to philodendron, it is irislike and forms appealing grassy clumps. The green-and-white foliage is useful for creating small landscapes in a terrarium or bowl garden. A miniature version, *Acorus gramineus pusillis,* grows 3 inches tall and forms dark-green tufts of flat spears. These plants actually like soil always between wet and moist. They grow well in open air if humidity is 30%

or more, but probably are happiest in a cool terrarium or bottle garden. In the hot, dry, stale air of winter heating, red spider mites are likely to attack. Soil allowed to dry will cause leaf tips to die. In a terrarium, acorus combines well with baby's tears, small ferns such as *Polystichum tsus-simense,* and miniature English ivy.

LIGHT: Two or 3 hours of sun in winter; adapts to light of a north window. Thrives in a cool, fluorescent-light garden.
TEMPERATURE: Survives average house heat in winter, but prefers to be on the cool side; suffers above 70 degrees and below 40 in winter.
POTTING SOIL: All-purpose or African-violet (see Chapter 3).
WATERING NEEDS: Water almost daily, enough to maintain a range between wet and moist. Check often. Mist often.
FEEDING: Feed all-purpose plant food all year; follow container directions for frequency of feeding.
PROBLEMS: Red spider mites (see Chapter 4).
CONTAINERS: Standard clay or plastic pot with drainage hole.
PROPAGATION: Plant root divisions, in any season.

Acorus (ACK-or-us). Calla Family • *Acorus calamus variegatus* (Sweet flag) A-255; *A. gramineus pusillus* (Miniature sweet flag) A-256.

TAHITIAN BRIDAL VEIL

LIVING WITH IT:
The plant shown is in an 8-inch hanging basket. Display on shelf or pedestal so the stems can cascade freely, or in a hanging basket. This plant has long, thin stems with small, olive-green leaves, blushed maroon on the back. From time to time it literally covers itself in tiny, delicate white flowers. If you buy Tahitian bridal veil as a large, mature plant, never let it dry out severely; if it does many of the older leaves will die along the stems; not only will these be unsightly, but removing them will be tedious work. If you start with a young plant, pinch back the tips after every few inches of new growth, to encourage maximum branching. This is especially important in the early stages and until the stems have grown thickly enough to nearly cover the hanging basket. Don't wait until stems are 12 inches or longer before pinching off the tips; this would produce heavy growth toward the bottom while the top remained sparse and unattractive.

LIGHT: Ideal is a sunny east, south, or west window. Tolerates the light of a bright north window.
TEMPERATURE: Average house in winter; suffers below 55 degrees.
POTTING SOIL: All-purpose (Chapter 3).
WATERING NEEDS: Keep soil evenly moist. Avoid extreme wetness, dryness. Mist foliage daily if possible, especially during winter heating.
FEEDING: Feed all-purpose all year; follow container directions.
PROBLEMS: In hot, dry, stale air, red spider mites may attack. Treat as instructed in Chapter 4.
CONTAINERS: Standard clay or plastic pot, or hanging basket.
PROPAGATION: Root cuttings, in any season.

Gibasis (jib-BAY-sis). Spiderwort Family • *Gibasis* (Tahitian bridal veil) A-257.

UMBRELLA PLANT; CYPERUS

LIVING WITH IT:
Plants shown are in 3-inch pots. The plant with larger, bolder leaves is *Cyperus diffusus;* the other is *C. alternifolius*. The plants shown are young; in a year, the stems will grow to 2 or 3 feet tall, each topped by a crown of green leaves arranged like the spokes of an umbrella. Plants are handsome, at that size, displayed on sill, shelf, table, floor, or pedestal. Greenish, insignificant flowers appear at the top where the leaves join the stem. These plants do not like hot, dry air, but present no further difficulties when grown indoors. No other house plant

shares their picturesque form, which recalls the umbrella plants that grow along the Nile in Egypt. (The related *C. papyrus* was used in the making of papyrus—forebear of paper— 3,000 years before Christ.) You can make a beautiful table scene by placing a tall umbrella plant next to a neat mound of baby's-tears or another small plant.

LIGHT: Ideal is a bright north window, near a sunny east or west window, or in similar brightness.
TEMPERATURE: Ideal is 60 to 70 degrees. Suffers over 75 degrees.
POTTING SOIL: All-purpose (see Chapter 3).
WATERING NEEDS: Keep soil between wet and moist. Never let dry out. Mist as often as possible.
FEEDING: Feed all-purpose all year; follow container directions.
PROBLEMS: Hot, dry, stale air causes dead leaf tips and encourages red spider mites (see Chapter 4 for treatment). If tall stems seem weak, support them on thin bamboo stakes.
CONTAINERS: Standard plastic or clay pot with drainage hole.
PROPAGATION: Plant root divisions, in any season.

Cyperus (sigh-PEER-us). Sedge Family • *Cyperus diffusus* (Umbrella plant) A-258; *C. alternifolius* (Umbrella plant) A-259.

UNGUENTINE PLANT; ALOE

LIVING WITH IT:
The plant shown is in an 11-inch pot. Never very large, it remains of a size suitable for display on a sill, shelf, or table. This succulent ought to be cultivated in every household. It is an attractive plant, and it is extremely easy to grow under ordinary house conditions. Furthermore, it is useful: When a leaf is broken off, the gelatinous pulp that oozes from it is an effective treatment for skin burns. Many other curative properties have been attributed to it. The white-spotted, translucent green or gray-green leaves have soft spines.

Although this aloe is widely cultivated, like many old-fashioned folk plants is not always easy to find commercially; it is rarely identified by its botanical name, *Aloe vera*. Several mail-order specialists in herbs and medicinal plants list it, as do some growers of cacti and other succulents. While it can take all the sun you can give it indoors in winter, be careful if you move it outdoors in warm weather. All-day sun can burn unsightly spots on the foliage.

LIGHT: Ideal is sunny east, south, or west window; survives north light.
TEMPERATURE: Average house in winter; suffers below 55 degrees.
POTTING SOIL: Cactus mixture (see Chapter 3).
WATERING NEEDS: Water well. An hour later, pour off any excess that has collected in saucer. Water again when surface feels nearly dry.
FEEDING: Feed all-purpose all year; follow container directions.
PROBLEMS: Soggy-wet, poorly drained soil, especially in winter, is likely to cause roots to rot. Too much outdoor sun will burn foliage.
CONTAINERS: Standard clay or plastic pot.
PROPAGATION: Root offsets, in any season.

Aloe vera (uh-LOH-ee VEER-uh). Lily Family • *Aloe vera* (Unguentine plant) A-260.

WANDERING JEW; STRIPED INCH PLANT

LIVING WITH IT:
The plants shown are in 5-inch pots. Display on shelf, table edge, pedestal, or in a hanging basket so the stems can fall free. All three leaf types pictured here are referred to as wandering Jew though they have different specific botanical names. All belong to the Spiderwort Family. The green leaf with white pin stripes is that of the striped inch plant, *Callisia elegans;* the green leaf irregularly striped with white is *Tradescantia fluminensis variegata;* the purple-silver-and-green leaf is *Zebrina pendula.* The way to grow a thick, full hanging basket of any one of these is to plant 6 short, stocky rooted cuttings in good, all-purpose soil in a 6- to 8-inch basket. Pinch out the tips; as soon as 2 to 4 leaves form on new branch, pinch out the tips again. Continue this procedure, turning the container a quarter to a half turn each week, so that all leaves receive an equal portion of light. You will soon have a dense bell of foliage that hides the basket.

LIGHT: Ideal is a sunny east, south, or west window. Tolerates the light of a bright north window.
TEMPERATURE: Average house in winter; suffers below 55 degrees. Avoid drafts of hot, dry air.
POTTING SOIL: All-purpose (see Chapter 3).
WATERING NEEDS: Keep soil evenly moist. Avoid extreme wetness, dryness. Mist often.
FERTILIZING: Feed all-purpose all year; follow container directions.
PROBLEMS: In hot, dry, stale air, red spider mites may attack. Treat as directed in Chapter 4.
CONTAINERS: Standard clay or plastic pot, or hanging basket.
PROPAGATION: Root cuttings in water or wet sand, in any season.

Callisia (kal-LISS-ee-uh). *Tradescantia* (trad-ess-KANT-ee-uh). *Zebrina* (zuh-BRYE-nuh).
Spiderwort Family • *Callisia elegans* A-261; *Tradescantia fluminensis variegata* A-262;
Zebrina pendula (Wandering Jew) A-263.

WAXPLANT; WAX FLOWER

LIVING WITH IT: The plants shown are in 3-inch pots. Display on sill, shelf, table, pedestal, or in hanging basket. There are plain green-leaved waxplants and others with variegated foliage. Miniature wax plant, *Hoya bella,* has smaller leaves set on arching rather than trailing stems like the others. All plants develop clusters of fragrant, waxy, five-pointed-star flowers, with white to pink petals and rosy-pink to maroon centers. The blooms grow from spurs. Once a spur appears, do not cut it off; it will produce more blooms year after year. Blooming is most reliable if plants are summered outdoors. Waxplants are among the most durable and adaptable of all house plants and are virtually pest-free. Cuttings root easily in water and may grow this way indefinitely; replace water once a month. One kind of waxplant has crested leaves that curl and twist into strange shapes. Breeders are developing new forms, so keep an eye out for an increasing selection of leaf types and flowers.

LIGHT: Sunny east, south, or west window; tolerates bright north light.
TEMPERATURE: Average house in winter; suffers below 55 degrees.
POTTING SOIL: All-purpose (see Chapter 3).
WATERING NEEDS: Water well; an hour later, pour off any excess. Water again when surface begins to feel dry. Water less in winter. Mist leaves frequently, especially *Hoya bella.*
FEEDING: Feed blooming plant food all year; follow container directions. For a young plant to grow quickly, feed all-purpose.
PROBLEMS: Soggy-wet soil combined with coolness may cause root rot.
CONTAINERS: Standard clay or plastic pot, or hanging basket.
PROPAGATION: Root leaf or stem cuttings; see Chapter 6.

Hoya (HOY-uh). Milkweed Family • *Hoya* (Waxplant; Wax flower) A-264; *H. bella* (Miniature waxplant) A-265.

LIVING WITH IT:
The plant shown is in a 5-inch pot. When small, display on sill, table; at maturity, it is large enough to join other plants in a floor arrangement. The shiny dark- to bright-green leaves of *Aphelandra squarrosa louisae* have prominent creamy yellow veins. Small white flowers emerge from a waxy, long-lasting, showy cone of brilliant yellow bracts at the top of the stems. The first time you forget to water and the soil dries out, the leaves will droop dejectedly. Within hours of watering the plant, the leaves will stand erect again, but most of the old ones will soon die and fall

off, leaving a bare stem. If this happens, cut off the 2 or 3 inches of bare stem and reroot it (or air-layer). Zebra plant grows easily from tip cuttings. Very young plants grow luxuriantly in a fluorescent-light garden, provided temperatures remain generally in the 60s or low 70s. Plants thrive in fresh, moist air that circulates freely.

LIGHT: Ideal is 2 or 3 hours of sun in winter, bright indirect light in summer; tolerates light of a north window.

TEMPERATURE: Average house, on the cool side in winter. Suffers over 75 degrees.

POTTING SOIL: All-purpose or African-violet (see Chapter 3).

WATERING NEEDS: Every day or two, or enough to keep the soil always nicely moist. Drying out causes rapid leaf loss. Mist often.

FEEDING: Alternate all-purpose foliage plant food and blooming plant food all year; follow container directions.

PROBLEMS: Dry soil and hot, dry, stale air cause the leaves to fall.

CONTAINERS: Standard clay or plastic pot with drainage hole.

PROPAGATION: Root tip cuttings, or air-layer, any time of the year.

Aphelandra (aff-uh-LAN-druh). Acanthus Family • *Aphelandra squarrosa louisae* (Zebra plant) A-266.

8
Dictionary of Seasonal Flowers and Gift Plants

The flowering plants included in Chapter 7 tend to be everblooming; those in this chapter usually produce one annual burst of bloom that lasts a few weeks or months. The rest of the year, they exist as foliage plants and may go dormant for a time. A few are dictatorial about their blooming needs. Short days and long nights trigger blooming of poinsettias (opposite) and jungle plants called Thanksgiving, Christmas, and Easter cactus (below). If any artificial light strikes them from sundown to sunup in autumn, they will think it is still summer, and leaves will grow instead of flowers. But most of the seasonal flowering plants can be kept flowering for a long time.   How to handle each appears here. If you give one of these plants as a gift, enclose instructions. This thoughtful gesture should help it last longer.

Easter cactus (above) is a hybrid of *Rhipsalidopsis,* a jungle cactus related to Christmas and Thanksgiving cactus. Poinsettias (opposite), in red, pink, white, and marbled, last for weeks if they are kept warm and moist.

Cyclamen, pink, rose, red, white, and variegated, bloom all winter and spring in a cool, bright, moist spot.

POINSETTIA: *Special care:* October 1 until flowers show, keep in darkness sundown to sunup; otherwise, flowering will be delayed. After flowering, cut back stems to 8 inches; repot into fresh soil. *Light:* Sunny east, south, or west window where no light is used at night. Or at night cover with large carton until flowering. *Temperature:* Average house in winter; avoid drafts of hot, dry, or cold air. *Potting soil:* All-purpose (see Chapter 3). *Watering needs:* It is important to keep soil evenly moist. If the soil dries, the leaves will wilt, yellow, and die. *Feeding:* Feed all-purpose in summer and spring; blooming in fall and winter. *Containers:* Standard plastic or clay pot. *Propagation:* Tip cuttings, in spring. Poinsettia is *Euphorbia* (yew-FOR-bee-uh) *pulcherrima*.

JUNGLE CACTI—THANKSGIVING, CHRISTMAS, EASTER: The first two are hybrids of *Schlumbergera* (schlum-BERJ-er-uh) and *Zygocactus* (zye-go-CACK-tus); the third is *Rhipsalidopsis* (rip-sal-ih-DOP-siss). *Special care:* For 8 weeks in autumn, avoid artificial light at night, high temperatures, overly moist soil, and feeding; these prevent normal flowering. *Light:* Sunny east or west window or similar brightness near a south window; adapts to light of a north window. Also, fluorescent light. *Temperature:* Ideal is 60 to 70 degrees, except as noted above. *Potting soil:* African-violet (see Chapter 3). *Watering needs:* Keep soil evenly moist, except as noted above. *Feeding:* Feed blooming-type plant food all year, except as noted above. *Containers:* Standard plastic or clay pot or hanging basket. *Propagation:* Tip cuttings, in spring.

CYCLAMEN: *Special care:* Keep evenly moist September-May; nearly dry June-August, so tuber can rest. Repot in September. *Light:* Ideal is a sunny east or west window, a fluorescent-light garden, or similar brightness. *Temperature:* Ideal is 60-70 degrees in winter; suffers in hot, dry air. *Potting soil:* African-violet (see Chapter 3). *Watering needs:* Except as noted, keep evenly moist. *Feeding:* Feed blooming-type September-May; do not feed in summer. *Containers:* Standard plastic or clay pot. *Cyclamen* (SICK-luh-men).

CALCEOLARIA; POCKETBOOK PLANT: (above) *Light:* Ideal is sunny east or west window, fluorescent light, or similar brightness. *Temperature:* Ideal is 60-70 degrees in winter; suffers in hot, dry air. *Potting soil:* All-purpose (see Chapter 3). *Watering needs:* Keep evenly moist. *Feeding:* All-purpose in summer and autumn; winter until end of flowering. *Problems:* Hot, dry air shrivels leaves, prevents flowering. Soggy-wet, poorly drained soil kills roots. *Containers:* Standard plastic or clay pot. *Propagation:* Sow seeds, spring or summer. Transplant seedlings to 3-inch pots; when roots fill, move to 6-inch. Discard after flowering. *Calceolaria* (kal-see-oh-LAY-ree-uh).

CINERARIA: (not pictured) These members of the Daisy Family grow from spring - or summer - planted seeds to produce bouquets of vivid-hued blooms in winter and spring. They need an atmosphere that is sunny, airy, moist, and cool. Follow the care outlined for calceolaria, page 203. Dwarf hybrids of *Senecio* (suh-NEE-see-oh) *cruentus*, the popular cineraria, are fairly easy to grow from seeds and can be brought to bloom even in a fluorescent-light garden.

JERUSALEM CHERRY: *Special care:* Feed blooming-type plant food June-March. Cut back stems to 8 inches in April; repot in fresh soil; keep soil moist, but do not start feeding again until June. *Light:* Ideal is a sunny east, south, or west window or a fluorescent-light garden. *Temperature:* Average house in winter; suffers below 55 degrees. *Potting soil:* All-purpose (see Chapter 3). *Watering needs:* Keep evenly moist. In dry heat, mist often. *Feeding:* Feed blooming-type plant food as directed above. *Problems:* Dry soil and temperatures below 60 degrees will prevent flowering. *Containers:* Standard plastic or clay pot. *Propagation:* Sow seeds, in spring, to have fruit-bearing plants in fall and winter. Jerusalem cherry is sometimes discarded when the fruits have shriveled; however, by cutting back the stems as described above, the plant can be kept year-round. Jerusalem cherry is *Solanum* (so-LAN-um) *pseudocapsicum.*

Shiny, orange-red fruits of the Jerusalem cherry remain attractive for several months. These fruits are poisonous; do not confuse them with peppers.

CHRYSANTHEMUM; MUM: Outdoors, these bloom in late summer and autumn as the days grow short. Florists bring them into bloom all year by using artificial light to lengthen short winter days. When the plants reach the desired height, shorter light days are provided to encourage flower buds to set. *Special care:* Mums will bloom for many weeks if you follow the care outlined below. When flowering ends, start new plants. Make 4-inch tip cuttings of new growth that has sprouted from the base after flowering. When the cuttings have rooted, pot them. In spring, plant the parent in a sunny outdoor bed; keep the young plants indoors for forcing. *Light:* Ideal is a sunny east or west window, a bright north window, or a fluorescent-light garden. *Temperature:* Ideal is 60 to 70 degrees in winter; hot, dry heat over 70 degrees withers flowers. *Potting soil:* All-purpose (see Chapter 3). *Watering needs:* Keep soil evenly moist. If leaves wilt because of dry soil, lower ones will die and flowers will wither. *Feeding:* Feed blooming-type from time buds show until flowers open; then all-purpose, to promote sturdy new growth for use as cuttings. *Problems:* Long light days, either natural (in summer) or artificial (electric light at night), prevent flowering. Pinch out tips of rooted cuttings every 2 weeks until 1 month before you want flower buds to set; this results in many more flowers. *Containers:* Standard plastic or clay pot. *Propagation:* Tip cuttings (see above). *Chrysanthemum* (kriss-ANTH-ee-mum).

BIRD OF PARADISE: (not pictured) These members of the Banana Family have attractive foliage; but until roots fill a pot 10 inches or larger, the birdlike, blue-and-orange flowers will not appear. *Special care:* Feed all-purpose plant food except November to February; when roots fill pot, feed blooming-type on same schedule. *Light:* Sunny east, south, or west window. *Temperature:* Average house; ideally 60 to 70 degrees in winter. *Potting soil:* All-purpose (see Chapter 3). *Watering needs:* Keep evenly moist; occasional dryness won't hurt. Mist often. *Feeding:* See above. *Problems:* Soggy-wet soil in winter may rot roots. *Containers:* Standard plastic or clay pot, or tub. *Propagation:* Plant seeds or divisions. *Strelitzia* (struh-LITZ-ee-uh).

Potted chrysanthemums will stay in peak bloom for weeks or months if the soil is never allowed to dry out and the air is fresh, moist, and circulates freely.

EUCHARIST LILY (above): Buy an unpotted tuber at any season; pot, and it will grow quickly into a handsome all-year foliage plant. Fragrant, daffodil-like white flowers bloom several times a year. *Special care:* Blooms when pot bound; to encourage, keep on dry side for 6 weeks. Shortly after you begin to water more freely, flowering should occur. *Light:* Ideal is sunny east, south, or west window. Tolerates bright north light. *Temperature:* Average house. *Potting soil:* All-purpose (see Chapter 3). *Watering needs:* Keep evenly moist. Mist often. *Feeding:* Blooming-type all year. *Containers:* Standard plastic or clay pot. *Propagation:* Plant tuber divisions, any time. *Eucharis* (YEW-kuh-riss).

HYACINTH: Buy unpotted bulbs October-November, to plant in soil or root in water in hyacinth glasses (photograph below, left). *Special care:* In all-purpose soil, plant so tip of bulb is exposed; in water, submerge ½ inch of base. Set to root in cool (40 to 50 degrees is ideal), dark place; keep moist. After 6 to 8 weeks, provide conditions below. They bloom 8 to 10 weeks after planting. *Light:* Ideal is sunny east or west window, bright north window, or fluorescent light. *Temperature:* Ideal is 50 to 60 degrees; tolerates 70 in fresh, moist air circulating freely. *Watering needs:* Keep soil evenly moist; change water once a week. *Feeding:* Not required. *Problems:* Too much heat results in half-developed stems. *Containers:* Standard plastic or clay pot, or hyacinth glass. *Propagation:* After flowers fade, remove their stems; continue to water; plant bulbs outdoors, in early spring. They will multiply. Do not force same bulbs again. *Hyacinth* (HYE-uh-sinth).

PAPERWHITE NARCISSUS: Buy unpotted bulbs in autumn. *Special care:* Plant several in a bowl, with bases ½ inch deep in moist all-purpose soil; or in aquarium gravel, with water to touch bases. Set to root in a cool (55 to 65 degrees), dark place for 3 or 4 weeks; then provide conditions for hyacinths, above. They bloom 5 to 7 weeks after planting. Paperwhites will succeed in slightly warmer temperatures than will hyacinths. In the South, plant the bulbs outdoors after they have flowered, or discard them.

Special hyacinth glass cradles bulb base so that it touches water and roots.

Paperwhite narcissus (and similar golden-flowered Soleil d'Or) may be coaxed into winter bloom when fall-planted in either moist soil or gravel.

Hybrids of *Camellia japonica,* a member of the Tea Family, produce single or double flowers in white, pink, red or variegated, from October to April.

CAMELLIA: These glossy-leaved evergreen shrubs, the pride of Southern gardens, are sold for container gardens as small shrubs or trees, to display on table or floor; some varieties bred for hanging baskets are also available from specialists. Blooms, depending on variety, may appear any time from October to April. There are hundreds of hybrids; start with one or two *japonica* hybrids, and if you are successful, add other varieties that naturally bloom early, midseason, and late. *Special care:* If you live in a warm apartment, camellias are not for you; but in a house that in winter has a sunny, airy, cool room, they will thrive. Keep outdoors in summer, if possible. *Light:* Ideal is a sunny east or west window in winter; less direct sun is needed in summer. *Temperature:* Ideal is 40 to 50 degrees in winter; tolerates 60 to 70 degrees if air is fresh, moist, and circulates freely. *Potting soil:* African-violet (see Chapter 3). *Watering needs:* Water often enough to keep evenly moist. Do not let dry out severely at any time. Mist often. *Feeding:* Alternate all-purpose and blooming plant food, following container directions (see page 22). *Problems:* If leaves begin to turn yellow, apply acid-type plant food. White flecking of leaves may indicate red spider mite; see page 25. *Containers:* Standard plastic or clay pot, tub, or hanging basket. *Propagation:* Cuttings of half-ripened wood, in spring. *Camellia* (kuh-MEE-lee-uh).

HYDRANGEA: You can't easily grow these indoors, but if you receive one in bloom from a florist, you can prolong its bloom. *Special care:* Do not allow to dry; if it wilts, flowers die. *Light:* Bright; no direct sun. *Temperature:* Ideal is 60 to 70 degrees; hot, dry air shortens bloom. *Watering needs:* Keep between wet and moist. When the flowers fade, transplant to partly shaded outdoor garden. In acid soil, flowers are blue, in neutral to alkaline soil, pink.

Hydrangea, in pink or blue, received from florist needs lots of water, to prevent wilting and to keep flowers in good condition for maximum time.

TULIPS, DAFFODILS, OTHER BULBS: Many spring-flowering bulbs can be potted and forced to bloom indoors in winter or early spring, before their natural flowering times. *Special care:* A pot of bulbs that have been forced into bloom will last longer if the soil is kept evenly moist, if the plants are given bright light (but no hot sun shining directly on the flowers), and if fresh, moist air circulates freely—ideally in a temperature range of 50 to 70 degrees. When the flowers fade, either plant the hardy bulbs in your outdoor garden or discard them; do not try to force them into indoor bloom again. To force your own winter flowers from spring-blooming bulbs, follow the procedure outlined here. Planting time: October-November. Select from catalogs of bulb specialists, choosing varieties that have been treated for forcing. *Light:* Darkness for an 8-week rooting period. Then move to a sunny east, south, or west window or a fluorescent-light garden. *Temperature:* Ideal is 45 to 55 degrees during rooting period, 55 to 70 degrees thereafter. *Potting soil:* All-purpose (see Chapter 3). *Watering needs:* Keep the soil evenly moist. *Feeding:* None is required. *Problems:* Dry soil and too high temperatures prevent proper rooting. Hot, dry, stale air causes flower buds to wither and fail to open. Aphids often attack tulips; see page 26 for treatment. *Containers:* Standard plastic or clay pot. In addition to tulips and daffodils, other hardy bulbs that can be forced into bloom include hyacinth (page 207), grape-hyacinth (varieties of *Muscari*), Dutch iris, *Iris reticulata,* crocus, puschkinia, glory-of-the-snow (*Chionodoxa*), snowdrop, squill, snowflake, and lily. Tender bulbs such as anemone, freesia, veltheimia, ranunculus, and ixia can be forced as described above, but cannot survive outdoor planting where temperatures are freezing.

AZALEA: These showy plants bloom for weeks and last as foliage plants forever if kept watered. *Special care:* Keep soil evenly moist. If leaves yellow, feed acid-type plant food. *Light:* Ideal, sunny east or west window or fluorescent light. Hot, direct sun ages flowers. *Temperature:* Ideal, 60 to 70 degrees; suffers above 70, below 40. *Watering needs:* Do not let dry out. Mist often. *Feeding:* Feed all-purpose spring and summer; blooming-type fall and winter. *Problems:* Red spider mites attack in hot, dry air (see page 25). *Containers:* Standard plastic or clay pot, or tub. *Propagation:* Root cuttings, in spring. Azaleas are species of *Rhododendron* (roh-doh-DEN-dron), of the Heath Family.

AMARYLLIS: Bulbs ready to plant or planted are sold fall and winter. First-year bloom—3 to 4 weeks after planting—is almost certain; future bloom depends on care. *Special care:* After blooming, cut off stem at soil level. Keep evenly moist November to August; then dry off, and let rest in dark closet for 8 weeks. Remove dead leaves; repot; place in bright light, resume watering and feeding to promote bloom. *Light:* Ideal is a sunny east, south, or west window. *Temperature:* Average house in winter (62 to 75 degrees); suffers below 55. *Potting soil:* All-purpose (see Chapter 3). *Feeding:* Feed blooming-type January to August. *Problems:* Mealybugs may attack (see page 26). *Containers:* Standard plastic or clay pot. *Propagation:* Plant offsets at repotting time. *Amaryllis* (am-uh-RILL-iss).

Azalea received in full bloom (above) needs cool, moist, fresh air and moist soil. Hybrid amaryllis (opposite) grow from bulbs and flower year after year.

9
Dictionary of
House-Plant Herbs

Herbs are fun to try as house plants, though some need pampering. Most thrive on a sunny sill or under lights. Group favorites in individual pots on the kitchen windowsill (page 230) or in a strawberry jar, as opposite. Though herbs grow in sandy soil outdoors, indoors they do best in all-purpose soil. Feed regularly. Basil and many others are weedy annuals, to start from seed and keep trimmed. Bathe basil and other thin-leaved sorts often, to prevent white-fly; provide fresh air. Sweet bay (below, right) and others are perennials, to buy as plants and grow to shrub size. Three popular basils are pictured below; left: green *(Ocimum basilicum)*, its purple-leaved variety 'Dark Opal,' and bush basil *(O. b. minimum)*, the one best suited to small spaces. All basils are great for seasoning tomatoes, salads, and Italian dishes. See Fennel, page 214, for culture. Sweet bay *(Laurus nobilis)* is used in bouquets, garnishes, soups, stews, and casseroles. For culture, see Lemon Verbena, page 215.

Three basils: green, purple, bush.

Sweet bay to grow indoors.

CHIVES AND FENNEL: *(Allium schoenoprasum)* are available much of the year in supermarkets and from nurseries. Repot in a container 2 sizes larger, using all-purpose potting soil. Snip away half the plant's growth to flavor salads, soups, or anything that will benefit from chives' mild oniony taste. Set the pot in a sunny east, west, or south window. Keep the soil evenly moist. With the approach of winter, put your chives outside the window for 2 or 3 weeks of mild frost, or give them their required cold treatment in the refrigerator. When you return them to their regular place, water sparingly until growth starts. Feed regularly with all-purpose plant food, following container instructions. Chives are easy to grow from seed, but since plants are so readily and inexpensively available, that is hardly worthwhile. Once a plant has been purchased, you can keep successive pots going by dividing the original plant. Trim when you need some for flavoring.

Fennel *(Foeniculum vulgare)*, like basil, is easily grown from seed. Although perennial, it is treated as an annual. Indoors in a pot, it will not develop into the large plant necessary to form the familiar edible white roots, nor will it produce seed. It is, however, an attractive plant with asparagus-fernlike leaves. Keep it pruned to house-plant size; use the snippings to flavor salads, fish sauces, soups, and stews. Pot both fennel and basil in all-purpose soil; give them as much sun as possible; feed regularly with an all-purpose plant food. Water enough to keep the soil evenly moist. Dill *(Anethum graveolens)*, whose feathery fronds resemble those of fennel, requires the same culture. Start seed in late summer or early fall, for winter clippings to use as seasoning.

Chives, a mild onion flavor.

Fennel, a flavor like licorice.

GINGER AND LEMON VERBENA: Ginger (*Zingiber officinale*) is the true ginger so highly prized in Oriental cookery for its root. The leaves also taste of ginger, but are milder. Start your own ginger plant from a section of root purchased in a Chinese or greengrocer specialty shop. Choose a fresh, succulent piece 2 or 3 inches big. Ginger root is a rhizome like that of an iris, and it will develop over the soil surface, so plant it in an azalea pot (wider than it is deep). Insert the cut end of the root into moist, all-purpose potting soil. Or lay the root across the soil surface with the knobby bits buried. Keep the pot in a dark, warm closet until growth begins; then move it into full sunlight. Keep the soil evenly moist, and feed the plant with all-purpose plant food. When the root fills the pot, remove a few inches of the tip to start a new plant. Use the rest of the root in Oriental dishes. Extras can be frozen or candied. Use the leaves in salads and in cooking.

Lemon verbena (*Aloysia triphylla*) does not go dormant in indoor heat as it does outdoors in the cold, but the stems of older plants become woody. It is best to raise compact new plants from tip cuttings each year. Sweet bay, whose needs are otherwise similar, does not need cutting back. It is propagated by division and root cuttings. Tip cuttings are slow to root. Both lemon verbena and sweet bay thrive with only a few hours of eastern or western sun daily and also under lights. Avoid a hot, stale atmosphere. Use all-purpose potting soil for both, and feed all-purpose plant food all year. Keep soil evenly moist; never allow it to dry out. The plants perk up outdoors in summer. Use fresh leaves of lemon verbena for salads, dried ones for potpourri and teas.

Ginger, grown for its peppery root.

Lemon verbena, for salads and teas.

SWEET MARJORAM AND MINT: The names sweet marjoram (*Majorana hortensis*) and oregano (*Origanum vulgare*) are often used in this country to denote just one plant. Most plants sold as oregano are sweet marjoram, the plant shown here. It is sweeter and less intense in fragrance and flavor than oregano and makes a delightful house plant. The small, woolly leaves on woody stems give off a sweet scent when crushed. Small white flowers are surrounded by green bracts. It is easily grown from seed or cuttings. Give it good sunlight or it will straggle. Pot in all-purpose soil, and feed with all-purpose plant food. Keep the soil evenly moist, and mist the plant regularly, to protect against red-spider attack. The fresh leaves may be used on tomatoes, the dried ones in soups, stuffings, and lamb dishes. *M. onites*, sometimes available, is known as French marjoram and is closer to real oregano in flavor.

Outdoors, mints multiply by underground roots and take over a bed in a few years. Confined to containers indoors, where they can't sucker, some lose their vigor and the leaves grow smaller. Tip cuttings root easily, so if this happens, start new plants. Spearmint (*Mentha spicata*) is less prone to spreading than is peppermint (*M. piperata*), especially if kept pruned. Orange mint (*M. citrata*) and apple mint (*M. rotundifolia*), as their names promise, smell strongly of oranges and apples. All the mints are tough and get by with an east or west exposure. They thrive under lights. Provide fresh air, and avoid a hot, dry atmosphere or red spider will appear. Use all-purpose potting soil; keep it evenly moist; feed regularly with all-purpose plant food. Use fresh leaves in cold drinks and jellies, dried ones in lamb sauce and teas.

Sweet marjoram, alias oregano.

Mints in many strong flavors.

PARSLEY AND ROSEMARY: Both curly parsley (*Petroselinum crispum*) and Italian parsley (*P. neapolitanum*) are easily grown indoors from seeds and will perform well if their simple needs are met. To accommodate parsley's long taproot, use a pot at least 4 inches deep. Since parsley is crotchety about being transplanted, keep it growing in the pot where it was sown. Soak the seeds in water for 24 hours; then plant in all-purpose potting mix. Set the pot on a cool, south-facing windowsill, and keep the soil evenly moist. Pinch off excess seedlings, to make room for the strongest ones. Parsley benefits from frequent misting. Curly parsley is the kind most generally used in this country, but seeds of Italian parsley are also readily available. The latter has a somewhat stronger flavor. You can use either in virtually any recipe. Almost any food tastes better with a sprinkling of chopped parsley. The curly variety is an especially pretty garnish for any serving platter.

Rosemary (*Rosmarinum officinalis*) is the evergreen perennial, with sharp, spiky leaves and wooden stems, beloved of most gourmet cooks. Pretty pink, lavender, or blue blossoms sometimes appear along the branches. Rosemary prefers a cool, sunny window and moist soil. If the soil is permitted to dry out at all, the plant will die. It does best in a glazed or plastic pot which retains moisture better than does a clay one. Pot in all-purpose soil, and feed once a month with all-purpose plant food. You can buy a plant and then start more plants from cuttings, which root easily. Summer the plants outdoors, if possible. Use rosemary to season all meats, to make teas, to scent bath water, potpourri, and sachets. You'll also find it useful in many Italian dishes.

Curly and Italian parsley.   Rosemary, gourmets' favorite herb.

SAGE AND WINTER SAVORY: Sage (*Salvia officinalis*) in its common variety performs better outdoors than indoors, probably because the average house is too warm for a plant that is winter-hardy in cold climates. Indoors, it can be kept growing satisfactorily if it can be placed in a cool, sunny, south window. An unheated, glassed-in sun porch would be ideal. If there is not enough sunlight, the plant will grow leggy and have few leaves. The variety 'Tricolor' seems to be happier and easier to manage under ordinary house conditions, as does pineapple sage (*S. rutilans*) (it truly smells like fresh pineapple). All the sages benefit from a summer outdoors. Sage is easily grown from seed or cuttings. Pot in all-purpose soil, and feed only once a month with all-purpose plant food. Sage is most generally used in pork dishes, sausage, and stuffing. Teas made with sage are reputed to relieve headaches. In days gone by, an infusion of leaves used as a rinse was believed to darken gray hair.

Winter savory (*Satureja montana*) is a small, shrubby plant with sharp pointed leaves and white or blue flowers. Winter savory, a perennial, does well as a house plant; whereas summer savory, an annual, does not. Start with a purchased plant, and raise new ones from cuttings or by planting root divisions of older plants. Use all-purpose potting soil, and water it enough to keep it evenly moist. Pruning will keep the plant compact. A sunny window or good light under fluorescents is needed to keep the plant from becoming straggly. Feed regularly with all-purpose plant food. Use savory to flavor stews, fish dishes, soups, and to make bath water aromatic.

'Tricolor', pineapple and plain sage.　　Winter savory as a house plant.

TARRAGON AND THYME: Tarragon (*Artemisia dracunculus*) isn't the best of house plants, but the flavor of the fresh leaves adds such a subtle, wonderful taste to casseroles and sauces and is so often called for in Italian recipes that it is worth trying. The problem is that it wants a cold rest when winter begins, and if you refuse to chill it, it will die. In late fall or early winter, put it outdoors on a sill for several weeks, or keep it in the refrigerator for a month. After the chilling, cut the branches back by two thirds; pot in fresh all-purpose soil; feed all-purpose plant food, and place in a sunny window. Keep soil evenly moist but never soggily wet. Propagate by tip cuttings, in August, or by root division. Buy only plants whose leaves are strongly aromatic when crushed. Not all tarragon plants sold are top quality.

Thyme (*Thymus serpyllum*) is the characteristic sprawling plant used for edging walks and rock-garden beds and filling chinks in stone walls and paths. Indoors, given enough sun, it will cascade gracefully from a hanging basket. Frequent pruning is necessary to keep it from becoming straggly. The tiny, pungent leaves of *T. vulgaris* form an attractive, upright, shrubby plant well suited to a window garden. The lemon-flavored variety (*T. serpyllum*) is not reliably winter-hardy in cold climates and is best of the thymes for indoor growing. It needs cool, fresh air and lots of sunlight, or good light under fluorescents. Pot in all-purpose soil; water well, then not again until the soil surface nears dryness. Start new cuttings in sand, in summer. Or grow plants from seed, or divide and pot the roots of an older plant. Use thyme to flavor vinegar, sauces for meat or fish, vegetables, and in sachets.

Tarragon thrives after chilling.

Thymes, variegated and plain.

Decorating with House Plants

Until recently, gardeners grew house plants and interior designers decorated with them. Now the two arts have come together. Gardeners have discovered the fun of displaying plants attractively, and designers have realized that plants have definite needs and can't exist just anywhere they look pretty in a room. In this chapter you will find ideas for decorating with plants of all sizes in natural and artificial light.

THE WINDOW GARDEN: The indoor garden shown opposite faces south and receives full sun from about 10 A.M. until 1 P.M. The natural-jute macrame holder makes a beautiful hanger to hold a rabbit's-foot fern (which will also grow well in less light). The mass of foliage to the right of the window is provided by several kinds of dracaenas. Remember, the area against a wall beside the sunniest window receives little or no direct sun, so low-light plants (see list, Chapter 11) will grow well there. A lipstick vine hangs from the ceiling (upper left), with a red-leaved climbing philodendron below. A seasonal-flowering pink azalea is displayed in the top of a yellow pedestal designed especially for plants. In summer, when this photograph was taken, a Rieger begonia and an orchid were doing well with their pots standing right on the air-conditioning unit. In winter, this becomes a heating unit, and two or three medium-size cacti replace the begonia and orchid. Lightweight wooden trellising screens the unit. Look for clear-plastic ceiling hooks and plant brackets to display the hanging baskets; they are the most attractive supports.

221

AFRICAN VIOLETS in a basket (above) make a beautiful centerpiece for a dining table. This space is about 6 feet from the partly sunny window garden pictured on page 220. Although the light is bright on the table, it is not sufficient for growing African violets; short, young Chinese evergreens, pothos, heartleaf philodendron, or small-leaved English ivy would grow well indefinitely in this kind of light. Since the African violets need more light, they are arranged and used on the table very much as cut flowers would be. After an evening or two serving as a dining-table centerpiece, they will be returned to the light in which they were brought into flower. Each pot placed in the basket has its own saucer to catch water that may drain from the soil. Florists' sheet moss hides the pot rims.

THE HOLIDAY SCENE (opposite) was photographed in another dining room, where sun streams in all afternoon from a west-facing window. Though it does not shine directly in the areas where these plants have been placed, they will come through the holidays with flying colors if the soil is kept evenly moist at all times and the foliage is misted frequently. English ivy trained, tied, and clipped into a wreath form, with a bow added, is displayed on a pedestal found on the street—a handsome piece of carved wood. Several poinsettias, each with its waterproof saucer, are displayed on the floor. The green foliage in the foreground (far right of photograph) is that of the spathiphyllum. In this room, it is 8 feet from the sunny window, where it thrives all year in the bright, but indirect sunlight.

BASKET GARDEN (opposite) grows in a sunny east window, with light-loving plants placed where they receive as much direct sun as possible and with others grouped on the floor and to the sides. Ferns that usually fill the basket in the foreground have been rearranged to allow room for the seasonal-blooming poinsettias. Heat-tolerant plants (see list, Chapter 11) grow next to the radiator. Two ordinary ovenproof baking dishes, placed on the radiator, are filled with pebbles and water to make the surface cool enough to hold pots. Water added as necessary to keep the pebbles wet evaporates around the plants, supplying needed humidity. The plants placed on these pebble trays have a special purpose—to hide a window air-conditioning unit during the winter, when it is not in operation. Architect's lamp equipped with a 75-watt floodlight supplements natural light when burned 6 to 8 hours each evening and, at the same time, dramatizes the flowers. When baskets are used to display plants, always place a waterproof saucer under each pot. Otherwise, excess water that drains through the soil will damage the baskets and wood flooring or carpeting below. Note: Unglazed clay saucers are not waterproof; plastic is preferable.

LOW-LIGHT PLANTS (upper right) may be used to decorate a sunless corner where daylight is bright enough to read or sew by. If the light is too dim, you can supplement it with floodlights, as described on page 17. For list of low-light plants, see Chapter 11.

Above: Two low-light plants—a tall bamboo palm and a fern—dress a dining-room corner. Below: Planting plan for basket garden.

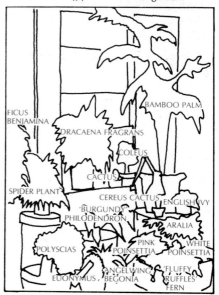

226

Decorating

DARK CORNER (opposite) is brightened by large Chinese evergreens in a red pedestal, *Dracaena fragrans massangeana* (left) and *Dracaena deremensis warneckei* (right). Both dracaenas are displayed in inexpensive woven baskets; they are growing in slightly smaller plastic pots with matching, waterproof, plastic saucers fitted under them to prevent damage to the baskets and carpeting from moisture seepage. The red pedestal appears to be an expensive planter; in reality, it was made by stacking two inexpensive plastic storage cubes. If a third cube were added, this bushy Chinese evergreen, which is only 2 feet tall and about 3 feet wide, would look like a full-size tree. This pretty bedroom corner is 16 feet from a south-facing window that receives sun several hours daily. No sun shines directly on the plants, but they thrive in low light. (See list, Chapter 11, for other low-light plants.)

BOOKSHELF GARDEN (below) thrives in the life-giving rays of two 20-watt fluorescent tubes held in a reflector attached to the shelf above. The unit is plugged into a timer, which automatically turns the lights on and off and provides uniform periods of light (15 hours) and darkness (9 hours) daily. In this fluorescent-light garden, the African violets bloom all year; additional color is provided by rose, white, and green coleus foliage, the yellow-spotted leaves of the gold-dust plant, and the dark-burgundy leaves of *Nautilocalyx lynchii,* a relative of the African violet—both are members of the Gesneria Family. The inexpensive yellow-plastic etagere bookcases divide living and dining areas, so the plants can be enjoyed from either side.

BASKET OF BEGONIAS (above), displayed on a bedside table, shows the effectiveness of grouping several related plants in a small space. The varieties here include miniature rhizomatous and rex types (see pages 71 to 74). One large plastic saucer placed inside the woven basket holds all the plants and protects the table from water spills. Scraps of pale-green florists' sheet moss hide the pot edges so the begonias appear to be growing in one container. Keeping them potted individually makes it a simple matter to remove one when it outgrows the others. The light cast by the table lamp is of some benefit to the plants when it is burned 6 to 8 hours each evening; but to grow properly, they also need 2 to 3 hours of sun daily.

If you would like to make a similar arrangement, designed to grow in bright natural light (without sun shining directly on the leaves) combined with evening incandescent light, select from small, low-light plants such as miniature sweet flag, short young Chinese evergreen, young bird's-nest fern, creeping fig, small-leaved English ivy, prayer plant, Pellionia, polystichum and pteris ferns, and strawberry-geranium. Small plants, begonias included, grouped this way grow better than when they are lined up, soldier-fashion, on a windowsill. Little pots standing alone dry out quickly. An arrangement like the one shown can be put together in 5 minutes—if you have an assortment of small plants from which to choose—yet it can have the effect of a charming spot in a woodland or wild-flower garden. Such a basket full of little plants would make a welcome gift, especially if you include instructions on how to care for them.

BATHROOM GARDEN (above) groups an assortment of small fancy-foliage plants in a shallow tray placed on the countertop near the washbowl. They grow 5 feet from a sunny south window, in bright light but without sun shining directly on them. Overhead bulbs give additional light. Small plants that need frequent watering are especially enjoyable, when displayed where you can see them up close, check them often, and water them from a nearby faucet. Bathrooms are unusually good places to grow plants because showering and bathing increase the humidity. If there is not enough natural light in your bathroom, add special fluorescent or incandescent fixtures (see Chapter 2).

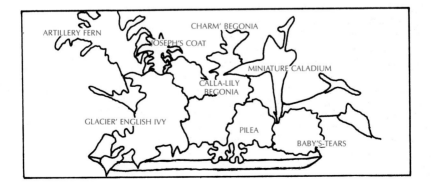

KITCHEN CONTAINERS (opposite, upper photograph) make interesting holders to display an assortment of fascinating little plants on a countertop. If natural light in a kitchen corner is not enough for good growth, arrange the plants where a fluorescent-light fixture gives supplemental light. For the plant arrangement shown here, a fixture could be attached to the bottom of the wall-hung cabinet. Small pots dry out quickly, and containers almost always hold excess water after watering; be sure to pour it off.

HERB PLANTS (opposite, lower photograph) are very much at home in a kitchen, handy for seasoning and easy to prune when growth gets weedy. (See Chapter 9.) As house plants, herbs need the light of an east, south, or west window, with an abundance of fresh air that circulates freely. If insects attack, rinse herbs in the sink every few days. Do not spray with harmful chemicals. A trim plastic tray is an ideal container for small plants when it is filled, as here, with pebbles and water that reaches just below pot bottoms.

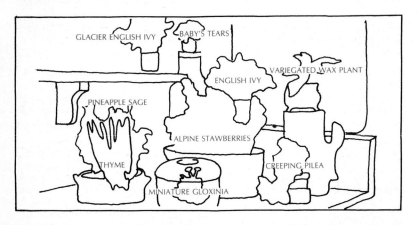

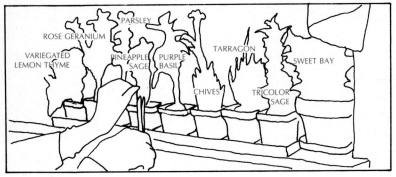

It's fun to mix and match kitchen containers to hold an assortment of interesting small house plants. Steam from cooking is fine for plants growing in tiny pots.

Collection of seasoning herbs grows on a sunny kitchen windowsill in a trim humidity tray filled with pebbles. Shower leaves with tepid water often.

Sprinkling of charcoal chips, to keep soil fresh, is added to base layer of gravel or marble chips.

Rolled newspaper page is used to grip thorny cacti while they are planted in a layer of cactus soil.

Layer of desert-colored sand makes pretty finish after all plants are in place in the potting soil.

DESERTSCAPE (opposite) is planted in a Mexican pottery casserole. You can create a similar garden by planting an assortment of small cacti and other succulents in an 8- to 10-inch clay pot saucer. Select plants whose size, shape, and color are miniatures of those in a real or imaginary desert scene. When you group several different plants, be sure all of them respond to similar care, temperature, kind of potting soil, amount of moisture and light. Most cacti and other succulents are compatible. To duplicate this desertscape, follow this procedure: (1) Since the container doesn't have a drainage hole, add a layer of gravel or marble chips ½ inch deep, topped by a generous sprinkling of charcoal chips. These two layers form a well for excess water, and the charcoal helps keep the soil fresh. (2) Add an inch of cactus potting soil (see Chapter 3). (3) Unpot plants for your desertscape, and gently arrange them in various positions until you are pleased with the planting plan. Firm each plant in place, and add enough soil to make all secure. Finish with a thin layer of sand.

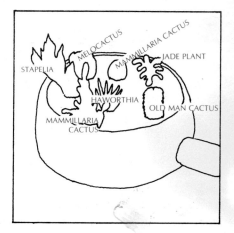

Sprinkle charcoal chips, to keep soil fresh, on 1-inch layer of marble chips lining brandy snifter.

Add 2 to 3 cups of moist terrarium soil; shape its surface into pleasing little hills and valleys.

Position roots of largest plants and cover roots with soil. Add tiny kinds and ground cover last.

BRANDY-SNIFTER TERRARIUM (opposite) with dollhouse tables and chairs suggests a shaded outdoor living space. Cacti and other succulents do best in containers (see pages 232, 233) where air can circulate freely. Shade-loving tropicals do best in a container like this or in a bottle garden or other terrarium with a small opening. The naturally miniature or small-growing plants in this little garden need constant high humidity. Provide it by covering the snifter's opening with a piece of glass,

MAIDENHAIR FERN ALUMINUM PLANT
MINIATURE GLOXINIA
SCILLA VIOLACEA
SELAGINELLA

Lucite, or Plexiglas cut to fit. To duplicate this terrarium, you will need a brandy snifter with an 8-inch opening. (1) Add an inch of marble chips or washed pebbles, then a sprinkling of charcoal chips, to keep soil fresh. (2) Add 2 to 3 cups of moistened terrarium soil. With your fingers, shape it into a pleasing terrain with hills and valleys. (3) Plant the largest plants first; cover roots with soil, and firm in place. Add tiny, tuft-forming and ground-cover plants. Carpet soil with wood moss or florists' sheet moss. Add barely enough water to make the newly planted roots moist and settle them in place.

What Kind of Plant Are You Looking For?

The lists in this chapter include all the plants discussed in this book. Cross-check the lists to find plants that meet your specific needs. Need a flowering plant for a semisunny spot? Check the Semisunny list against the list of Flowering Plants. Then see Chapter 7 for complete information on the plant(s) chosen. If the plant you are seeking isn't in the alphabetized group in Chapter 7, then look in the Index and you'll find the number of the page on which it appears. The (A-1) (A-2) numbers after some of the plant names designate varieties within a genus.

LIGHT: Plants have highly varied light requirements. Whatever indoor garden spaces you have, you can find a plant that will thrive there.

Sunny
(Unobstructed south window)

Agave	Fittonia
Amaryllis	Gardenia
Asparagus-fern	Geranium
Basil	Ginger
Bay, sweet	Gloxinia (large hybrids)
Bishop's cap	Gold-dust plant
Bougainvillea	Haworthia
Bromeliad	Hibiscus, Chinese
Browallia	Jade plant
Cacti	Jasmine
Calamondin	Jerusalem cherry
Chenille plant	Kalanchoe
Chives	Lantana
Chrysanthemum	Lavender, fernleaf
Coleus	Lemon-verbena
Copperleaf	Living stone
Croton	Maple, flowering
Donkey- or burro's-tail	Mint
Echeveria	Moses in the cradle
Euphorbia	Myrtle
Fatshedera	Night-jessamine
Fennel	Onion, pregnant

Oxalis
Palm: A-181
Parsley
Pepper, Christmas
Pink polkadot plant
Poinsettia
Ponytail
Purple passion plant
Redbird cactus
Rosary vine
Rosemary
Rose, miniature
Rouge berry
Sage
St. Augustinegrass,
    variegated

Savory, winter
Schefflera
Screw-pine
Shrimp plant
Snake plant
Star of Bethlehem
Strawberry, Alpine
Swedish-ivy
Sweet marjoram
Tahitian bridal veil
Tarragon
Thyme
Unguentine plant (Aloe)
Wandering Jew
Waxplant
Zebra plant

-------------------------- Semisunny --------------------------
(Unobstructed east or west window)

Asparagus-fern
Aspidistra
Avocado
Azalea
Baby's-tears
Basil
Bay, sweet
Begonia
Bishop's cap
Bougainvillea
Bromeliad
Browallia
Cacti
Caladium
Calamondin
Calceolaria
Camellia
Chenille plant
Chives
Christmas cactus
Chrysanthemum
Cineraria
Coffee tree
Coleus
Columnea
Copper-leaf
Coralberry

Croton
Cyclamen
Donkey- or burro's-tail
Dracaena
Dumbcane
Echeveria
Episcia
Eucharis
Euonymus
Exacum
Fatshedera
Fennel
Fern
Ficus
Fittonia
Fuchsia
Gardenia
Ginger
Gloxinia
Gold-dust plant
Grape-ivy
Hawaiian ti plant
Haworthia
Impatiens
Ivy, English
Ivy, German
Ivy, red or flame

Jade plant
Jasmine
Jerusalem cherry
Kalanchoe
Kangaroo vine
Lantana
Lavender, fernleaf
Lemon-verbena
Leopard plant
Lily-turf
Lipstick vine
Living stone
Maple, flowering
Mexican foxglove
Mint
Moses in the cradle
Myrtle
Narcissus, paper-white
Nephthytis
Night-jessamine
Norfolk Island pine
Onion, pregnant
Orchid
Oxalis
Palm
Parsley
Peperomia
Pepper, Christmas
Philodendron
Piggyback plant
Pilea
Pink polkadot plant
Pittosporum
Pleomele
Podocarpus
Poinsettia
Polyscias

Ponytail
Pothos
Primrose
Primrose, Cape
Purple passion plant
Redbird cactus
Rosary vine
Rosemary
Rose, miniature
Rouge berry
Sage
Sago palm
St. Augustinegrass,
    variegated
Savory, winter
Schefflera
Scilla violacea
Screw-pine
Shrimp plant
Snake plant
Spathiphyllum
Spider plant
Star of Bethlehem
Strawberry, Alpine
Strawberry-geranium
Swedish-ivy
Sweet flag
Sweet marjoram
Tahitian bridal veil
Tarragon
Thyme
Umbrella plant
Unguentine plant (Aloe)
Wandering Jew
Waxplant
Zebra plant

Semishady

(In bright north window or near a sunny window but with little or no sun striking leaves)

Anthurium
Aralia
Aralia, false
Asparagus-fern
Aspidistra

Avocado
Azalea
Baby's-tears
Begonia: Rex; A-22;
    Rhizomatous; A-14

Bromeliad: A-30;
  Neoregelia; Vriesia
Browallia
Caladium
Calathea
Chinese evergreen
Christmas cactus
Coffee tree
Columnea
Coralberry
Croton
Cyclamen
Dracaena (all types)
Dumbcane
Episcia
Eucharis
Euonymus
Exacum
Fatshedera
Ferns
Ficus
Fittonia
Ginger
Gloxinia
Gold-dust plant
Grape-ivy
Hawaiian ti plant
Impatiens
Ivy, English
Ivy, German
Ivy, red or flame
Kangaroo vine
Leopard plant
Lily-turf
Lipstick vine
Mexican foxglove
Moses in the cradle
Narcissus, paper-white

Nephthytis
Norfolk Island pine
Orchid
Palm
Pellionia
Peperomia
Philodendron
Piggyback plant
Pilea
Pittosporum
Pleomele
Podocarpus
Polyscias
Ponytail
Pothos
Prayer plant
Primrose
Primrose, Cape
Rosary vine
Sago palm
St. Augustinegrass,
  variegated
Schefflera
Scilla violacea
Screw-pine
Selaginella
Snake plant
Sonerila
Spathiphyllum
Spider plant
Strawberry-geranium
Swedish-ivy
Sweet flag
Tahitian bridal veil
Umbrella plant
Wandering Jew
Waxplant

Shady

(Near a bright window, but no sun striking leaves)

Asparagus-fern
Aspidistra
Baby's-tears
Calathea
Chinese evergreen

Dracaena
Dumbcane
Fern: Holly
Ivy, English
Nephthytis

Palm
Pellionia
Philodendron
Pothos
Selaginella

Snake plant
Sonerila
Spider plant
Swedish-ivy
Umbrella plant

———————— Plants for Dark Corners ————————
(Daylight bright enough to read by)

Aspidistra
Calathea
Chinese evergreen

Dracaena
Pothos

Selaginella
Snake plant

———————————— Fluorescent Lights ————————————

African violet
Anthurium scherzerianum
Azalea
Baby's-tears
Basil
Bay, sweet
Begonia: Angelwing;
  Cane, A-21, A-22;
  Rhizomatous, A-14
Bromeliad: A-30
Browallia (young plants)
Cacti (small varieties)
Caladium: A-50; A-51
Calathea
Calceolaria
Chinese evergreen
Chives
Cineraria
Coffee tree (young plants)
Coleus
Columnea
Copper-leaf (young plants)
Coralberry
Cyclamen
Dracaena 'Florida Beauty'
Echeveria
Episcia
Eucharis
Euonymus
Exacum
Fern (young, small
  plants)

Ficus: A-102
Fittonia
Gardenia
Geranium: A-109
Gloxinia
Grape-ivy
Hawaiian ti plant
  (young plants)
Haworthia
Hibiscus, Chinese
  (young plants)
Impatiens
Ivy, English
Ivy, German
Ivy, red
Jade plant
Jerusalem cherry
Kalanchoe
Lavender, fernleaf
  (young plants)
Lemon-verbena
Leopard plant
Lily-turf
Living stone
Mexican foxglove
Moses in the cradle
Myrtle
Nephthytis
Night-jessamine
  (young plants)
Orchid
Oxalis

What Plant Where?

Parsley
Pellionia
Peperomia
Pepper, Christmas
Philodendron (young plants)
Piggyback plant
Pilea
Pink polkadot plant
Polyscias (small plants)
Pothos
Prayer plant
Primrose
Primrose, Cape
Purple passion plant

Redbird cactus
Rosemary
Rose, miniature
Rouge berry
Scilla violacea
Selaginella
Shrimp plant
Sonerila
Strawberry, Alpine
Strawberry-geranium
Sweet flag
Waxplant
Zebra plant (young plants)

TEMPERATURE: Most of the plants in this book will grow well in the temperatures of the average house during the winter heating season —generally speaking 62–75 degrees. Kinds that like to be unusually cool or warm are noted here.

—————————————————— Cool ——————————————————
(60–70 degrees during winter heating season)

Aralia
Asparagus-fern
Aspidistra
Azalea
Bay, sweet
Begonia, Rieger
Browallia
Calamondin
Calceolaria
Camellia
Chives
Chrysanthemum
Cineraria
Coralberry
Cyclamen
Euonymus
Exacum
Fatshedera
Fern
Fuchsia
Gardenia
Geranium

Gold-dust plant
Grape-ivy
Ivy, English
Ivy, German
Jasmine
Kangaroo vine
Lantana
Lavender, fernleaf
Lemon-verbena
Leopard plant
Lily-turf
Living stone
Maple, flowering
Mint
Myrtle
Night-jessamine
Norfolk Island pine
Oxalis
Parsley
Piggyback plant
Pittosporum
Podocarpus

Primrose
Rosemary
Rose, miniature
Sage
Sago palm
St. Augustinegrass,
  variegated
Savory, winter

Shrimp plant
Star of Bethlehem
Strawberry, Alpine
Strawberry-geranium
Sweet flag
Sweet marjoram
Tarragon
Thyme

————————————— **Warm** —————————————
(65–75 degrees during winter heating season)

African violet
Agave
Anthurium
Caladium
Calathea
Chinese evergreen
Episcia

Gloxinia
Philodendron
Pilea
Pothos
Schefflera
Sonerila

HUMIDITY: If all other conditions are to the liking of a plant, it will tolerate less than ideal humidity. Most of the plants included in this book will exist and thrive on 20–30% relative humidity. Kinds that really prefer more are listed here.

————————————— **High Humidity** —————————————
(50% or more)

Anthurium
Begonias: A-22; A-15
Calathea
Columnea
Episcia
Fern: A-92; A-95
Gloxinia

Lipstick vine
Orchids
Primrose, Cape
Selaginella
Sonerila
Sweet flag

————————————— **Moderate Humidity** —————————————
(30–50%)

African violet
Aralia
Aralia, false
Avocado
Begonia (except rex and
  tuberous)
Bougainvillea

Bromeliads
Browallia
Caladium
Calamondin
Chinese evergreen
Coffee tree
Coralberry

Croton
Dumbcane
Euonymus
Exacum
Fatshedera
Fern: A-91; A-89; A-90; A-86; A-88; A-94
Ficus
Fittonia
Gardenia
Geranium
Gold-dust plant
Hibiscus, Chinese
Ivy, English
Ivy, German
Ivy, red or flame
Lantana
Lavender, fernleaf
Leopard plant
Lily-turf
Mexican foxglove

Norfolk Island pine
Oxalis
Pellionia
Philodendron
Piggyback plant
Pilea
Pink polkadot plant
Pittosporum
Podocarpus
Pothos
Prayer plant
Rose, miniature
Sago palm
Shrimp plant
Spathiphyllum
Star of Bethlehem
Strawberry, Alpine
Strawberry-geranium
Umbrella plant
Wandering Jew

SOIL MOISTURE: Most of the plants included in this book thrive in soil that is kept evenly or nicely moist at all times. Exceptions —both to the dry and to the wet side—are listed here.

─────────────────── **Wet** ───────────────────
(Maintain soil in a range between wet and moist)

Chinese evergreen
Piggyback plant
Sweet flag

Umbrella plant
Zebra plant

─────────── **Near Dry Between Waterings** ───────────
(Water well; water again when the surface soil begins
to feel dry when you pinch some of it between your fingers)

Aspidistra
Bishop's cap
Bougainvillea
Cacti
Croton
Donkey- or burro's tail
Echeveria
Euphorbia

Ficus
Hawaiian ti plant
Haworthia
Jade plant
Kalanchoe
Living stone
Onion, pregnant
Peperomia

Ponytail
Redbird cactus
Rosary vine
Sago palm

Schefflera
Snake plant
Sonerila
Wax plant

PLANTS FOR SPECIAL USES: The lists that follow will help you to locate plants for special purposes—flowering and basket plants, plants to grow from seed, plants to scent your rooms. Plants for terrariums are also suited for growing in bottle gardens.

──────── **Terrarium Plants** ────────

African violet, miniature
Anthurium (young plants
  of small varieties)
Aralia, false (young plants)
Begonia: A-22; hybrid miniatures
Bromeliad: A-30
Caladium: A-51
Coralberry (young plants)
Dracaena sanderiana
Episcia
Euonymus
Ferns (young, small plants)
Gloxinia, miniature
Ivy, English
Leopard plant

Mexican foxglove
Neanthe bella palm
Norfolk Island pine (seedlings)
Oxalis
Pellionia
Philodendron sodiroi
Pilea
Prayer plant
Scilla violacea
Selaginella
Sonerila
Strawberry-geranium
Sweet flag
Waxplant

──────── **Hanging Basket Plants** ────────

African violet
Asparagus-fern
Baby's-tears
Begonia: Angelwing; Cane; A-22;
  Rhizomatous; A-14
Bougainvillea
Browallia (older plants)
Cacti: A-47; A-48; A-49
Caladium hybrids
Chenille plant
Coleus rehneltianus
Columnea
Donkey-tail
Episcia
Exacum
Fern: A-87

Ficus: A-102
Fittonia (older plants)
Fuchsia
Geranium: A-110
Grape-ivy
Impatiens
Ivy, English
Ivy, German
Ivy, red
Jasmine
Kangaroo vine
Lantana
Lipstick vine
Maple, flowering
Moses in the cradle
Nephthytis

Night-jessamine
Oxalis
Pellionia
Peperomia
Philodendron
Piggyback plant
Pilea
Pink polkadot plant
Ponytail
Pothos
Prayer plant
Primrose, Cape
Purple passion plant
Redbird cactus

Rosary vine
Rose, miniature
Rouge berry
St. Augustinegrass,
   variegated
Screw-pine
Shrimp plant
Spider plant
Star of Bethlehem
Strawberry-geranium
Swedish-ivy
Tahitian bridal veil
Wandering Jew
Waxplant

Flowering Plants

African violet
Amaryllis
Anthurium
Azalea
Begonia
Bougainvillea
Bromeliad
Browallia
Cacti
Calamondin
Calceolaria
Camellia
Chenille plant
Chinese evergreen
Chrysanthemum
Cineraria
Columnea
Coralberry
Cyclamen
Echeveria
Episcia
Eucharis
Euphorbia 'Bojeri'
Exacum
Fuchsia
Gardenia
Geranium
Gloxinia
Hibiscus, Chinese
Hyacinth

Hydrangea
Impatiens
Jasmine
Jerusalem cherry
Kalanchoe
Lavender, fernleaf
Lily-turf
Lipstick vine
Living stone
Mexican foxglove
Moses in the cradle
Narcissus, paper-white
Night-jessamine
Onion, pregnant
Orchid
Oxalis
Pepper, Christmas
Poinsettia
Primrose
Primrose, Cape
Rosary vine
Rose, miniature
Scilla violacea
Shrimp plant
Spathiphyllum
Spider plant
Star of Bethlehem
Strawberry-geranium
Waxplant
Zebra plant

Calamondin
Coffee tree
Coralberry
Eucharis
Exacum
Gardenia
Hyacinth
Jasmine

Narcissus, paper-white
Night-jessamine
Orchid: A-167
Pittosporum
Rose, miniature
Spathiphyllum cannaefolium
Waxplant

──────── **Trees** ────────
(Or large shrubs)

Aralia
Aralia, false
Avocado
Calamondin
Coffee tree
Croton
Dracaena
Dumbcane
Euphorbia
Fern: A-96
Ficus
Gardenia

Gold-dust plant
Hawaiian ti plant
Hibiscus, Chinese
Maple, flowering
Norfolk Island pine
Palm
Pleomele
Podocarpus
Polyscias
Ponytail
Schefflera

──────── **House Plants You**
Can Grow From Seeds ────────

African violet
Amaryllis
Asparagus-fern
Avocado
Basil
Begonia
Bishop's cap
Bougainvillea
Browallia
Cacti
Calceolaria
Chinese evergreen
Chives
Coffee tree
Coleus
Coralberry
Cyclamen
Dill

Exacum
Fennel
Fern
Geranium
Gloxinia
Impatiens
Jerusalem cherry
Kalanchoe
Lily-turf
Living stone
Mexican foxglove
Mint
Norfolk Island pine
Palm
Parsley
Pepper, Christmas
Ponytail
Primrose

Primrose, Cape
Rose, miniature
Rouge berry
Sage

Schefflera
Strawberry, Alpine
Sweet marjoram
Thyme

─────────── Good Plants for Beginners ───────────

African violet
Aspidistra
Begonia: Angelwing;
Cane; A-14
Chinese evergreen
Coleus
Dracaena
Eucharis
Euphorbia
Fern: A-86; A-87; A-88
Grape-ivy
Ivy, English
Ivy, red
Jade plant
Kangaroo vine
Lipstick vine

Nephthytis
Onion, pregnant
Palm: A-179
Philodendron
Pilea
Ponytail
Pothos
Rosary vine
Scilla violacea
Snake plant
Spathiphyllum
Swedish-ivy
Unguentine plant (Aloe)
Wandering Jew
Waxplant

INDEX

249

255

A ROBYN KELLY MYSTERY

MASQUERADE

LIZ OSBORNE

FIVE STAR

An imprint of Thomson Gale, a part of The Thomson Corporation

Detroit • New York • San Francisco • New Haven, Conn. • Waterville, Maine • London

THOMSON

GALE

LIBRARY OF CONGRESS CATALOGING-IN-PUBLICATION DATA

Osborne, Liz.
    Masquerade : a Robyn Kelly mystery / Liz Osborne.—1st ed.
      p. cm.
    ISBN-13: 978-1-59414-538-4 (alk. paper)
    ISBN-10: 1-59414-538-5 (alk. paper)
    1. Hospitals—Employees—Fiction. 2. Legislators—United States—Crimes
against—Fiction. I. Title.
PS3611.R34M37 2007
813'.6—dc22
                                            2006035682

First Edition. First Printing: March 2007.

Published in 2007 in conjunction with Tekno Books and Ed Gorman.

Printed in the United States of America on permanent paper
10 9 8 7 6 5 4 3 2 1

To my grandchildren, Jake Hulett, Trevor Hulett, Jeneveve Osborne, and Keegan Mallon, for the joy and fun you've brought into my life, I love you all.

ACKNOWLEDGMENTS

I'd like to thank the members of my two critique groups, Megan Chance, Elizabeth DeMatteo, Linda Lee, Jena MacPherson, Melinda McRae, Karen Muir, Joanne Otness, and Sharon Thomas for their suggestions, advice, support, patience, and friendship. Thanks to those who worked with me at Group Health Cooperative, the physicians and staff, especially Kristine Leander, Sandra Matisse, Beryl Schulman, Glenda Anderson, Harry Shriver, M.D., Jim deMaine, M.D., Hal Leland, M.D., and James Van Ostrand, M.D., all of whom made a challenging job manageable, and even fun at times. Thanks to Cyndi Osborne for sharing her police expertise. Thanks also to members of the Society for Healthcare Consumer Advocacy, especially Donna Davison-Smith, Ellen Martin, and Lolma Olson. Any mistakes in medical or police procedures are all mine.

CHAPTER 1

You know it's going to be a bad day when. . . .

I knew it was going to be a bad day when the hospital alarm bells went off at six a.m., pealing so loudly that only the profoundly deaf could have ignored them.

My name is Robyn Kelly and I manage the Patient Relations department for Madrona Bay Hospital and Medical Center in a small suburb east of Seattle's Lake Washington. Last weekend, I turned forty. I am not thrilled with the prospect of searching my black hair more frequently for silver, but at least I don't need glasses to do it. Yet.

I had come in early that Monday to avoid the usual rush-hour gridlock, planning to finish some paperwork before the phones started ringing. But as I sipped my Starbucks latté in the outer office with my assistant, Connie, who had also come in unexpectedly early, the alarm bells startled us.

"What the heck is that?" Connie asked. She had graduated from college earlier in the year, and working here was her first job. She was usually full of youthful confidence, but, right now, her brown eyes were wide with concern.

"The alarm," I said, trying to remain calm for her sake. Unannounced drills did not occur at six a.m.

Connie rolled her eyes. "I know it's the alarm. Why is it going off?"

"I don't know why. You're the one who claims to be psychic," I quipped.

"I'm working on it. You're the one who's fey."

"Not me, my grandmother. And, she wasn't fey; she had dreams about family members."

She scowled. "It's just that—"

I waved my hand to stop her. A muffled voice was coming over the PA in the hall. Our office was not wired for the PA system, so we opened the hallway door to hear the announcement.

"This is a Code Yellow. I repeat, this is a Code Yellow. This is not a drill."

My heart pounded as I tried to remember the different kinds of codes. Code Yellow. It wasn't a fire; that was Code Red.

"What should we do now, boss?"

"Lock up your purse and bring your keys." To mask my own growing nervousness, I hustled into my office and grabbed the red "Disaster Manual" off the shelf. The hospital had disaster drills twice a year, and even though we took them seriously, there was always an element of play-acting. This was the real thing. "It doesn't matter what the color code is. We go to A103. Ready?"

I pulled my cell phone from my purse and propelled Connie through the door, locking it behind us. I wished I knew what we were getting into. At this time of day, there were not many staff in the building to handle it. Whatever "it" was.

We strode down the hall toward the closest elevators. As we walked, Connie undid her long blond hair, then twisted it into a coil and reclipped it in the back. I recognized it as her version of a nervous twitch.

The four-story hospital-clinic complex was shaped like a rectangular box with three wings sticking out, to the south, west, and north, each with a stairwell and a pair of passenger elevators.

Connie and I rounded the corner to the west wing. The

lighted numbers above the doors indicated both elevators were stopped on the floor below us and heading down.

"Let's take the stairs. It'll be faster." I was grateful that this forced exercise was down, not up. I glanced at Connie. With the naiveté of youth, she now appeared more excited than anxious about whatever it was we faced.

When we reached the basement, we joined the smattering of people trickling into the large meeting room. I didn't know most of them since they usually left before I arrived in the morning.

Charley Anderson stood at the far end of the room, urging everyone to take a seat. Charley is about my age, and a registered nurse who rose up through the ranks to be the ER manager. Tall and lanky with a dry sense of humor, he's also a great person in a crisis, having worked in war zones prior to coming to Madrona Bay. I was relieved to see him in charge.

"Come on, people," Charley called out. "No time for chit-chat."

The urgency in his voice rippled through the group, and we quickly gave him our full attention.

"The State Patrol has notified us that there's been a multi-vehicle pile-up on Snoqualmie Pass—"

My stomach roiled. *Oh God, anything but that.* I swallowed hard, forcing myself to stay seated, concentrating on the present, not the past.

"—It sounds like black ice turned I-90 into a skating rink. We don't know the total number of casualties, but it's high. The worst will be airlifted to Harborview, the next worst will go to Overlake, then what's left will be sent to us. The best guess is we could get thirty to fifty victims in the next hour."

We listened in stunned silence. Thirty to fifty victims? In an hour? We were a two-hundred-bed community hospital. Our ER would have injured people stacked in the halls, and ancillary services such as Radiology and the lab would be inundated.

"We can do this," Charley said, his voice calm, his determined gaze scanning the room. Then, he smiled. "O.R., your docs are already en route for this morning's surgeries. Cancel your schedules, but tell the urgents to wait. Maybe we can fit them in later in the day. Who's here from Two-West and Three-West?"

Several nurses raised their hands.

"Good. I need a free-bed count in the next ten minutes. Housekeeping? We need a full-moon-Saturday-night's worth of supplies in the ER in the next fifteen minutes."

That broke the tension and everyone chuckled, knowing how busy Saturday nights are anyway, even without the lunacy factor.

"Any questions?" Charley looked expectantly at the group, then clapped his hands. "Okay, let's do it. Rob? You come with me."

I nodded, then shoved the disaster manual at Connie. "Take this to the main lobby," I said hurriedly. "Everything you need is in here. Find a phone to call Social Services. They'll help with victims' families. Then, call Human Resources for backup. Then snag some volunteers in case we need runners for something."

Connie nodded, her eyes wide with tension.

"It will be fine. Just like Charley said." I patted her shoulder. "Everything you need is in the manual. Okay?"

She nodded again.

"I'm going to the ER. Call me if you need anything." I watched her blend into the crowd moving quickly out the door.

One floor up, I caught Charley as he strode down the long hallway toward the reception desk and ambulance entrance. Double-timing it, I followed him past supply, special treatment, and staff rooms on one side, and exam rooms on the other. We dodged people rushing with supplies, calling and shouting to

12

each other as they raced to prepare for the worst.

"This is a nice way to start the week," I quipped.

Charley snorted. "Yeah, right."

"How can I help?"

"Call the family practice docs from the clinic. And the P.A.'s. I'm hoping most of the victims sent here will be T-and-R's," he said, referring to treating and releasing rather than admitting patients to the hospital.

We reached the front desk. Charley opened a cupboard and pulled out his disaster manual. Actually, his was divided into two very thick volumes because the ER had a lot of responsibility.

"Here's the list," he said, releasing the page and handing it to me.

Before I could comment, a nurse rushed over and dragged Charley away. I took the list into a small physician-dictation room and shut the door. If any of the docs questioned the urgency of the situation, I figured I would just open the door and let them hear for themselves.

I was surprised how quickly I lined up half a dozen docs and a couple of P.A.'s, or physician assistants. It was probably more than we needed, but they would have to be here for rounds in another hour or so anyway. None of them wasted time asking me for details and they all sounded energized about being part of the action.

I stepped from the dictation room into an empty hall, then found everyone gathered quietly around the front desk, watching the ambulance entrance. It reminded me of a scene from the television show, *ER:* that moment of total silence before all hell broke loose. But this was not fiction.

Then, from a distance, we heard it. A siren. Then another. The ebbing and soaring wails grew louder as they approached.

I swallowed hard, suddenly nervous. This was my first real

disaster. Could simulation drills possibly prepare me for the real thing?

The first docs I had called arrived in a rush of controlled intensity. They quickly traded raincoats for white coats, pinned on their name tags, and shoved stethoscopes into pockets. Charley teamed each of them with an ER nurse as the ambulances began pulling in front.

He signaled for me to follow. Filled with trepidation, I caught the pair of latex gloves Charley tossed me and pulled them on as I followed him and an ER nurse, Jamie Rice, out the door. The first of the victims were being pulled from the ambulances—

The squeal of tires. The sickening crunch of metal against metal. Shattered glass. Blood everywhere. David. Oh, God. No—

"Rob!" Charley's sharp call pulled me back to the present. Taking a deep breath, I donned the emotional armor worn by those who deal with people's fears and anxieties on a daily basis, the only thing that keeps us sane, and hurried to his side. I blocked out the groans and whimpers, the metallic smell of blood. The memories.

The rain had stopped, so at least the victims lining up in the circular driveway did not have that added misery. I could only hope we had everyone moved inside before the next downpour.

Charley did the initial triage of each new victim, an assessment of how serious the injuries were, then Jamie or I tagged the patient with a colored card that identified for the docs which patients to treat first. If Charley suspected something critical, we looped a red tag around the victim's arm and waved for an orderly to take him straight to an exam room. Broken bones got a yellow tag, while cuts and bruises earned a green tag and an interminable wait inside.

At one point, I looked up. The scene unfolded, wild and chaotic at first glance, but amazingly efficient. Not quite *Gone With The Wind* when Scarlett walks through the hundreds of injured soldiers, but as close as I wanted to get.

"Yellow tag," Charley called out, then moved on to the next victim with Jamie close behind.

I moved to the yellow-tag victim. He looked vaguely familiar, a handsome man I guessed to be in his mid-thirties, with dark wavy hair and those long, thick eyelashes that are wasted on a man. He grabbed my arm and jerked me toward him.

"Where's the doctor? I hurt."

I wrapped the yellow tag around his arm. He needed help, but not until after the red-tagged victims. "What do you need?"

He squeezed my arm hard enough to bruise and I flinched. "Get the doctor," he snarled. "I want something for the pain."

I extricated my arm and glanced around. All the docs had gone inside with the red-tag patients. "They will be with you as soon as they can. They're all with other patients right now."

"I don't care." The man struggled to sit up. "I want something for the pain and I want it now."

I tried to ease him back down, surprised at his strength despite his injuries. "I know this is hard for you. I'm sorry. But we can't give you pain medication until the doctor has thoroughly examined you. He could miss a serious injury if you can't feel—"

"Come on, nurse." His voice took on a whiny, cajoling tone that gave me the creeps. "Just a little shot."

"I'm sorry, sir," I said again. "I'm not a nurse. I can't give you anything, but I will check to see how much longer it'll be until a doctor can see you."

"You're not a nurse?"

"No, I'm a patient representative."

The man looked at me, an oddly speculative expression crossing his face. "What's your name?"

"My name's Robyn. A doctor will see you soon."

"But, I want—"

"Rob! Red!" Charley hollered. He was getting ahead of me. I didn't have time to linger. I moved to the "red" patient and waved for someone to take her inside immediately.

Within a relatively short time, Charley, Jamie, and I had finished, leaving yellow-tagged victims lining the halls on gurneys, while green-tagged people overflowed the waiting room, many grumbling into cell phones. During a lull in new arrivals, I slalomed around the line of gurneys, taking names and numbers of relatives to call. I tried to give each victim a kind word and a reassuring pat on the shoulder. Not being a doctor or nurse, there wasn't much more I could do for them, but it seemed to calm several people down. Most responded with a hesitant smile, but I saw the fear ease from their eyes. I took a deep breath and had a good feeling that, for some people, I had made a difference today.

Finally, all I wanted to do was take a break, even if only for a few minutes. I found an empty spot outside some exam rooms and leaned against the wall. My eyes closed, I breathed deeply and felt the tension start to seep away.

I heard something. A moaned scream. A giant pit formed in my stomach. Then I heard the rattle of curtain hooks pulled across a metal rod. A woman dressed in green scrubs stepped into the hall.

Darlene Skaggs, one of our midwives, cast me a sardonic look. "I suppose you're the best I'm going to get under the circumstances. Get over here, Rob." She disappeared into the exam room and I heard the curtain whipped closed.

How could I refuse such a gracious request for help? I rounded the curtain and saw a laboring mom in the throes of a contraction. I moved to the other side of the bed and waited until the exhausted woman sank against the pillows as her contraction ended.

Darlene smiled gently at the patient. "This is Linda. She lives in Ellensburg. She was on her way to Sea-Tac to pick up her mother when they were in the accident. She's a bit early, but this baby decided he wants to pick up Grandma too."

"Who's on upstairs?" I asked, since there was always an obstetrician in our hospital.

"Dr. Kyler. He's doing an emergency C-section not related to the accident. We'll take care of Linda here, then move her upstairs." Darlene turned to the patient. "This is Robyn. I know you wanted your mother to be your coach, but it looks like Rob will have to stand in for her. Okay?"

Linda nodded and smiled weakly. Then she groaned, signaling another contraction. I took her hand, and she squeezed so hard I lost my breath. I tried to mimic the Lamaze breathing technique. If it helped with labor pain, it should help my hand. As the contraction subsided, Darlene excused herself and left the room.

I wiped the woman's forehead with the corner of the sheet. "How are you doing?"

"Okay." Her chin quivered. "I really wanted my mom to be here." Her ash-blond hair was damp, lying limp around her face.

"I know," I said, patting her hand. "At least she'll be here to help you with the baby."

Darlene returned, and Linda looked at her anxiously. "Have they found my husband?" Her fear was palpable, or was it my own memories causing my heart to pound, my knees to weaken?

"Not yet," Darlene said. "We'll call the other hospitals. Don't worry about him right now. You have your hands full delivering this baby."

"What's your husband's name?" I asked, the calmness in my voice belying my inner turmoil.

"Ben. Ben Tucker," Linda said. "We were in a white Toyota."

"Can you describe Ben to me?"

"He's my age. Twenty-eight. And he's real good looking."

I smiled. "I'm sure he is. What color is his hair, and how tall is he?"

After Linda gave me more details, I took a minute between contractions to call Connie at the information desk, and asked her to have Social Services locate Linda's husband.

"Sure, Rob," Connie said. "I called the Human Resources people too, and they're on their way. But it's pouring rain outside and rush-hour traffic is awful."

"Are you doing okay?" I asked.

"So far. I've been listening to the radio, and it sounds like all the reporters went to Harborview with the most serious cases."

"It's probably too much to hope the reporters will stay there."

I hung up as Linda started another contraction, and I focused on this young woman and her breathing. In between contractions, Linda told me her story. This was her first baby after three miscarriages. She'd spent the last four months in bed. It sounded like a high-risk pregnancy to me. Alarmed, I glanced at Darlene.

As if reading my mind, Darlene said, "I called her OB in Ellensburg. Keeping her pregnant through the second trimester was the hard part. She's been doing fine since her contractions started."

Darlene checked Linda, who was amazingly calm. I figured she was now so totally focused on delivering her baby that nothing could distract her.

"Okay," Darlene said. "I see the head. Next contraction, I want you to bear down and push."

Linda nodded, her mouth set in a straight line of determination, and I squeezed her hand in support. The contraction came and we pushed, Darlene calling out instructions, and me offering encouragement.

"Okay, here he comes . . . here he . . . oh, he's a beautiful baby boy, Linda." Darlene quickly cleaned the infant, swabbed out his mouth and made sure he was breathing before she wrapped him in a blanket and handed him to his mother. Then she massaged Linda's stomach to finish the birth process. I looked over Linda's shoulder, a lump forming in my throat as she checked the baby's fingers and toes and cooed with maternal pride and delight.

Reminded of my own son's birth, I swiped at the tears blurring my vision. That was the happiest day of my life, rivaled only by the day I married David. Josh had been a joy to me, but now, in his late teens, there was an underlying friction between us and I struggled to understand it.

"Well, how are things in here?"

I turned to see the obstetrician. "Hi, Stan."

"This is Linda Tucker, Dr. Kyler," Darlene said. She proceeded to give him a technical status report.

There was nothing more for me to do here, so I washed my hands and waved to Linda, who smiled back, then I slipped from the room. In the hall, I hesitated a moment.

Wow.

That was all I could think. Wow.

I had just helped bring a new life into the world. Me. I smiled broadly, feeling quite pleased with myself.

The self-administered pat on the back lasted only a moment before I remembered what I was doing before I heard Linda's groan. Oh, yes. I had been taking a break. The hallway was now empty of gurneys, so I hurried down the hall to the reception desk.

"Hi, Patti," I said to the receptionist as I leaned on the high counter. "How are things?"

"All the reds and yellows have been seen. Some are in the O.R., and the rest were admitted. All that's left are the greens."

"Do you need me?"

"Not unless you want to take temps and prep rooms."

I laughed. "I'll pass."

Patti grinned back. "I thought so. Now leave. Having you here makes me nervous."

"I don't know why. You're the one who got six compliments from happy patients last month." One of these days, I planned to observe her in action, maybe even video her with patients, to use as examples in customer-service training for other receptionists.

"Seven compliments. But, who's counting?"

I waved good-bye. The adrenaline rush had worn off. I wanted a shower, and I wanted either a nap or a caffeine IV. I was accustomed to mentally strenuous days, but this morning I'd run the gamut of emotions. And, it was barely 9:00 a.m., a long way from going-home time at 5:00.

When no one rushed forward to offer me the rest of the day off, I started down the hall toward the front entrance. We needed to prepare for the reporters who would show up eventually and for the accident victims' families.

I pushed through the double doors to the main lobby and was immediately caught up in the crush of day-surgery patients. I had forgotten all about what the disaster response had done to them. It was worse than the airport with last-minute flight cancellations. The situation was ugly, and looked about to get worse.

From behind the registration desk, the beleaguered lone receptionist was dealing with patients one at a time. In her early thirties, Nicole was soft-spoken, and probably weighed one hundred pounds dripping wet. She said something quietly to the man in front of her. He was in his late fifties and overweight, with a baseball cap pulled low over his unshaven face.

The man scowled and boomed, "What'd you mean, my surgery's been cancelled? I missed breakfast and drove all the way from Kent in this storm, and I'm not going home until my hernia's repaired."

I sighed. Handling this agitated crowd wasn't a receptionist's job, but the supervisor wasn't in yet. I pushed my way through the throng, vaguely aware of the sour looks as I passed by, as if I was cutting in line ahead of them. I ducked behind the counter and put my hand on Nicole's shoulder. She looked at me, relief shining in her eyes.

"Mind if I say something?" I asked her.

"Please do." Nicole couldn't scoot her chair away fast enough.

"Folks, could I have your attention?" I called out. "Quiet down, please?"

It took a moment before the cluster of people stopped talking and milling and I could continue in a more normal voice. "My name is Robyn Kelly, and I'm the manager of Patient Relations."

"Well, you better start relating, lady, 'cause—"

"Sir, if you would give me a moment, please." I gave the man my "icicle manager" stare, then returned my attention to the whole crowd.

"I'm really sorry about this delay. I'm sure you're all aware that we've had an unexpected event," I said. "There was a serious multi-vehicle accident on Snoqualmie Pass this morning."

"So why's that my problem?" It was the same man. Were some people just born obnoxious?

"We are one of the hospitals responding to the accident," I said calmly. "We had a number of victims brought here who needed emergency surgery, so we had to cancel elective or nonurgent surgeries. I don't know about you, but I'd be willing to accept some inconvenience if it meant saving someone's life."

Many of them nodded in agreement. Most people were reasonable if you were up front and treated them with respect. The others were sent to departments like mine.

"I'm really sorry this has happened," I said. "If you'll give Nicole some information, we'll call you to reschedule your surgeries. Thank you for being so understanding."

I wanted to make a blanket offer to write-off their insurance co-pays as a good-faith gesture, but Will Slater, the administrator, would have a fit if I didn't run it by him first. As my Irish grandmother used to say, he'd skin a flea for a ha'penny and sell the hide.

Stepping out of Nicole's way, I watched the people talk quietly among themselves, with only a minimum of grumbling.

When it looked like Nicole had matters under control, I ducked into the restroom to salvage what I could of my appearance. The mirror view was worse than I had imagined. The best I could do was run wet fingers through my hair and dab around my face and neck to rearrange the remnants of my make-up. At least the waterproof mascara had lived up to its advertised claims.

My new blue silk blouse, however, was a total loss. It had been my birthday present to myself, along with dinner at the Metropolitan Grill and tickets to the Seattle Symphony with my friend, Andrea Van Dree. The blouse had been a real splurge. What had possessed me to wear it today? Now it was covered with a variety of "mystery spots." Even Nordstrom would balk at accepting it as a return.

My shoes were wet too, and I didn't look forward to a day of cold, clammy feet. Thank heaven for the cell phone. I called home to ask Josh to bring a change of clothes before he left for the university. He had heard about the accident on the news and wanted all the gory details. It took some fast talking to deflect his quizzing. I was left wondering if the only reason he agreed so readily to bring the clothes was to get a closer look at the action.

I couldn't hide in the bathroom until I was presentable, so I headed across the lobby where Connie had stationed herself. One reporter was already on the scene with a cameraman in tow.

"Hi, I'm Robyn Kelly. Can I help you?" I extended my hand to the reporter.

"Melanie Cole, Channel Eight. We tried to interview someone in the ER, but they told us to leave." She gave me what was supposed to be a disarming smile. "Can you give us some information?"

I had never been "the spokesperson" before, but a quick look around the lobby offered no other volunteers. "I don't know how many accident victims we received, but it went as smoothly as could be expected. We canceled our scheduled surgeries for the emergencies, but it's going okay. Only a few people with minor injuries were left untreated as of a few minutes ago."

"Anything newsworthy?"

I thought for a moment, then smiled. "Well, we did deliver a baby." Before I said another word, the reporter and cameraman bolted down the hall. "Wonder where they think they're going? Call Social Services, Connie, and see if they've located Linda Tucker's husband yet."

"That's just the kind of human-interest story reporters eat up," Connie said as she punched in the extension.

While Connie was on the phone, I saw Irene Hamstead, a nurse manager, rushing by with a clipboard in one hand and a portable radio in the other, her long black braid swinging in rhythm with her steps. At night, when all the administrators were gone, a nurse manager was in charge of the hospital.

"Irene, are you 'it'?"

She changed direction and headed for me. "I'm 'it.' Wouldn't you know, today's the big executive retreat at Port Ludlow. No one's scheduled to be here at all today." She sighed, then looked at me with an impish grin. "Although, that may not be all bad.

Thank goodness Charley came in early. And you, I understand you've been a busy girl this morning."

"I came in early to avoid the traffic and try to catch up on paperwork. At least I avoided the traffic."

She gave a short laugh. "An empty in-box is an urban myth. If we caught up, we wouldn't know what to do with ourselves."

I nodded in agreement. "By the way, the first reporter's already arrived. There will probably be more soon. I'm media relations until PR shows up."

"Lucky you."

Ignoring her quip, I asked, "Any info on the victims that I can share without violating privacy laws?"

"Charley's supposed to call any minute with the numbers." At that moment, her radio beeped. She pushed the speaker button. "This is Irene."

"Where are you?" Charley's voice.

"The main lobby with Rob."

"What's the extension there?"

Connie glanced at the phone in front of her. "Five three two four."

"Five three two four," Irene repeated into the radio, then turned it off. "Whatever it is, he doesn't want to say it over open radio waves."

That didn't sound good at all. What could he say that he didn't want heard by the other two departments listening to the radio, Security and Engineering? Curiosity building, we stared silently at the phone. When it rang, Connie picked up the receiver and handed it across the counter to Irene.

"Charley? What've you got?" Irene crooked the receiver between her ear and shoulder and started scribbling on her notepad.

"Uh-huh . . . uh-huh . . . okay . . . Great. Thanks. What?" She looked at me and frowned.

"What? You've got to be kidding?" Irene sighed heavily. "Yeah, Charley, I've got it. I'll take care of it. Thanks."

"Well? What is it?" I asked as Irene handed the receiver back to Connie.

"Charley gave me the numbers you can share with the press. They saw forty-three people. Sixteen are either in surgery or waiting to get in. Another seven were admitted for observation. The rest were treated and released."

I frowned. "That isn't privileged. He could have said that over the radio."

"I know," Irene said with a pained expression. She squeezed the bridge of her nose and sighed again. "One of the patients filed a complaint against you."

Her answer stunned me. That was the last thing I expected her to say. "A patient complained—oh, I know who it was. That man who demanded pain meds." I shook my head. "I told him a doctor would be with him as soon as the more serious injuries were treated."

"Well, that's not why he's complaining."

"It's not?"

"No. He wants to file a formal complaint that you were rude, unprofessional . . . and that you deliberately downgraded his color code when he asked for help."

"I what? I'd never do that. Charley triaged him as yellow, and that's what I put on his arm."

"There's more, Rob. The man who filed the complaint is Jake Hamilton."

"Jake Hamilton?" I repeated. "That name sounds familiar."

Irene nodded. "It should. He's Congressman Jake Hamilton."

CHAPTER 2

"A . . . a . . . a congressman?" I sputtered. "Filed a complaint? That I deliberately . . . you must be joking."

I could tell from Irene's grimace that she wished she were. Indignation—no, fury welled up inside me. Ten years and a wealth of compliments, and now someone had filed a totally false complaint against me. And not just any someone, a congressman, a well-known congressman. I'd thought he looked familiar, but under the circumstances, I probably wouldn't have recognized Brad Pitt in that crush of bandaged and moaning people.

I shook my head in dismay. This was the kind of thing that destroyed careers. "Where is he?"

She flipped her long braid over her shoulder. "He was admitted, but I don't know where."

"Hmmm." A vindictive congressman. Just what I needed.

In a hospital, we dealt with unhappy people every day. Let's face it, patients seldom wanted to be here. Even happy occasions are fraught with anxiety, like Linda having her long-awaited baby, but not knowing where her husband was, or if he was even alive.

A story like Linda's might make today's news, but this was different. This could stay in the news for weeks. Jake Hamilton was not only a political figure, he was a prominent person. Every word he spoke would be parroted by the press and scrutinized by the public. And, his complaint was a serious one—that I had deliberately tried to harm him.

But, why? Then I remembered that odd look that had crossed his face when I said I was a patient rep. Good heavens, did this have something to do with the patient-rights legislation we were trying to push through Congress?

I groaned. "PR's going to kill me. If Will doesn't do it first." I glanced at Irene. "I don't suppose we can forget to call them?"

Irene shook her head. "Wish we could. But you can't talk to the press if this complaint gets out. Call PR. I'll page Will and another administrator. They get paid the big bucks to protect the hospital's reputation, right?"

Her implication that I had jeopardized our reputation made me wince. "Right. But we're here and they're not. In fact, if they are already at Port Ludlow, it'll take hours for any of them to return." I thought for a moment. "I wonder how long we can keep this quiet? I don't suppose we can keep Hamilton sedated until the press finds a serial murderer to focus on?"

Irene shook her head again, but smiled sadly. "No, Rob, we can't sedate him unless it's medically indicated."

Another reporter and cameraman came through the front entrance, Channel Three this time. "This is going to be a very long day. I want my Excedrin," I said with a heavy sigh.

"I'm out of here." Irene eased away from the reception counter.

"Coward," I muttered after her.

She squeezed my hand and said, "Hang in there. I'll be back when I have something to report. We'll keep the complaint quiet for a while."

I turned to Connie. "Ready?"

She nodded, her mouth may have been in a serious straight line, but her eyes sparkled with anticipation.

She wasn't disappointed. For the next hour, we were swamped. Security helped us convince the local press that if they stayed in one area, we would give them regular updates. With promises of coffee, donuts, multiple phone lines, a fax machine, and all the victim information we could legally provide under HIPAA regulations, they were happy. At least for the time being.

Until they learned one of the victims was a congressman.

A congressman who had filed a serious complaint about me.

Despite all the chaos, I had borrowed a clean white jacket and slipped it on to cover my bedraggled blouse. It made me look more official, but caused minor confusion whenever someone assumed I was a doctor or a nurse. I wished Josh would hurry up with my change of clothes.

Connie contacted Dietary to place the food order and argued about whose budget to bill it to, while I sent another E-mail to all departments that combined all their latest status reports. The worst of the crisis may have been over for the ER, but the effects were rolling through the building like a storm surge.

At the opposite end of the building, the clinic was open for regular appointments, but the surgeons were behind schedule from the emergency consults and surgeries. I hoped the clinic patients were as reasonable as most of the cancelled day-surgery patients.

At one point, Tom Geralding, the security manager, strode by. A barrel-chested, retired marine, he had a way of drawing himself up that made him seem taller than he really was. That, and his booming voice, made Tom someone I wanted on my side if things got ugly. He slapped the counter and stopped in front of us. "You two doing okay? Can I get you anything?"

"Thanks, Tom, but we're fine. And you?" I asked, partly for our next update and partly because everyone expected me to know what's going on.

"I've got our guys stationed at the main entrance. They'll let in staff, patients and their families, and, unfortunately, reporters," he grumbled. "Everyone else is turned away. And, I got rent-a-guards at the other doors. Only people with hospital photo ID get past them."

I glanced at Connie and saw that she was adding it to the next all-department E-mail. I told Tom, "We caught some reporters sneaking down the back hall. One was in a wheelchair and the other was wearing a white lab coat and pushing him."

"Hmm. That was smart," Tom said. "I'll add masquerading as staff and the need to control access to lab coats and wheelchairs to my final report when we wrap this up. How'd you recognize them?"

"The local TV reporters are easy to identify. We shooed them back to the clinic waiting area."

"The guy behind them lugging camera equipment was a dead giveaway," Connie piped in. "It's the radio and newspaper people we don't recognize."

"The last thing we need is reporters running amuck. Slater will have my head if we lose control of the building." Tom scowled and shook his head. "He'll have my head anyway when he sees what this extra security is costing us, but there's no getting around it."

I nodded in sympathy and tried to reassure Tom. "It's not like he can blame you for something like this."

"Don't be too sure. You should've seen him when we called in snowplows to clear the parking lot two years ago. We do that, what, every four or five years? It's not something we budget for. And, we sure as hell didn't budget for this."

Tom leaned over the counter and lowered his voice. "It's bad enough we got police all over the place investigating the accident. Not to mention the families running around, not knowing which hospital they should be at. But with a congressman involved, the press is gonna go nutso." He looked around to be sure no one was standing too close. "That's when the you-know-what hits the fan."

"I guess we just wait and hope it doesn't happen until after we've gone home," I said.

Tom must not have recognized my attempted humor, because he nodded sagely and pushed himself away from the counter. He slapped the laminated surface again. "I better call for more security guards to watch the stairwell entrances. That's the only way we'll keep reporters out of the rest of the building."

"I'd just block the doors or lock them," Connie said as she picked up the ringing phone.

"Too easy," Tom replied. "Fire codes say no can do. You ladies stay out of trouble, you hear?"

That was easier said than done, I thought with a sigh. The whole thing with the congressman had given me a headache. Or maybe it was all the noise and confusion.

Connie hung up the phone and laughed. "Do you want to hear the latest one?"

"Sure." Rumors and stories were running rampant.

"A trucker going to a rendering plant skidded on the ice and dumped a load of beef carcasses all over I-90. The State Patrol's closed it again to all westbound traffic. An environmental group is holding a press conference," Connie said in a clandestine whisper. "They're citing this as an example of why we should pay more attention to the hazardous waste hauled by trucks every day."

I shook my head as I sorted through the most recent internal E-mail updates. "What a mess. Ice and grease."

"Where is he?"

I looked up to see a young woman in her early twenties. Her shoulder-length brown hair was tousled and her silk blouse collar lay half-in and half-out of her tailored suit jacket. Her distraught gaze jumped from me to Connie and back again.

"I'm sorry, where is who?" I asked.

"Jake. Jake Hamilton." She had a soft, girlish voice that clashed with her professional clothing.

"Are you a relative, Miss . . . ?"

"I'm Jake's—Congressman Hamilton's aide, Cynthia Martin."

"I'm sorry, Ms. Martin, but he's not—"

"You don't understand. I have to see him. I have to know he's all right." From the way she clawed at the attaché case she clutched to her chest, hysteria was not far away.

"I'm sure he's going to be fine, but I don't know if he's been assigned a bed yet. If you'd like to wait over—" The woman started down the hallway. I hurried around the reception counter and caught up with her. "Wait, Ms. Martin? Cynthia, where are you going?"

"To Administration."

"But I can—"

"My mother's Brenda Martin," she said, lifting her chin. "She'll help me see him."

It clicked then. Cynthia was a willowy version of her mother, our Director of Nursing Services. I touched her arm to comfort her. "I'm sure she would, Cynthia, if she was here, but she's not."

"What do you mean?" Cynthia wailed as she spun away from my hand. "Of course she's here."

"There's a management retreat at Port Ludlow today."

Cynthia sagged against me, and for a moment I was afraid she'd fainted. I felt her shudder and then, her body shook as she began to sob. Over her shoulder, I gave Connie a raised eyebrow look. This was one very loyal congressional aide. Given this reaction, if it turned out her feelings were more than strictly professional, I wouldn't be surprised. Congressman Hamilton had a reputation for eliciting the total devotion of any female who came in contact with him, regardless of her age. Not that I could understand it, based on my own encounter with him. I must be the glaring exception to that phenomenon.

I led Cynthia to the empty waiting area and settled her into one of the overstuffed chairs.

She fumbled for a linen handkerchief and glanced around to see if anyone was watching. "I'm glad Ja—Congressman Hamilton didn't see me fall apart." She blew her nose. "He says emotional displays are a sign of weakness."

"I see," I said finally. I could understand why he needed to be careful about his own behavior, but why his young aide? "How did you know to come here, Cynthia?"

She blew her nose again. "I flew in last week from D.C. We're hosting hearings around the region on salmon runs. I was leaving for the Renton hearings when I heard about the accident on the news. I just knew he was involved."

Connie would have appreciated Cynthia's psychic abilities. Over the young woman's shoulder, I saw the Channel Three reporter and cameraman coming down the hall and silently groaned. I didn't need to be clairvoyant to know I had to get Cynthia out of the public area.

"Do you usually live in D.C.?"

She nodded. Good; chances were the local media wouldn't recognize her, but I didn't want to risk it, especially with her as fragile as she seemed to be.

"You know, Cynthia, we don't have any information on Congressman Hamilton. We could use his address and phone number, and the name of his regular physician," I said in a calm, soothing voice. Keeping myself between Cynthia and the reporter, I eased her from the chair and guided her into the confines of the Business Office.

The Business Office staff was amazing when it came to ferreting out information, but it was the quickest way to get Cynthia out of public view. "Maybe you could help us with that,

32

and I'll let you know when you can see him. How would that be?"

Cynthia nodded meekly. Relieved that she had acquiesced so easily, I turned her over to an admitting clerk.

I had barely returned to the reception counter when the phone rang again and Connie answered it. "Uh-huh. Uh-huh." She glanced at me, and I didn't like the way her expression went from animated to bland. "Uh-huh. Okay. Thanks for the warning." She hung up the phone and scowled at it. "Thanks for nothing."

"Are you going to keep me in suspense?" I asked.

"Oh, you're going to love this one. That was Daniel in PR. Essentially, he said, they'll be here when they can, but it'll be a while. The bridges and interstates are still a mess because of the storm."

"When they can?" I looked at her in disbelief. "You're kidding. Someone must live on the Eastside. And what about beepers and cell phones?"

"I don't know," Connie said, shaking her head. "Maybe you can get a better response from him."

"Does he know about Congressman Hamilton?"

"No. He didn't give me a chance to say anything."

"Hmm. That might not be all bad. If he doesn't know a congressman is here, he doesn't know about the complaint."

"Good thought, boss. Oh, and Social Services found Ben Tucker. He was taken to Overlake and he's doing fine, but he'll be there for a day or two. Social Services called the airlines too, and found Linda's mother. Somehow they'll get all three—I mean all four—of them together."

"That's a relief," I said. "Remind me to send a note to Social Services complimenting their efforts."

"Hey, Rob, how are you doing?"

I looked up to see who was feeling so cheery. Charley and

Irene were standing on the other side of the counter. Relieved to see some friendly faces, I thought maybe I had found Daniel's replacement. "Just ducky. Say, Charley, how'd you like to be the hospital spokesman? You don't have anything else to do now that you've cleared out the ER."

"Sorry. I already have a job," he said with phony regret. "I appointed myself Irene's assistant. It's a whole lot easier."

"He's good too. He makes phone calls and runs errands. But I haven't been able to get him to make coffee," joked Irene.

"Excuse me. Where's Congressman Hamilton?"

We turned to face a reporter I didn't recognize. How did he know about the congressman? I pointed down the hall. "The pressroom is—"

I didn't have a chance to say more. The reporter shoved a microphone between us, and his cameraman started rolling. Then, the tidal wave hit. The other reporters must have seen enough to think they were being scooped. They poured from their comfortable makeshift newsroom and charged over. Charley and Irene quickly found themselves trapped behind the counter with me. Connie had disappeared, and I didn't blame her.

I had seen these assaults on TV before. Microphones dangled like a swarm of mosquitoes, bright lights glared from the videocams, and cameras clicked like machine guns. It was one thing to view a scene like this from the comfort of your living room, and something entirely different to be on the receiving end. At least we had the reception counter to barricade us from them.

Charley, Irene, and I stood together, stoic but united, as if facing a firing squad. As long as we stayed calm—and kept breathing—we would get through this. We had worked enough crises over the years to handle just about anything. Even a journalist assault.

Irene was trying to silence the crowd when I saw Connie

fast-talking a man who had been pointed out to me earlier as a police detective. I nudged Charley, who glanced quickly in that direction. The detective pushed his way through the shouting throng of reporters. He looked to be about fifty, physically trim, with more than a touch of gray to his dark hair, a firm jaw now softened by age, and brown eyes that had seen too much.

I stepped back as he moved into the spot where I'd been standing behind the counter. "Is there a problem, Detective?"

He looked at me as if I was the village idiot. "I'll handle it from here." He brushed by and inserted himself between Irene and the counter.

Incredulous, I looked at Charley. "I thought we were handling it," I muttered.

"Not anymore," Charley said with an amused glint in his eyes, amusement I didn't share.

Equally surprised, Irene had stepped back too, and the three of us watched the detective go into action. I had to admit, begrudgingly, that he seemed to know what he was doing.

He silenced the crowd of jabbering reporters with his sharp look before he addressed them in a deep gravelly voice. "I'm Detective Matthew Pierce, Madrona Bay Police Department. As you already know from listening to the police and fire scanners," he said sardonically, "a major accident occurred this morning on Snoqualmie Pass. It involved multiple cars and semi-trucks. The most seriously injured were airlifted to Harborview. Some trauma cases were taken to Overlake, and the rest came here to Madrona Bay. The State Patrol has asked our department to help with the interviews. At this time, it appears the accident was an unfortunate chain reaction that occurred when a semi hit a patch of black ice and lost control."

"What about Congressman Hamilton?" The news was out. A rumble grew as the rest of the reporters realized they had almost missed the biggest part of the story.

The detective appeared unruffled by the questions thrown at him. He glanced at the three of us, then settled on Irene. "You prepared to talk about this?" he asked in a low voice.

She nodded once. I watched how he took her arm to ease her in front of him, a gentle gesture at odds with the rest of his brusqueness.

Irene blinked at the flashing lights before her and swallowed hard. Her voice quavered only slightly when she said, "Congressman Jake Hamilton has been admitted to our hospital. His condition is stable. HIPAA regulations prohibit me from saying anything more. His family will be the ones to release any information."

Matthew Pierce reinserted himself in front of her. "That's all for now."

"Ms. Kelly, tell us what it was like to deliver a baby in the middle of a disaster," a voice called from the back, a deep melodious voice that made me gasp.

I squinted to see past the bright lights, but even the faint profile was enough. At the sight, my stomach clenched.

It was Peter.

Peter Armstrong, ace reporter for a cable news service. First at every war and scene of mass destruction. Pulitzer Prize winner for his sensational exposés. What the hell was he doing in Seattle?

After the initial shock, I was suddenly, unreasonably angry. How like him to distort reality for the sake of a story. "That's a total exaggeration," I snapped. "The disaster was up on the pass, not in our ER. The baby was delivered by a qualified midwife who had the full resources of the hospital supporting her." Okay, so I had morphed the truth a little. I didn't think Linda Tucker would want the story sensationalized any more than it already was.

Detective Pierce stepped in front of me. "That's all for now, folks. The hospital has provided you with a comfortable place to wait. They will keep the coffee and donuts coming, and sandwiches?" He glanced at Irene. She nodded. "And sandwiches. All we ask is that you not bother the victims, their families, other patients, or the staff. We'll let them know you're here so they can come to you for their fifteen seconds of fame."

A couple more questions were thrown out amidst the chuckling, but the reporters started moving away. I turned my back on them, not wanting to know if one reporter in particular had chosen to linger.

"Guess that'll keep them happy for a while," Detective Pierce said in his throaty growl as he watched the crowd disperse.

Irene groaned. "Can't those reporters read?"

I turned around again to see what she was talking about. The television reporters had moved to different corners, their cameras turned on for live transmissions. Print journalists were standing in front of Radiology, talking rapidly on their cell phones.

"How many signs do we post saying do not use cell phones because they interfere with the equipment?" She went for the closest reporter and tapped his shoulder, gestured to the posted signs, then pointed at his cell phone. When he started to argue, she signaled for one of the security guards. She made her way down the hall, waylaying every reporter who was in a "no cell phone" area.

Detective Pierce watched her progress, a hint of amusement lifting the corners of his mouth. "We could use someone like her for crowd control during the Taste of Madrona Bay festival."

Charley looked at the now-empty space in front of the reception counter. "I'm going to the ER. Call me if something comes up." He squeezed my shoulder and left me standing there with the detective.

Detective Pierce grunted. "Well, that's over."

"For a while at least," I said, wishing I was alone and anywhere else, but here. Thinking about the complaint against me, I sighed. "They'll be back for all the gory details."

"About that baby?" He glanced at my chest where a nametag should be, and I realized I wasn't wearing it. "Are you a nurse?"

I winced at his mistake. "No. I manage the Patient Relations department."

"The what?"

"Unhappy patients come to my department and we try to sort it out."

He smirked. "Bet you're not very popular around here."

"What do you mean by that?"

"I mean, if you take the patient's side in an argument, the rest of the employees are probably leery of you, at best. At worst, they don't like you. You're like IA."

"No, Detective. It's not like Internal Affairs at all." I told myself not to be defensive. "You would be amazed how often the staff calls and asks us to contact an unhappy patient."

"If you say so." He wasn't a tall man, but he had a patronizing way that made me feel small and I didn't like it.

"Hey, Mom!"

I turned to see Josh loping across the lobby, his long rangy body still waiting to be filled out. A baseball cap covered his dark-brown hair and he grinned broadly as he took in the cameras and reporters loitering nearby. A coat hanger with a clean blouse and slacks hung over his shoulder and he held a plastic bag with shoes. The clothes didn't match, but at this point, I didn't care. I briskly introduced Josh to Detective Pierce.

"Call me Matt," Pierce said as they shook hands.

"Nice to meet you. Mom, I gotta go. I'm double-parked in a fire lane." He grinned at Pierce, who merely shook his head as Josh raced out the door.

"Good kid you have there."

"Thanks. I think so too," I said. Most of the time. "He's a sophomore in mechanical engineering at the U."

"His dad must be real proud of him."

"Yes, he would be. David died when Josh was five, in a car accident. A drunk driver crossed the center line." *He died in my arms.*

"I'm sorry."

I turned to look at him and shrugged, pushing the nightmare back into the memory box I usually kept tightly locked. "It was a long time ago, Detective."

"That kind of hurt never goes away completely."

A lump formed in my throat and I swallowed hard. He was right. David's death had been forever, while the driver had been released after only three years in jail to drink and drive and kill again. Pierce's compassion brought the pain back unexpectedly, pain I had thought was long past. I twisted the gold claddagh ring on my right hand, a gift from David that I still wore. The Irish symbol of a crowned heart embraced by hands represented love, loyalty, and friendship, everything David and I meant to each other.

Nodding, I looked at the clothes Josh had brought. "Guess I better change before the next media assault."

"Are you coming back?"

"Of course. This is my designated place."

"Your what?"

"The disaster plan says I'm supposed to be here and direct the flow of information to employees, victims' families, and the media."

"That's a big job."

Did I hear an underlying condescension in his bland statement? It was hard to tell. "It's nothing we can't handle, Detective. Well, I really do need to change."

I started to leave, then turned back, basic courtesy winning over my desire to escape from this man who saw too much. "Thank you for helping us with the reporters."

He nodded and remained to talk to Connie, who apparently liked the detective, if her easy chatter was any indication. I slipped down a back hallway to a restroom. The brown slacks were snug, reflecting the few extra pounds I had put on since last winter, and the variegated blue blouse would have looked better with my navy slacks and navy shoes, not the taupe pumps Josh had brought. He had been in a hurry, I knew, and even in the best of times, his sense of fashion was a minus two on a scale of one to ten. At least these clothes were clean and un-wrinkled. I didn't tuck in the blouse, convincing myself it made me look taller. And thinner. Delusional maybe, but I felt better.

After wrapping the dirty clothes in the plastic bag, I tried to do something with my hair. If I ever made it back to my office, I'd fix my make-up, but for the time being, this was as good as it was going to get.

Impatient to get back to Connie, I came barreling out of the restroom. The sight of a man lounging against the wall, his arms crossed casually over his broad chest, brought me to a stop.

"Hello, Rob."

"Peter. It's been a long time." I hoped I sounded insouciant rather than the way I really felt, like a stammering adolescent with a pounding heart.

Peter pushed away from the wall. The fluid ease of his move-ment told me he still worked out, although his tapered waist and taut neck were also evidence of a disciplined lifestyle. His jaw was still square, his cheeks hollow, and his eagle-sharp brown eyes missed nothing.

"What's it been? Five years?"

I laughed, but there was no humor. "Try more than ten. It was right before your career-making exploits during the Balkans wars." I silently berated myself for letting my hurt and Irish temper show.

"You look great, just the same," he said. Amazing how sincere he sounded. I raised a skeptical brow. He had the honesty to laugh at himself. "Okay, not the same, but you do look great, Rob. That blue blouse you were wearing before looked real nice on you. Matched your eyes."

"Thanks." The compliment caught me off guard. I took a couple of steps toward him and noticed some gray mixed with his tawny hair. "You've aged well too."

He ignored the jab. "What are you doing here?"

"I work here. The Patient Relations department," I said, beginning to feel like a broken record. He was close enough now that I picked up a hint of his aftershave. Stetson. What he wore ten years ago. I breathed in more deeply, then stopped myself as the fragrance brought back heady memories.

"Really? Patient relations. That sounds interesting. I bet you know where all the bodies are buried."

His attempt at humor irritated me, and snapped me back to the present. "So why're you here? A freeway pile-up is a little tame for you. Shouldn't you be in the Middle East or some other hot spot, bringing man's inhumanity to man into our living rooms every evening?"

"Actually, I was at Sea-Tac when the network beeped me. It's an interesting change of pace, navigating through traffic on I-405 instead of through a war zone."

He looked away for a moment, and his expression turned boyishly wistful. "I had no idea you were here. I'm glad I found you, Rob." He took a step towards me.

His voice was so soft, I almost missed the words. But the implication slammed home to me. I hesitated before saying, "I didn't know you were looking."

"In between assignments, when I'd get back to the States, I

would make a few phone calls, but no one seemed to know where you'd gone." He stepped closer.

I didn't tell him that the few who knew wouldn't have told. They had stood by me when David had died, and, for years, they feared I'd never fall in love again. Then I met Peter. When he disappeared from my life, they'd had to stand by in silent support as I struggled to pull myself together again. No, they would not have told.

"I've missed you, Rob. I've missed this." He tilted my chin up, and, for a moment, time stood still. He bent to kiss me.

I froze. My breath caught in my throat and then, his lips were on mine, warm and achingly familiar. Instinctively, I leaned into the kiss, hungrily tasted him, breathed in the smell of him as if I had been starved for it. The years slipped away, along with the anger at his rejection, replaced by the flames of the passion we had always fanned in each other.

Slowly we parted. Still confused by his sudden reappearance in my life, I searched his face for signs of what he had meant by kissing me. His gaze had softened and his mouth formed that quirky smile that always made my heart somersault.

A deep cough from behind startled me. I pulled away and turned to see that police detective. My face heated with embarrassment. I had never done anything like this before, never lost myself in a passionate embrace in a place where anyone could walk by, and, of all the people to see us, why did it have to be him? How long had I been standing here with Peter? How long had the detective been watching? How much had he heard?

"Can . . . can I help you, Detective?"

Detective Pierce eyed Peter with a cold stare, then turned a bland look at me. "Connie needs you to read some report."

"Thank you, Detective. I'll talk to you later, Peter." Not daring to glance at either one of them, my emotions in a complete tangle, I hurried to the reception desk.

CHAPTER 3

Suppressing my embarrassment, I returned to Connie and the front desk, but the next few hours were a blur. I know I approved the in-house communiqués only because I saw my initials on them later, and I must have acted in a reasonably coherent manner because Connie didn't ask if anything was wrong. To say I was distracted, though, would be a gross understatement. Even the congressman's complaint against me faded from my mind.

Peter is back. Peter is back. The words swirled around and around in my head.

For a moment, I'd felt as giddy as a schoolgirl, thrilled down to my toes that he was here, yet bemoaning that I had been caught at less than my best when we were finally reunited.

But only for a moment. Then reality settled in. We were not reunited. If I had been an inveterate romantic, I might declare it was synchronicity, a fateful, unplanned crossing of paths. The skeptical realist in me insisted that he'd been on his way to somewhere else in the world; this meeting was a fluke, an accident. He had not sought me out.

At some level, my subconscious wish all these years had been that he would come to understand how much he loved me, how much he needed me, that he was willing to give up all the fame and excitement. Just for me. No woman wants to believe a man would choose action and danger over her passionate embrace.

Unfortunately, I had never given much thought to what happened next if he did declare his love and begged me to take him back. That was one of the problems with fantasies; they left out the nitty-gritty details. So now what?

Ten years was a long time, but I still remembered every moment we spent together. It had been the beginning of summer. I had put Josh on a plane to spend the vacation with my parents on their Colorado ranch, then rushed to a press function at the New York City hospital where I worked. Peter represented a local news station. Even then, he radiated energy, driven to succeed. He wanted to be *the* reporter. Not the anchor, but the one in the field who recounted the news as it happened without benefit of script writers or make-up artists.

It was pure chemistry. We started talking and gradually realized that everyone else had left and the clean-up crew was almost finished. We found our way to an intimate little basement bistro, one with a patio that looked through a charming wrought-iron fence to the sidewalk above. We sipped cabernet and toyed with our linguine, each reluctant to release the other's gaze. The next two months had been a whirlwind. When we weren't at work, we were together, and if one of us had to work late, the other one came to help.

I was the happiest I'd been in years, since before David had died, and I'd never thought to find that kind of happiness again. Yet, it was different. With Peter, I felt an intensity I never experienced with David.

As quickly as our relationship had flamed, it was snuffed out. Josh was coming home at the end of the week, and I didn't feel right living with a man in front of my young son. I arrived home planning to talk seriously to Peter about the future. Instead of finding Peter preparing another exotic feast, I found a note. It seemed that several months before, he had applied for a position with a cable news organization. The call had come that day. He'd been hired and was being sent to the Middle

East to cover a war. Just like that, he was gone.

While the rest of America listened to his voice-overs on nightly news reports from a secret location behind enemy lines, I turned the television off. I found myself restless in the big city; everywhere I went reminded me of him. Of us.

The position at Madrona Bay came open at the right time, near what was then touted as the most liveable city in the States. Nine-year-old Josh loved the idea of a house with a yard and playing ball in the cul-de-sac with other neighborhood kids. I escaped the memories of New York and made a fresh start for myself.

We had made a good life here, Josh and I. Now, I asked myself: did Peter want me back in his life? More to the point, did I want Peter back in mine? If that searing kiss we shared was any indication, I would have to say "I think so" to both questions.

By mid-day, the storm continued unabated, but the hospital had settled into its usual routine. The ER was open again for business, and the O.R.'s were finishing up with the last of the accident victims. We still had a few empty beds available, but not many.

Connie had returned to our office, where a slew of voice-mail messages guaranteed we'd be swamped for days. I had remained at the registration desk, but one more E-mail update and I could get back to my office.

Everyone knew the congressman was being monitored closely in a private room near ICU that could be guarded and cordoned off from the curious public and relentless reporters determined to get the scoop on *"How did it feel, Congressman Hamilton, when you saw the jack-knifed semi looming in front of you?"* and other such ridiculous questions.

No one had approached me for a good ten minutes, so I

decided to take a look around. I slipped through a door that led to the now-quiet ER. I peeked out the ambulance entrance where I had a reasonably good view of the parking lot.

The spaces closest to the building had been reserved for victims' families so they could come and go without running the gauntlet of reporters. Two uniformed police officers patrolled the perimeter of the lot, which was marked off with bright yellow crime-scene tape to keep away reporters and the curious.

I didn't see Detective Pierce anywhere. In fact, I hadn't seen him since the embarrassing encounter in the hallway, and that was fine with me. The man grated on my nerves, which was unusual because I don't often have an immediate dislike of someone.

From behind the yellow police tape, a few reporters waited like vultures for victims or their families to depart. Peter stood off to the side, gesturing broadly as he talked on his cell phone. I shut the door before he saw me, although I was hard pressed to explain why I was avoiding contact. Maybe I needed more time to sort out my feelings.

I checked in on our makeshift pressroom, and the scene reminded me of those old black-and-white movies with all the foreign correspondents sitting around a dark bar sharing war stories. Only this time there was no Scotch-on-the-rocks and no thick layer of smoke in the air. Instead, it was coffee by the giant urn-full, soft drink cans and yogurt cups in huge ice-filled bowls, a portable sandwich bar cart, and small bags of chips and cookies under glaring lights. If nothing else, the reporters wouldn't leave hungry. Those who wanted to smoke went outside. Otherwise, they munched and hunched over their laptops.

Melanie Cole, the Channel Eight reporter, approached me. She didn't have a microphone or notepad in her hands, so I relaxed. She followed local politics and knew everybody who was anybody, including the behind-the-scenes movers and shakers. In her mid-thirties, she was smart, articulate, and had a reputation for telling the story straight, rather than hyping it up. The word "shocking" was not part of her vocabulary, and I respected her for not caving in to network demands to sensationalize the news.

"How's it going, Melanie?" I asked as if we were old friends.

"I've seen election night losers' parties livelier than this." A quick grin brought a twinkle to her hazel eyes. Then, she wrinkled her nose and nodded toward the food table. "You're feeding us too well. I won't need to eat for days."

She was much thinner than she appeared on TV, lending credence to the theory that the camera added ten to twenty pounds. Her heart-shaped face was free of wrinkles and her frosted brown hair was cut in a layered bob. A lightweight black sweater fitted softly over her curves, and black boots met her black wool skirt at mid-calf. The black-and-tan plaid jacket she wore on camera was draped over the back of her chair, ready to slip on at a moment's notice.

"We don't want you guys getting cranky from sugar or caffeine deprivation. Is there anything you need in here?"

The quick grin appeared again. "Yeah, you can make something happen."

"I'll see what I can do," I said with a laugh.

"When will you have a press conference?"

I handed her a copy of the latest update. "Will this do?"

She glanced at it. "Not really. We need a real person so we can ask questions about Congressman Hamilton."

I grimaced. "Like that mob scene we had earlier this morning?"

"Well, maybe not like that. But an interview would be great, especially since we're so close to the evening news lead-in commercials. It would be even better to talk with the congressman himself."

"Hmm. I'll see if I can arrange for something to happen and a press conference. Anything else?"

"That about does it. Thanks, Robyn. I know this hasn't been easy."

"You guys have been reasonable," I said. "Except for those tabloid reporters who brought their own lab coats and pretended to be doctors to sneak upstairs."

Melanie laughed and shook her head. "That took balls, all right. I'm glad you let the rest of us stay after Security threw them out."

I left her then, remembering how Tom had been apoplectic when he discovered two reporters had brazened their way past a rented security guard and were fast-talking the police officer guarding the congressman's door into letting them examine Hamilton. After that, *anyone* not wearing the hospital's picture ID was denied access upstairs.

I returned to the front desk to corral a doc to talk about Congressman Hamilton, and someone to talk about disaster preparedness in general. That should keep the reporters happy, and put in a good plug for all the planning we did throughout the year.

As I punched in the number for the ICU nurses' station, two people came roaring through the front door.

"Robyn, what the hell is going on?" Will Slater's voice ricocheted off the lobby and echoed down the hallway. I winced as everyone within earshot turned to look at us, including Melanie and several other reporters who came to the doorway of our makeshift pressroom.

Will must have noticed as well, because his bristliness subsided as he strode toward me. He was a tall, lean man in his late forties, with a shock of silver through his black hair. An accountant at heart, he was an excellent money manager, with little patience for the unanticipated or the exception. My department dealt mostly with the unanticipated and the exception, and so our working relationship was troublesome at best. We just did not speak the same language.

"Will, I'm so glad to see you," I said more warmly than I felt. "We've had quite a time here."

"I can't leave this place for a single day. We'll be lucky to get any new program funds," he fumed, referring to the allocations scheduled to be made at this corporate-wide retreat.

"What's the status, Robyn?" asked the woman who had followed him in, her kind tone a sharp contrast to Will's. Brenda Martin, the Director of Nursing Services, was only about ten years older than me, but it often felt more like a generation separated us. Her gray-streaked hair was wound into a tight bun every morning, and by the end of the day, not a strand had dared escape. Her business suits were functional and unimaginative, devoid of any softness or decoration except for a large silver cross on a chunky chain, while her shoes could only be described as "sensible." Short and square, she seemed better suited for a military operation with her no-nonsense approach. But she was a staunch advocate for her nurses, who loved her and would follow her into hell if she asked them. Underneath her all-business demeanor, I occasionally sensed a bit of the zealot, but she never shared any personal opinions.

In answer to her question, I handed both Brenda and Will copies of the in-house E-mail updates and gave them a quick verbal summary of the day's events, finishing with, "Did you hear that one of the victims was Jake Hamilton?"

Will's head shot up. "Who?"

"Congressman Hamilton?" Brenda asked. "My daughter, Cynthia, works for him."

I nodded. "That's him. He had a number of injuries, nothing

critical, but serious enough that he was admitted." I decided now was not the time to mention that the congressman wasn't totally delighted with all aspects of his care. "I'm in the process of setting up a press conference so the reporters can ask questions."

Will frowned, as if he couldn't decide if a press conference would be a good thing or bad, for the hospital or for himself. He was not big on impromptu events, so I quickly added, "I'm trying to get a doc to summarize the victims and maybe Charley to talk about our disaster planning."

"That should be okay, Robyn." He straightened his already straight tie. "I'll be there too, of course. To address any questions that might be best for me to answer."

Remembering the assault Irene, Charley, and I had survived, I swallowed a smile and wondered how Will would have reacted to it. And, to Detective Pierce stepping in to take charge. Now that would have been worth the price of admission to watch. "I'll let you know when it's set up. Oh, and Brenda? Your daughter's here."

"Cynthia's here?" Brenda appeared flustered, as if surprised her daughter was even in Seattle. "Where is she?"

"She's probably in the cafeteria or upstairs with Congressman Hamilton."

Brenda's lips tightened—with disapproval? I wasn't sure. "Thanks, Robyn. Will, maybe we can meet later this week with the CEO to discuss our budget requests before he flies back to L.A." Brenda headed in the direction of the back stairwell.

Will absently drummed his fingers on the laminated counter as he looked around the busy lobby, then he scowled. "I better take a look at these reports and figure out how much this fiasco cost us. Let me know when you have the press conference set up, Robyn."

I watched him leave, his eyes moving like a radar dish, scanning everything, missing nothing. I remembered Tom's comments about today's extra security costs and was relieved I hadn't spent any money. Or had I? Which department did Connie and Dietary settle on to pay for the reporters' food? I decided not to check on that. I'd hear from Will soon enough if it was my problem. Instead, I resumed my efforts to organize a press conference so I could get back to my real work.

It was mid-afternoon when I finally escaped my lobby post. After the press conference, most of the reporters had left the hospital to find more exciting stories. They had squeezed out all the human-interest bystander interviews that television viewers could tolerate. The congressman was stable, but unavailable for interviews. Not much news there.

I started toward the stairs to grab a roast beef sandwich in the cafeteria and order my afternoon tonic, a latté with a double shot of espresso and chocolate syrup. Instead, I decided to take a detour first to pay a courtesy call on Congressman Hamilton. I still couldn't believe he had filed a complaint against me. All I did was tell him I couldn't give him pain meds, and that the doctor probably wouldn't order any until after a thorough exam. I certainly had not mis-tagged him, deliberately or otherwise. Charley said yellow, and that was the tag I put on Hamilton's arm.

It must be something else. Maybe he was on the congressional committee hearing Louisa's testimony. Was this a ploy to discredit our profession and undermine the patient-rights legislation? That wasn't possible. It was too far-fetched for even a moderate conspiracy theorist.

Maybe I could smooth things over so the congressman wouldn't follow through with his complaint. I hoped he was ready to listen to reason. Some people were much more pleasant when they felt better and had not just gone through a horrific experience. And surely he'd had enough treatment by now that he was feeling properly attended to. If not, there was a part of me that was tempted to point out the possible press interpretation of the congressman's aggressive demands for drugs. Only as a last resort, mind you.

Of course, I knew full well that such a tactic, regardless of how satisfying in the short run, could backfire in a big way. Jake Hamilton was an up-and-coming congressman from our state, and he would vote on a lot of patient rights and health-insurance bills over the next two years. My professional association would appreciate my keeping good relations with him. Sometimes, I thought with a sigh, a person had to keep the big picture in mind and stifle justifiable human reactions.

I reached the double doors that marked the entrance to 3-West. Like the other patient wings at Madrona Bay Hospital, the unit had a U-shaped hallway, with patient rooms along the outside walls, and staff offices and supply rooms down the middle.

Congressman Hamilton's corner room was at the far end of 3-West. "Wet floor" triangles had been used to cordon off the area, funneling all who came and went past the uniformed police officer outside Hamilton's door. The officer was a tall young man, dark-haired with the requisite macho mustache. Probably because I wasn't wearing either of the hospital's uniforms, a white lab coat or scrubs, he shifted his position to stand taller. His huge belt creaked the way only stiff leather can.

I glanced at his nametag and extended my hand. "Hello, Officer Tomlin. I'm Robyn Kelly, manager of Patient Relations. How're you doing?"

"Ms. Kelly." Noting the picture ID on my blouse, he seemed to relax, even smiled a bit. I was probably the first person to talk to him as if he were a real person. He shook my hand and I found his hand damp to the touch. For a fleeting moment, that puzzled me because he didn't appear overly warm.

"I've never spent time in a hospital before," Officer Tomlin said, his hands resting on his belt. "It's like a three-ring circus. I'd hate to be a patient. You never get any rest."

I almost chuckled, but it was not a laughing matter for most patients. "People don't come to hospitals to rest anymore, Officer. These days, they're treated and discharged as soon as they can sit up. Has it been busy?"

"People with charts and trays of pills and needles have been going in and out all day. And then there's the accident investigation. Several people have talked to Mr. Hamilton about the crash."

So Irene hadn't been able to keep him sedated. I only hoped the congressman hadn't taken those opportunities to share his opinion of me with investigators.

"I was wondering if I could pop in for a moment to say hi and see if there's anything we can do to make him more comfortable." And see if I could settle his complaint before it made the news.

Officer Tomlin shrugged. "Don't see any reason why not. No one's come by for at least fifteen minutes or so. He may be asleep."

"I'll check quietly," I promised.

The door to Hamilton's room was closed. Taking a deep, calming breath, I steeled myself for another unpleasant encounter with this man. I knocked softly, but didn't hear a response, so I slowly opened the door and peeked into the semi-darkened room. A cart rattled noisily down the hall. I ducked inside the room and shut the door quickly.

This time of year, there wasn't much sun in the Pacific Northwest, and even with the blinds tilted open, only a little light entered the room. The overhead fluorescents were turned off, but the bathroom door was ajar and a narrow stream of light escaped through the crack.

"Congressman Hamilton?" I said in a hushed voice. If he was asleep, I didn't want to wake him.

It was then that I was struck by how quiet it was, what could only be described as a chilling silence. I rubbed my arms as if to ward off the cold.

Shaking off my unease, I stepped farther into the room. The congressman lay in the bed, his face turned away from me. I raised myself on tiptoes to see. It seemed the congressman's eyes were open.

"Congressman?" I said in a conversational volume.

When he did not respond, I moved closer until I rounded the foot of the bed. A prickly feeling crawled up my spine as I leaned forward. Even in the dim light, I could see a glassiness in his eyes, and I realized he wasn't breathing.

Chapter 4

An icy-hot wave of nausea hit me. I backed away, then ran to the door and flung it open.

Officer Tomlin grabbed my arm as I lurched from the congressman's room. "What's wrong?" he asked.

I escaped his grasp and ran to the nurses' station. "Code Blue. Hamilton's room."

Susan Wong, the nurse manager, blanched and hit the intercom button. "Code Blue . . . Three-West . . . Code Blue . . . Three-West." She flipped off the intercom and ran into a supply room, reappearing with a crash cart. She raced with it toward the congressman's room, and two other nurses met her at the door.

I sank into Susan's chair and started deep breathing. Although I work in a hospital, my exposure to dead patients was limited. I held family members' hands while they made difficult decisions, or talked to them about their complaints. I spent time with patients who weren't happy. But I did not do dead people.

Some patient reps became very involved with patients and their families, and stayed with them during the final moments. Those reps usually worked for hospitals with large cancer or research units, and the patients were there so long they were more like family. But Madrona Bay replaced hips and delivered babies, and took out gall bladders, a general purpose in-and-out local hospital. And that was fine with me. Drained of emotion and overwhelmed, I buried my face in my hands.

As my shock at finding the dead congressman subsided, I began to worry. This should not be happening. He'd been listed in stable condition. A few broken bones and lacerations, and a possible concussion. He wasn't critical. He wasn't even connected to any monitors.

The door to Hamilton's room was half open, and the team inside was still trying desperately to revive him. Officer Tomlin was talking into his shoulder-mounted radio and from his grim expression, the response was not going well. Beyond the barriers already set up around the room, a crowd had gathered, staff and visitors, trying to see this latest installment of a very bizarre day.

At last, the team in Hamilton's room seemed to pull back from his bed as one. Several of them snapped off their latex gloves. A quick glance at the clock told me they had tried for half an hour.

But, this was not the end of it, not by a long shot. I didn't want to begin to contemplate the furor that was coming. At the very least, Will Slater would have an apoplectic fit, and the press would go into another feeding frenzy. At the thought of it, my stomach flip-flopped.

And, as selfish as it sounded, I worried about the congressman's complaint against me. Where was it? If I was lucky, it was only in Charley's notes where it could easily be forgotten. After all, who would we follow-up with? At worst, it was written up formally with copies floating through the inter-office mail system.

Hoping to escape before all hell broke loose, I slipped down the hallway to my office. Connie was just starting to make a telephone call. She looked up and must have seen something awful on my face, because she dropped the receiver and came to me at once.

"Rob, what happened? You look like you've seen a ghost." She guided me to the small couch in our waiting area and sat me down.

"That's so close to the truth, your psychic training must be working," I said ruefully. I told her about finding Hamilton's body and the unsuccessful efforts of the crash team to revive him. "So now, it's going to be worse than this morning. Call PR and tell them to get someone over here *now.*"

I didn't care about excuses. Public Relations was handling the next round of press conferences. They were paid a lot more than me, and I wasn't letting them off the hook this time. With a groan, I sagged against the back of the couch and closed my eyes. "I don't even want to think about it."

At a knock on the door, my eyes popped open. "See," I said. "It's beginning already. Go away." The last was in a half-hearted whisper.

Connie frowned, at me or the interruption, I didn't care, and went to answer the door. As she reached for the knob, the door opened.

Detective Pierce stepped into the office. His rapid scrutiny of the room stopped when it landed on me. His eyebrow quirked, but his quick assessment must have told him that my supine position was not from terminal causes. Through half-open eyes, I saw his solid steadiness and felt a flash of calm. But that was ridiculous; he followed in the wake of trouble. I wrote off my momentary relief as a semi-hysterical reaction. If one can be semi-hysterical while leaning listlessly against a couch.

"Ms. Kelly?"

"Yes, Detective?"

"You look like hell," Pierce said.

"Detective, this has been a very difficult day," I said with a scowl, and decided this man really was annoying. I struggled to sit up, but my bones felt like mush.

"Don't get up." When I sank onto the couch again and closed my eyes, he added, "Perhaps I should rephrase that. You don't have to get up, but don't go to sleep."

"What do you want?"

"I have to question you about Congressman Hamilton."

I opened my eyes to study him. "Why me? I don't know anything."

"An injured, but not seriously injured, congressman is unexpectedly found dead. A lot of people think that's a problem. You found him, so I'm starting with you."

"There's not much to tell. When I entered his room, he looked like he was dead. Not breathing. Glassy-eyed stare." I shuddered at the memory.

"Why did you go to Congressman Hamilton's room?"

This probably wasn't the time to mention that I visited the congressman because he had filed a complaint against me and I wanted to resolve it before it went any further.

"I decided to pay a courtesy call on Congressman Hamilton. Volunteers visit all the new patients. Part of our patient-relations thing. But, since he was a VIP, I thought it would be best if I did it myself."

I pushed myself to a full sitting position. "When I discovered he wasn't breathing, I ran out and called a Code Blue."

At that point, Connie came over and put a comforting hand on my shoulder.

"A Code Blue," Detective Pierce said.

"Yes." I sighed. "Code Blue means someone has stopped breathing, or their heart stops."

"I know what it means," Pierce mumbled to himself. He looked toward the window for a moment, and I had the oddest suspicion he was pulling himself together. When he turned to face me again, he appeared to be his usual brusque self.

"Tell me exactly what happened when you went into the

58

congressman's room. Everything, no matter how trivial you think it might be." He sat down at the other end of the couch and slipped on a pair of half-glasses that magnified his weary brown eyes. He took out his notepad and pen, and looked at me.

"I introduced myself to Officer Tomlin and we chatted for a moment. He seems very nice. I hope you have a lot of officers like him."

"As opposed to crusty old farts like me?" Detective Pierce looked at me over the top of his glasses.

From the heat on my face, I figured I was blushing furiously. His attempt at humor surprised me. Maybe he wasn't as arrogant as I'd first thought. "That's not what I meant at all, Detective. Experience and maturity are also very necessary for a police department. Besides," I added with a placid smile, "you're not old, just well-seasoned."

"Like a good steak, huh?" He gave a tired chuckle. "I've been called a lot of things, Ms. Kelly, but never well-seasoned. Now, you were telling me about finding the congressman?"

"Where was I?"

"You chatted with Officer Tomlin."

"Oh, yes. Very nice young man. I said that already, didn't I? Okay, so I knocked on the congressman's door and started to open it when a cart came rattling down the hall. You know, Detective Pierce, we have these on-going debates about whether the floors should be carpeted or vinyl," I said earnestly, leaning forward. "Carpeting is so much quieter, but the carts are easier to push on vinyl and—"

"Ms. Kelly."

"Hmmm? Oh. Sorry. Guess I'm still a bit upset by the whole thing." I shifted my position and took a moment to gather my thoughts. I rested my hands on my lap in gentle fists and stared at a spot on the carpet. "The cart was making a lot of noise and

I didn't want to wake the congressman if he was asleep, so I ducked into his room and shut the door."

A bone-chilling cold settled into my bones. I started to shake. Even my teeth chattered. Then came the tears, cascading down my cheeks like a waterfall.

"Get her a coat or a blanket," Detective Pierce snapped at Connie. She ducked into the storage area and returned with my Eddie Bauer jacket. Detective Pierce grabbed the jacket from her and slipped it over my shoulders, pulling it close and hugging me to him.

"It's okay, Ms. Kelly . . . may I call you Robyn?"

He patted my back as a parent would a child. I felt uncomfortable with his closeness, but not enough to pull away. I sniffed and nodded against his shoulder.

"Good. You'll be okay in a minute, Robyn. You're just having a delayed reaction." He held me for a moment until I stopped shaking, then set me back in my corner of the couch.

"Feel better?" he asked.

I nodded.

"Ready to continue?"

I nodded again and dug a handkerchief out of my coat pocket. He was being so nice, I thought maybe he wasn't so bad after all. After blowing my nose and swiping at my eyes, I reached for the steaming cup of coffee Connie held out for me. I took a sip and shuddered at the bitter taste. It had been sitting in the pot for several hours, but it was hot and that was most important.

"I'm sorry, Detective. I don't usually fall apart." I took another sip of coffee before setting the cup on the floor.

"You don't fall apart period, Rob," Connie chimed in. "She doesn't, Detective. She's always calm. No matter what."

She stood next to me, a worried look on her face and a box of tissues in her hand. I pulled one out and blew my nose again.

After taking a deep breath, I said, "Okay, I went into the

room and shut the door. Then I felt the cold. It was like nothing I ever felt before. Do you know what I'm talking about?" I searched his face for confirmation.

He nodded. "I do. It's a feeling I get whenever I walk into a room where someone's recently died. It's as if the warmth of that person's soul has departed, leaving the body to face the chill of the grave alone."

His poetic description caught me by surprise. Some of the tension slipped away too; he understood.

"That's exactly what it felt like, but I didn't know it at the time. I called Congressman Hamilton's name quietly, but he didn't respond."

"Describe where he was."

"He was lying in bed." From Detective Pierce's glowering, he wanted more than that.

I closed my eyes and tried to recreate the scene in my head. "He was lying in the bed. On his back. Looking away from me toward the window. The covers were rumpled around his waist. His arms were bandaged from all the cuts and his left"—I shifted my shoulders—"no, his right arm was in a full cast. The left was all bandaged up, including his hand. Both arms were at his sides, but not straight. More of a forty-five-degree angle. Slightly bent at the elbows."

I opened my eyes, surprised but pleased I remembered so much.

"Then, what did you do?"

"I stepped toward him. Quietly, because I didn't want to disturb him if he was sleeping. I rounded the foot of the bed and leaned forward to see if he was awake. That's when I saw his eyes were open and it looked like he wasn't breathing. I ran from the room and called the code."

"Did you touch anything while you were in the room?"

"I don't think so. It all happened so fast."

He nodded. "That should do it for now. But—"

The office door opened and Peter stepped inside. He stopped for a moment as he took in the scene, then his expression hardened.

"Rob? Is everything okay?" He came to me and, when I stood up, threw a protective arm around my shoulder. "What are you doing here, Detective?"

Part of me was gratified by Peter's macho protectiveness, and part of me found it smothering. I eased away from him. "I'm fine, Peter. Really I am. Detective Pierce has been asking me to describe what I—"

"That's fine for now, Ms. Kelly."

Detective Pierce flipped his notepad closed and stood. The wary distaste I'd seen in his eyes earlier when he caught Peter and me kissing had returned. It irritated me that he didn't mask his personal opinion.

"I'll check back with you if I have any more questions. In the meantime, it would be best if you didn't talk about this. With anyone."

Although he gave Connie a passing glance, Detective Pierce glared at Peter, leaving little doubt exactly who he meant. Of course, Peter stiffened, but had the sense not to open his mouth. Under the circumstances, being allied with a reporter might not be a good thing. I felt caught in the professional crossfire between the press and the police.

"Mr. Armstrong, the third floor is off limits." Detective Pierce opened the door and I saw another uniformed officer standing outside. "I'm sure you know that. Officer Leeds here will escort you back to the first floor."

Peter scowled. "I need to talk to Robyn for a few minutes. Then, I'll come down." Peter glanced at me. "She'll see that I don't go where I'm not supposed to."

Detective Pierce frowned, his gaze shifting between me and

Peter. Finally, he stared hard at me. "Five minutes. Then, I want him downstairs."

After I nodded my agreement, Detective Pierce and the officer left. Connie shuffled a stack of papers on her desk and glanced at Peter and me from downcast eyes. "I, uh, I remembered I have to go to the mail room."

Connie was barely out of the room when Peter turned his frown of concern toward me. "I was so worried about you." He rested his hands on my shoulders. "We heard about the congressman, and that you were involved."

Peter pulled me closer. He was still devastatingly attractive and the chemistry was still there, even after all these years. Then, I couldn't help but be annoyed for capitulating to his charms so easily. Determined to prove, if only to myself, that I wasn't a complete pushover, I asserted some willpower and pushed away before it went any further. I found his penitent expression almost amusing.

"I'm sorry, darling. I can't help myself when I'm around you. Never could, could I?" he said with a sheepish grin, one of his most endearing expressions.

"That's okay, Peter, except this isn't the time, and this certainly isn't the place."

His grin broadened and he ruffled my hair affectionately. "It didn't used to bother you."

I refrained from rolling my eyes. His playfulness and spontaneity were part of what I had loved about him. Instead of giving in, though, I chided him. "That was in a locked office late at night after everyone had gone home. This office is open to the public, and that door is unlocked."

Now too warm, I took my coat to the storage room. When I returned, Peter was standing beside the couch. "We could always lock the door."

Was he testing me? Memories flooded back, memories stuffed

into a dark corner where I did not have to see them. Memories of a time when I had been deliriously happy, so in love with Peter that any risk was worth it to be with him.

But that was then, and this was now, and I wasn't the same person anymore. Well, maybe I was the same person, but an older, wiser version, and I'd worked too hard to risk everything for a moment's pleasure. The jury remained out as to whether or not I was still in love with Peter. Or trusted him. I wanted to believe, but could I?

As quickly as his countenance turned serious, it changed back to frisky. He wiggled his eyebrows and leered blatantly at me. "Baby, when two people have that special something, time doesn't matter."

"Oh, for heaven's sake, Peter, you sound like a bad B movie." Smiling now, I wondered if maybe I was taking this all too seriously.

"I want to see you again, Rob. But not here. Someplace where we can talk."

He sounded sincere, which meant I had to reconsider my earlier worries. This time, I thought with my head and not my heart before saying quietly, "I don't know, Peter. I have to think about it. Come on, let's get you downstairs before Detective Pierce comes looking for you."

Peter frowned and touched my arm. "Is there something I should know about?"

Bewildered, I said, "What? What are you talking about?"

"You and the cop. Is there something going on? I saw the way he looked at you."

I laughed then, a hearty laugh, the first and only one in a long, difficult day. "Honestly, Peter. Don't be ridiculous. I just met the man this morning."

Shaking my head, and still laughing, I opened the door and ushered Peter from the office.

"Then, you don't owe him anything." Peter stared at me so intently his eyes could have burned holes through my skull to see into my brain. He gripped my arms. "Look, Rob, everyone knows Hamilton is dead. Do you know how it happened?"

I had forgotten the congressman's death was already common knowledge; the hospital grapevine can disseminate news faster than the Internet. I slipped from his grip and said, "You'll find out when everyone else does, Peter."

I didn't say anything more until I opened the stairwell door to the 1st floor and we stepped around the corner to the makeshift pressroom.

He leaned forward to kiss me, but this time I was prepared. I side-stepped as if unaware what he was attempting. He looked hurt, but he'd have to live with it. I wasn't about to provide another public spectacle.

"Ms. Kelly, I have some more questions."

With a silent groan of dismay, I recognized Detective Pierce's voice from behind me. I felt like a teenager caught sneaking a cigarette behind the gym. Peter cast a withering look at Pierce, but he moved away and entered the pressroom without saying another word.

"Yes, Detective, I'm ready." I noticed he had gone back to the more formal address. Maybe he only used first names when witnesses were hysterical.

Wordlessly, we crossed the waiting area to the west wing elevators. When we got in, Detective Pierce pushed "Three." I expected to return to my office when we stepped off the elevator. Instead, he led me in the opposite direction. I shuddered as we walked down the 3-West hallway toward Congressman Hamilton's room.

Bright yellow crime-scene tape covered the door. "Why is that here?" I asked.

Pierce only shrugged. With the help of the officer standing

guard, he pulled the tape aside and we passed through.

I held my breath as we entered the room, but the chilling cold I felt before wasn't there. I slowly started to breathe again and looked around to see an ordinary patient room waiting to be cleaned by housekeeping.

"Why are we here?" I asked.

"Procedure." Pierce shrugged again, but I wasn't buying it. An underlying current of energy ran through him. He wasn't as blasé as he wanted to appear.

Intrigued, I asked, "What do you think happened?"

Pierce ignored the question, which only heightened my curiosity. "Okay, Ms. Kelly, I want you to run through the scene again. You walked into the room and came around the end of the bed."

He signaled for me to retrace my steps. "Did you touch anything?"

I thought for a moment, before I reached out to put my hand on the bed. "Yes. I put my hand here. Only, I touched the pillow."

It wasn't there now, which wasn't surprising given the efforts of the crash team to revive Congressman Hamilton. I looked around and saw it lying on the floor in the corner, and bent to pick it up.

"Wait!" Detective Pierce grabbed my arm. "Don't touch it."

"Why not?"

"Think about it. Why was the pillow at the foot of the bed?"

Annoyed at this one-sided game of his, I snapped, "How should I know?"

"Are patients automatically given a pillow or is it an option?"

"I expect it's placed under their heads automatically. Congressman Hamilton was probably sedated when he was brought here, so, yes, it's safe to assume he was using one."

Detective Pierce stared at the empty bed as if willing it to confess. "Could he have moved the pillow himself if he had a seizure or something?"

"You mean thrashing around?" When he nodded, I approached the other side of the bed. "I don't think so. If he had thrashed around, it would have fallen on the floor next to his head." I tried to think of other scenarios. "His right arm was in a cast over the elbow, so he couldn't bend it. And his left hand was bandaged, making it difficult to hold onto anything. Either way, I can't see him grabbing the pillow and tossing it to the foot of the bed. If anything, he'd push it on the floor."

"What about a nurse, would she put the pillow there?"

"I don't think so," I said again. "She'd be more likely to toss it into a chair."

"Get me a large plastic bag to put this pillow in."

"Sure. I'll be right back."

I left Detective Pierce mumbling to himself while I tried to figure out why the pillow was such a big deal. I walked the short distance to the nurses' station. "Hi, Susan," I said to the nurse behind the counter.

Susan Wong, the manager for 3-West, looked up, and I saw her harassed expression. A petite bundle of energy, Susan always stood tall and wore a heavily starched, immaculate white lab coat over her street clothes. Now the lab coat looked like my blue silk blouse, spotted and wrinkled, and her shoulders were slumped with fatigue. Usually her long black hair was neatly tied up, but strands had slipped from the hair clip and she didn't seem to notice, which worried me.

"Rob. Do you believe it? This morning was bad enough, but this. I didn't like that man in the first place," she grumbled. "If I had known. . . ."

"You didn't like him?"

"Oh, I don't know. Maybe like is too strong. I mean, he was pretty much out of it when he transferred here. But later. . . ."

She frowned. "I guess he just, well, I don't know. Maybe I just dislike all politicians on general principle. Even the good ones turn out to be smarmy on closer inspection."

"This whole thing is a nightmare. Important people aren't supposed to die at little ol' Madrona Bay. It's crazy." I wanted to ask her more, but Pierce was waiting for me, so I said, "Listen, do you have those plastic bags we put patients' things in?"

Nodding, she went to a supply closet and returned with one. "Are you checking in?"

"Don't I wish," I said. "No, this is for the police. The detective wants to take a pillow."

She looked unnerved. "A pillow? Why?"

"Who knows?" Shaking the bag open, I turned to leave, then stopped. "Susan? Who's been here today?"

"Who?" She thought for a moment and shrugged. "Only the whole western world. Let's see," Susan continued, counting on her fingers. "The police were here, of course, investigating the accident. Brenda came, representing Admin. Will wouldn't want corporate to hear we annoyed a congressman—"

I winced inside; what would corporate say if they learned a congressman had complained about me?

"—We had eight victims admitted to this unit, so all their families. And the staff. But everyone checked in with me about the clinical stuff, and then again with that darling officer standing guard at the door."

I smiled; so she wasn't too tired to notice him. Married with four kids, Susan was old enough to be Officer Tomlin's mother. "Okay, thanks." I started down the hall when Susan called after me.

"Wait, Rob. His assistant, that girl. She was here too. A real nuisance, crying and carrying on after she saw him." Susan shook her head. "I had to call a social worker to get her out of here."

"When was that?"

"Sometime this afternoon?" Susan shook her head. "I don't know. The whole day's been a blur."

Returning to Hamilton's room, I kept mulling over the list of "the whole western world." In a hospital, that covered a wide territory: lab and pharmacy techs, physical and respiratory therapists, doctors, nurses, housekeeping. I did not envy Detective Pierce his task.

In the room, I found Detective Pierce facing the bed, one hand fisted and resting on his hip, the other hand covering his mouth. He started when I entered.

"Penny for your thoughts, Detective."

He raised an eyebrow. "I don't think you really want to know."

"Try me."

He paced the room once, twice, then stopped again. "With someone as prominent as the congressman, a lot of people will be peering over our shoulders, telling us what we should have done."

He sighed and wiped his hand over his face. He motioned for me to hold the plastic bag open while he pulled on a pair of latex gloves and picked the pillow up by the corners and very carefully set it into the bag. Then he marked the bag with an adhesive label he dug out of his pocket and sealed the bag with a tie from another pocket.

"What are you afraid you might have overlooked?"

"I don't know," he said thoughtfully. "We had a uniformed officer outside the door at all times."

"What do you mean?"

He gave me a quelling look, then started for the door, the bagged pillow in his hand. Stunned by his implication, I hesitated, then quickly followed, not eager to stay in the room alone.

It had finally sunk in: Detective Pierce believed Congressman Hamilton was murdered.

Murder.

I couldn't get it out of my head. Detective Pierce thought Congressman Hamilton had been murdered. I reeled at the possibility, and I wanted nothing more to do with any of it. After all, I had withheld information from the police.

When questioned by Detective Pierce earlier, I had deliberately not mentioned that the real reason I went to Congressman Hamilton's room was because he'd filed a complaint against me, and I hoped to change his mind. Would that be considered a motive?

And I was the last person to enter the room. Would the police believe Congressman Hamilton was already dead when I went in? Surely they wouldn't suspect me. Or would they? I certainly hoped not!

When I left 3-West, Detective Pierce was on the phone. Again. What could he hope to find from a pillow tossed on the floor? The Code Team had made a mess of the room when they tried to revive the congressman. The Crime Scene Unit would have a nightmare sorting through the evidence left by all the people in and out of that room.

I figured an autopsy had been ordered, and it was a safe assumption that Congressman Hamilton was at the top of the medical examiner's waiting list.

It had already been a demanding day, but if I thought this morning had been challenging, it paled compared to what was coming. At least this time a corporate PR person was dealing with the media. I really hoped I would escape notice.

As I left 3-West and crossed the waiting area, I spotted Cynthia Martin standing near the window. Despite my plan to not be involved, I couldn't help but respond to Cynthia's obvious distress. Her shoulders were hunched and her face rested against the window while she gazed in the direction of the concrete wall that made 3-North.

"Cynthia? Are you okay?" I asked in a soft voice as I approached her.

At first, she didn't respond, but then she shuddered and turned to face me. Her face was blotchy and swollen from crying. "He's dead," she said in the most pitiful voice I had ever heard.

"I know, dear." I put my arm around her shoulder. "I'm really sorry."

She leaned into my shoulder and started to sob. "Why? Why did he . . . have to . . . die? He was . . . he was so wonderful," she sputtered.

"I don't know. But I'm sure we'll know when the autopsy's done."

She jerked away from me, her eyes wide with horror. "Autopsy? They're going to do an autopsy?"

"Well, yes," I said slowly. "Whenever someone dies unexpectedly, they usually do."

"No. Oh, no," she wailed, backing away from me. She turned and ran. At that moment, the elevator doors opened and she pushed past the elderly couple coming off and frantically hit buttons until the door closed.

I stood for a moment, stunned. Was it the volatile reaction of youth? Or was it something more? I sighed heavily. That was Pierce's problem, not mine.

Thinking it must be close to midnight, I glanced at a wall clock; it was only late afternoon. Not even quittin' time yet. All I wanted was to go home, take a long, hot shower, turn on the gas fireplace and sip a glass of Cab-Merlot.

Any thoughts of leaving early disappeared when I saw Connie's beleaguered expression as she talked on the phone, the flashing lights on the telephone that indicated people on hold, and my overflowing message box. I grabbed my messages and sifted through them as I hurried to my desk.

I picked up the phone and punched one of the flashing lights. "This is Robyn Kelly. I'm sorry you had to wait. How can I help you?" I grabbed a pad of paper and a pen.

"This is Myrna Flanders. I'm not sure what I should do."

I sighed and set aside all thoughts of murder. Mrs. Flanders sounded like an older lady, the kind who never complained, because she didn't want anyone to get in trouble. Most of the time, I only talk to patients on the phone, but I'd met a few women like Mrs. Flanders in person when they came to see Margie. They were always a bit fluttery, and soft and round, and smelled faintly of vanilla. On their next visit to the medical center, they brought home-baked cookies to the office to thank us for helping them.

"Why don't you tell me what the problem is, Mrs. Flanders?"

"Well, dear," she said with a hint of an English accent. "I had this surgery and I . . . oh, I don't want to make trouble."

"It's okay, Mrs. Flanders. You are not making any trouble. We want you to be happy with the care you received here. What kind of surgery was it?"

"It was for my gall bladder. Terrible gallstone attacks, you know." She tsk-tsked at the memory.

"I've heard gallstones can be very painful. When did you have the surgery?"

"Let's see, it was two weeks ago. On November third."

"And you're having problems now?"

"It seems very odd, dear. But since the surgery, I keep feeling this cool breeze across my pancreas, as if they left me open. I can't find a hole, but I must say, it's quite put me off my porridge. I don't know what to do."

I struggled not to laugh at her description. She sounded very sincere. I reassured her that Dr. Davisson would want to see her again and offered to call his office. She seemed so relieved that for the first time all day, I started to relax.

Then I shuddered, remembering how I'd been too late to help Congressman Hamilton. But if he was murdered, and if I had arrived earlier . . . I could have walked in on the murderer.

Snapping back to the problem at hand, I gathered some additional information from Mrs. Flanders, then called the surgeon's office. He wasn't in, so I talked to his nurse, who thought Mrs. Flanders was a sweetheart. Gladys assured me she would get the patient in right away to talk about her cool breeze.

When I finished, there were no more flashing "hold" lights, so I quickly documented my conversation with Mrs. Flanders, then sorted the telephone messages by urgency.

"Ms. Kelly?"

I looked up to see Detective Pierce standing in my doorway. He did not look happy. In fact, his expression was downright hostile.

"Detective. Come in." I gestured hesitantly for him to sit down.

"You left out something when I questioned you earlier. You want to remember it now?"

I winced inwardly. "And that would be?"

Detective Pierce scowled. "You forgot to mention a little detail, the one about Congressman Hamilton complaining about you. About how you tagged him wrong during triage."

"First of all, that's blatantly untrue. Charley said he was a yellow, and that's the tag I gave him." I sighed. "I was hoping it would go away. How'd you find out?"

"Back-tracking to follow the congressman's movement from the time he arrived until when you found him. So he was real angry with you?"

"Look, things like that happen all the time when patients are upset," I said. "As soon as the trauma is over and they calm down, they usually forget the whole thing."

"So, if he was supposed to forget the whole thing, why did you go to see him? And don't give me this business about him being a VIP so you went instead of a volunteer. Wouldn't an administrator go, not a middle manager? Even if she is in charge of patient relations, and especially if he had complained about her."

"We try to have the staff person involved in the complaint try to solve it first. It's standard procedure. In fact, I can show you the brochure we hand out to patients when they're admitted. But that's beside the point. Why do you think he was murdered?"

"You don't see dead bodies very often, do you?"

"Actually, Detective, I don't see dead bodies at all." I shivered. "Until today."

"Let's just say I saw some things that said the cause of death wasn't natural." From the way he crossed his arms over his chest, I gathered he wasn't going to share any details with me.

"Are you going to arrest me?"

CHAPTER 5

Detective Pierce started. "Am I—? For what? Withholding evidence? Obstruction of justice?"

His expression softened just a bit. "No. Of course not. Like I said before, this case is going to be scrutinized by everyone so I want all the t's crossed and the i's dotted. All the lines of questioning taken to their logical and accurate conclusions. You just wasted my time, is all, by not being up front from the beginning."

I leaned back, feeling like an overblown balloon that had released some of its extra air. "That's a relief."

"You really thought you were a suspect?"

"Didn't you?"

Detective Pierce shrugged. "Maybe. For a minute. Until I figured out there's no way you could have killed him in the length of time you were in the room."

So, he had considered me a suspect. A cold shiver ran down my spine at the thought of being fingerprinted and forced to wear a bright orange jumpsuit. "I guess I'm glad you calculated the timing."

"Now we only have two hundred ninety-nine other possible suspects to rule out." Pierce stood and flipped his notepad closed. "Don't leave town, in case I need to talk to you again."

I might have worried if I hadn't caught the hint of a smile as he turned to leave. As it was, I kept quiet, relieved that the truth was now out in the open. Hopefully it would go no further. The last thing I needed was for Will to hear about my problem with Congressman Hamilton.

After the detective left, I flipped through the phone messages and decided they were routine and could wait until tomorrow. I surveyed my office. Damn. On the desk, a teetering stack of case reports I needed to write up before I could no longer decipher my notes. On the table, a staggering mound of data waiting to be interpreted and summarized for my section of the Quality Committee Report. And, in the in-box, copies of E-mails from members of my professional association telling me what to include in the congressional testimony I was drafting on patient rights. No wonder a bottle of Excedrin had a permanent spot next to my phone. If the message light started flashing again, I planned to ignore it. It could only be more bad news.

Which pile to tackle first: Eeny, meeny, miney, mo—the Quality Committee would be understanding if the report was late, but the association's lobbyist needed that draft. And I really needed to do something with that Insurance Commissioner's complaint about Nancy Stone.

I pulled the Stone case file from the teetering stack of folders and medical records, the pile labeled "Urgent," and flipped it open. Some of the tension from Pierce's visit dissipated as I threw myself into the comfortingly normal task.

On top in the file was the Insurance Commissioner's office cover letter, then Mrs. Stone's complaint letter to him, followed by my acknowledgement letter to the IC, my letter to Mrs. Stone asking her to sign and return a medical-records release form for the non-plan physician, Dr. Chin, whom she had seen, a copy of the signed form she returned to me, and copies of Dr. Chin's and Mountain View Hospital's bills that Mrs. Stone wanted Health Assurance to pay. I shook my head. A whole lot of paperwork and nothing had even happened yet.

The case log sheet showed we mailed the original signed

release to Dr. Chin's office two weeks ago, but the records had not arrived. The deadline for my response letter to the IC was next Monday.

Mrs. Stone was requesting an exception to the "no coverage for non-plan physicians" clause in her insurance contract because she felt one of our docs had given her poor medical care. I had our records, but I needed Dr. Chin's records before I could send the case to Dr. Weiser to review.

Two phone books later, I called Dr. Chin's office and asked to speak to the office manager.

"This is Nadine," the office manager said when she picked up the phone.

"Hi, Nadine. This is Robyn Kelly. I'm the patient-relations director at Madrona Bay Hospital. I'm calling about your patient, Nancy Stone. We sent a records-release form two weeks ago for the care Mrs. Stone received from Dr. Chin last spring."

"Yes, I remember seeing it."

"Well, I'm calling to see if the records have been sent yet." I try very hard not to say "you" in these conversations, having learned that "you" puts the other person on the defensive. Hard to keep things neutral, but I've developed a repertoire of phrases for these kinds of calls.

"What did you say your name was?" Papers rustled on her end of the line.

"Robyn Kelly. Patient relations at Madrona Bay."

"Hmm. Oh, here it is. We get to these requests when we have a chance, but frankly, it's not a priority."

"I see. Well, Mrs. Stone is asking for Health Assurance to pay Dr. Chin's bill, which was. . . ." I flipped through the file to the billing statement. "Which was about five thousand dollars. I'm ready to send the case out for review, but without Dr. Chin's records, I can't start."

"What's your fax number?"

I smiled and gave it to her. It was a sorry fact of healthcare life that if a request did not generate income, it fell to the bottom of the pile.

While I waited for the faxed records, I sifted through our medical records, flagging the pages I needed to copy, then checked Mrs. Stone's insurance coverage to be sure her Health Assurance policy was in effect for both the care she received here and the care from Dr. Chin.

A few minutes later, Connie brought me the faxed records. I try to do a quick assessment before sending cases to Dr. Weiser, but today I didn't have time. Instead, I made the copies that Dr. Weiser needed, wrote a cover memo to him with the due-date for his response in bold, organized it, stuck it in an oversized envelope, and asked Connie to take it downstairs to the Medical Staff office in the Admin suite.

That done, I pulled out the stack of E-mails and tried to outline a coherent statement of our association's opinion for Louisa.

Before I knew it, Connie was standing at the door of my office. "It's almost six, boss. Okay if I turn the phones off?"

I nodded and took the opportunity to stretch. "Nothing we can do for someone who calls now anyway. How're you getting home?"

"Philip's picking me up at the teriyaki place across the street so he doesn't have to drive through all this mess."

I glanced out my window. In the summer, the view from my office sweeps west across a sailboat-filled Lake Washington to Seattle's skyscrapers. Not that I have much time to enjoy the view, but it wasn't summer or sunny. It was still November, and rain still pelted my windows. A few police cars remained in the circular drive, along with a horde of reporters with cameras and lights stationed around the perimeter, waiting for the next news release. They reminded me of vultures, lurking, waiting to pounce when their prey weakened. I stood up to see the hospital entrance and thought I spotted Detective Pierce. Sinking back into my chair, I considered the long day he'd had, and the even longer night facing him.

"I'll be leaving soon too, Connie. Do you think Louisa will forgive me for not sending a polished draft of this testimony if I explain a congressman's been murdered?" I tried to smile, but there was nothing funny about the day.

"It's been all over the news. She'd have to be in a monastery not to have heard. See you tomorrow."

She was right. I flipped from my word-processing program to E-mail. Maybe Louisa had sent me a message. While I waited for the download, I called out to Connie, "Any more messages I need to know about?"

She came back, shrugging into her coat, and wincing, which told me she didn't want to be here when I read one of the messages she'd taken.

"How bad is it?"

"Debbie called from Admin. Will scheduled a debriefing meeting for tomorrow."

"I expected that. If nothing else, this morning was a good test of our disaster preparedness."

"Bet you didn't expect the meeting to be at six a.m."

"You're kidding." I slumped back in my chair. "Please say this is a joke."

Connie shook her head. "Sorry. He wants the meeting over before he meets with the CEO."

A quick glance at my E-mail did not find the hoped-for reprieve. I threw up my hands. "Okay. I surrender. I'm sending this as-is to Louisa with my apologies and a referral to the eleven o'clock news. Then I'm going home."

"Good idea. I'll see you in the morning."

I waved her away, then spent another few minutes preparing

my draft for E-mail.

I'd just clicked the "send" key when I heard the outer door open. Connie should have locked the door behind her. Nothing like a murderer running loose to keep the imagination in overdrive. Suspicious, I stepped out of my office, but relaxed when I saw it was Pham Nguyen from housekeeping.

"Pham, you're here early tonight."

He bowed slightly. "Sorry, Miss Kelly. I not disturb you. Three-West is closed by policemen, so I cannot clean."

"Yes. I imagine they don't want anyone in there for a while. Come on in. I'm just about to leave." I turned around and went into my office to start picking up.

"Miss Kelly?"

I looked up from my desk, surprised to see Pham standing in the doorway. He was older than me and well-educated, but when he first immigrated, he'd been unable to find a job that matched his training because of his limited English. We had talked on numerous occasions and he told me of escaping from Vietnam with his family, and living in refugee camps until finally obtaining a visa to come to the United States. He had put six children through college. Now he had a doctor and a lawyer in the family, as well as a stock broker and a teacher. He was fiercely proud of his children, including the one he least understood, the independent filmmaker.

"Yes, Pham. What is it? What cause are you raising funds for now?" With a smile, I gestured for him to sit in the chair next to my desk.

Pham stepped inside my office, but didn't take the offered seat. "I hear about the murder, Miss Kelly."

"It was awful. I'm the one who found the body."

"I sorry you find him, Miss Kelly." Pham's face darkened. "But I am not sorry he dead."

Surprised, I asked, "What do you mean? Congressman Hamilton was considered by many to be a good man." So what if I wasn't one of them. No point in defaming the dead.

Pham shook his head violently. "No. No."

Before I could ask him why, I heard the outer office door open again. "Wait here, Pham."

I stepped from my office and saw Detective Pierce with yet another uniformed officer. "Detective?"

He glanced at the housekeeping cart, then back at me. "Is Mr. Nguyen here?"

"Yes," I said. "He hasn't touched Three-West, if that's what you're worried about."

Detective Pierce nodded. "I know. Where is he?"

Puzzled by Detective Pierce's grim expression, I pointed toward my office. "What's this about?" I asked, following behind him.

He turned and gestured for me to back up. "Wait over there, Ms. Kelly." He signaled for the policeman to come with him.

I didn't wait by Connie's desk, I followed him. The last thing I expected, though, was to hear Detective Pierce say, "Pham Nguyen? I'd like you to come with me for questioning about the murder of Jake Hamilton."

I stumbled back against Connie's desk. What was going on? Why Pham? What could he know?

The officer led Pham from the room. His eyes pleaded with me. "Miss Kelly? Help me. I not do this."

I grabbed Detective Pierce's arm as he tried to pass by. "This is crazy. You don't think Pham had anything to do with Congressman Hamilton, do you? This is a mistake. He's a highly respected member of the Southeast Asian community. He—he sponsors refugees and finds them housing and raises money for children's programs and—"

Detective Pierce looked at me with those sad brown eyes, then shook his head. And I knew what he suspected.

"But why?" I cried. "Why would Pham possibly do such a thing?"

"He had opportunity." Detective Pierce sighed heavily. "And he had motive."

My hand slipped from the detective's arm. "You're wrong. You've made a horrible mistake."

He patted my shoulder, and I sensed he wished I hadn't seen this. "Go home, Robyn. It's been a long day." He shut the door quietly.

Stunned, I stared at the closed door, unable to believe the cruel twist this nightmare had taken. Random thoughts. Detective Pierce was wrong. What motive? What opportunity? And how had Hamilton been murdered, anyway? The questions tumbled over themselves as I struggled to make sense of what I had just witnessed.

I don't know what it was that finally jolted me out of my daze, but I had to do something. At least there was one thing I could do to help Pham now. I used my security clearance to access his employment records in the Human Resources database and called his home. Fortunately, one of the kids answered rather than Mrs. Nguyen who spoke almost no English. I explained the situation and left it to him to find a lawyer.

I hung up the phone and plopped into my chair, fuming at the injustice. No matter what the police thought, I could not, would not, believe that Pham murdered Congressman Hamilton. I had volunteered for some of Pham's projects. I had seen him work with people, pulling a diverse refugee community together. It just didn't make any sense.

The storm had returned by the time I sprinted across the hospital parking lot with my useless umbrella and climbed into my Ford Explorer. I breathed in the cold fresh air and listened to the rain pounding its rhythmic tune on the top of my car.

Then, I turned on the radio to check the traffic. The highways, bridges, and arterials were all moving at a crawl. At this rate, the Puget Sound area would redefine rush hour as five a.m. until ten p.m. There were simply too many people on too little asphalt, and with our topography, there was no room to build more.

I started the engine and began my trip home, following circuitous routes I had worked out in advance using my *Thomas Map Guide*. Maybe it's because I grew up in the wide open spaces of Colorado, but I refuse to be stuck in traffic. I probably knew every alternate route on the Eastside. My friend, Andrea, laughs at me, but my feeling is that moving steadily is far better than just sitting. Other people must have thought the same thing tonight because even some of my most secret routes had more than the usual amount of vehicles.

At last, I turned into my cul-de-sac. As I drove to the end of the street, I noticed few cars in the driveways, but lights on in almost every home. Except mine. It was totally dark.

Damn. Josh wasn't home. I wanted to hear about his day, all those ordinary things that would reassure me that what I'd been through had been an aberrant nightmare.

I pulled into the garage and, after hanging up my wet coat to drip on the concrete floor, let myself into the house, anticipating the assault I knew was coming. "Oopf," I groaned as eighty pounds of golden retriever pounced on me. "Taffy. Down. Good girl."

I talked to her as I pushed past, left my damp shoes in the laundry room, and entered the kitchen. When I snapped on the lights, I was relieved to see signs that Josh had been home, even if it was dirty dishes in the sink. Taffy hadn't been waiting for me to let her out and feed her. I glanced at her and smiled. She was sitting now, doing her hungry dog imitation, looking at me, looking at her dish, looking at me.

"Oh, no, you're not conning me." Her ears drooped and I had to laugh as I rummaged in the cupboard for a biscuit. "Here you go, girl."

With her taken care of, I poured myself a small glass of wine. From the kitchen, I went through the dark dining room to the equally dark living room where I turned on some table lamps and sat down on the sofa. A collage of Irish landscapes and black-and-white photographs of people from bygone eras adorned the wall over the used-brick fireplace.

"Hello, ancestors." I lifted my glass in a toast. "Bet you never had the kind of day I had today."

The pictures had come from my paternal grandmother's home after she died. I wasn't sure who they all were, but my dad rattled off their names and relationships every time he visited. One of these times, I would write it all down.

The phone rang next to me and I glanced at caller ID before picking up the receiver. Speak of the devil. "Hi, Da."

"Robyn Anne, are you all right?"

"I'm fine, Da." Lying to a parent was allowed if it reduced their anxiety over something they could do nothing about. "It's been a busy day, though."

"Hrmph. I keep telling you the city's not a safe place for a young girl—"

I grinned at his standard refrain to lure me home. It hadn't worked when I lived in New York City, and it certainly wasn't going to work now.

"—no place to bring up a child."

"Da, Josh is nineteen. He's not a child anymore. Besides, Colorado has crime too."

"Well, you stay away from those politicians. They's nothing but trouble and taxes."

"I'll stay away from them." As far away as I could get, especially if they were cranky or dead. "Listen, Da, I just got home and haven't even had time to change. Can I call you back later?"

"Naw. I just wanted to check on you."

"Thanks, Da. I love you."

Before he hung up, he mumbled something that might be interpreted as him loving me too, but he was not one to express emotion. In his mid-sixties, my father was still hale and hearty, capable of putting in a full day's work on the ranch. He was a charming fellow with twinkling blue eyes and believed family was the most important thing in the world. He called me once a week, and when he thought I was in trouble or danger, like tonight.

I worried about him being alone, but it was his choice. After my mother passed away, he was inundated with cakes, pies, and offers of home-cooked meals—and probably more—by ladies in a twenty-mile radius. He turned them all down, preferring to hire a housekeeper to cook and clean while he was gone all day, and have his evenings to sip beer and watch ball games on TV in peace. He had his ranch hands and he had married friends to socialize with, so I didn't fuss with him about being lonely.

Now where was I? I finished my wine and turned to Taffy. "Let's get out of these clothes, and take a nice hot shower, shall we?" I wasn't sure if it was the too-tight waistband on these slacks or the obscene amount of coffee I'd consumed, or maybe it was just the events of the day, but I was getting a stomach ache.

A knock on the door scared the daylights out of me. Taffy went nuts, barking and wagging her tail as if she just knew her best friend was on the other side of the door.

I shoved her aside to look through the peephole. Peter. I groaned, leaning heavily in the direction of not answering the door.

"Rob? I know you're there. Please let me in."

I looked at Taffy, who was always ready to make new friends. With a sigh, I unlocked the door and glared at Peter. "It's been a long day. What do you want?"

He held up a bottle of wine, and I felt myself weaken. I stepped back and let him pass. "Wine glasses are in the cupboard to the left of the sink. Taffy will help you find them," I said, pointing him in the right direction. "Excuse me while I change."

He smiled that little smile that made my insides flip-flop. "Come on, Taffy. Maybe you'll even show me where the good silver is," he said, obviously referring to goldens' reputation for being extremely friendly toward strangers.

I watched him shed his jacket and disappear through the dining room before I went to the bedroom to slip out of my mismatched work clothes. I hesitated for only a moment before deciding to jump into a hot shower. After all, I had promised it to myself, and just because Peter had shown up, uninvited, didn't mean I had to alter my plans.

It didn't take me long. My hair dried quickly, and I dabbed on only a touch of make-up before I slipped into my northwest casual uniform of well-worn jeans, an oxford shirt, and comfortable loafers.

I took a quick look in the mirror, then chided myself. I didn't care what Peter thought of me.

He was part of my past. True.

We were over. Probably.

Through. Maybe.

With a sigh, I realized the only thing I knew for certain was that a charming man had brought a bottle of wine at the end of a horrendous day. I would sip some wine, keep the conversation light, then graciously escort him to the door. No one was asking for a lifetime commitment, right?

My resolve was tested as soon as I entered the living room.

He had settled comfortably on the couch, the gas fireplace was lit, the bottle of wine stood open on the coffee table. A familiar aroma drifted from the kitchen.

When he saw me sniff, he smiled. "I thought you might be hungry and I remembered you always kept nibbles in the freezer." The timer went off and he went to the kitchen, Taffy following close behind.

I raised an eyebrow. So, he had rummaged in my refrigerator and made himself at home. I felt invaded, but perhaps I was being churlish for not appreciating his efforts. Even my dog thought he was great. But then, she wasn't the most discriminating judge of character.

Rather than say something stupid, I poured two glasses of wine, took the half-filled one, and sank into my favorite over-stuffed chair. Peter returned with a plate and napkins. I had to admit, the mushroom canapés were delicious after a long day, and the wine was excellent. I closed my eyes and enjoyed the silence.

"I meant what I said earlier today," Peter said.

With a start, I straightened in the chair. Had I dozed off? Maybe I had. Vowing to keep my eyes open, I asked, "What was that?"

"When I said you look good. I meant it. The years have been good to you, Rob."

"So I have changed."

He was leaning forward, his elbows resting on his knees. He stared at the glass he held like a snifter and chuckled. "Yeah. In some ways, you look softer now. But you're more wary. Life teaches us that."

"You should know. You were one of my best teachers." I wished I could bite back the words as soon as I spoke them, but it was too late.

"I'm sorry about that, Rob. It was wrong. Arrogant. To think

I could take off and you'd wait around for me to return in a couple of months for a brief visit before I was sent on another assignment."

"You expected me to wait?"

"Yes."

"But you never said anything."

"I know. That's the arrogant part. I didn't think I had to say it, that you would just know."

I laughed at his audacity, then drained my glass and held it out for a refill before I curled my feet under me. "What a time we had."

I took another sip before I cocked my head and said, "It's hard to believe that two people who spent two months practically inside each other's skin could have made such wrong assumptions."

"Guess communicatin' wasn't high on our list." The smoldering look in Peter's eyes reminded me of why we had not spent a lot of time talking. I looked away quickly; I wasn't sure I wanted to go down that path again.

"So, Peter, what are you working on these days?" Discussing work was much safer.

"That's the one thing that doesn't change, Rob." He shrugged. "Man's need for power and control. His willingness to do anything to get it. And the hatred. God, I get so tired of it." He slumped against the couch. "I'm so weary of trying to understand why what your grandfather-to-the-x-power did to my uncle-to-the-y-power over five hundred years ago to get some land makes any difference now. Why it means we can't live together peacefully today. So often it's based on something as ridiculous as that. And then you throw in some religion. Christians, Moslems, or Jews; they're all as bad. If they aren't fighting each other, they're fighting within. Just so long as they're fighting. They always need to have an enemy, someone they can hate."

He stopped, and looked sheepish. "Whoa. Where did that diatribe come from?"

I was surprised at his assessment of what he had seen, and the passion in his response. He sounded so . . . so mature, but then, even Peter would have changed in ten years. Hopefully we all were wiser than we were in our youth.

"Could be you've thought this for a long time, but haven't been anywhere safe to say it. If you told someone you were interviewing that they were at war for greedy or stupid reasons, I suspect you'd be the next casualty. And the networks don't want to hear it. They want more blood and gore to boost the ratings."

"You're right. But you left out something."

"What's that?"

"You're very easy to talk to. Something about you inspires confidences."

I had to laugh, thinking about the Mrs. Flanders' I had met over the years. "Peter, you'd be amazed, or maybe appalled, at the confidences I inspire at work. All day long I listen to people."

"Whatever you're doing, it must agree with you."

I didn't argue because I did enjoy my job. On most days. But right now, I needed to know why Peter was here. So, I asked him, "Peter, why are you here?"

"Why?" he asked as if the question surprised him. "I thought I told you. I was at Sea-Tac waiting to change planes when I heard about the crash. So I rented a car and headed to the hospital."

"I know that. I mean why are you here?" I asked, pointing to the floor.

"That should be obvious, Rob. I wanted to see you again. The hospital wasn't a good place. Too much going on, too many distractions." He shrugged again, a gesture he used a lot. "I guess I wanted to see if the old flame still burned."

Caught off guard, I choked on my wine. That was the last thing I expected him to say. "Wanted to see an old friend" or "catch up on old times," maybe. But not "see if the old flame still burned." Coughing and sputtering, I set the glass on the coffee table and tried to catch my breath.

Peter crossed the room and patted my back. "You okay?"

I nodded, and the pats turned into gentle rubbing. He perched on the arm of the chair, and I was acutely aware of his closeness. I shifted away from his touch. I took a deep breath, then wished I hadn't because his aftershave was another reminder of the past.

I stood up and crossed the room before turning to face him. "Look. Peter. I'm not sure this is a good idea." I gestured at the whole scene, the fireplace, the wine, the canapés.

He rose from the chair, a fluid sinewy movement that reminded me of one of the big cats. He approached, his intent gaze never leaving my face. Mesmerized, I let him almost reach me before I moved again, this time toward the door, scooping up his jacket on my way. I held it on my crooked finger.

He grimaced as he snagged the jacket and shrugged into it. "I can't believe you're throwing me out."

I sighed. "Peter, today was a very long day. So, quite frankly, I'm just not up to this right now."

I reached for the doorknob, but he caught my hand. I almost laughed. This whole thing really was becoming more and more like a bad B movie. I stopped laughing, though, when I saw the heated look in his eyes.

Then, Taffy pushed her way between us with a low growl, a sound so foreign for her that it broke the mood. Surprised at Taffy's behavior, I pulled away from Peter to see headlights flash through the side windows as a car pulled into the driveway.

Josh was home. Yup, good time for Peter to leave. I didn't

want to explain him to Josh, especially not tonight.

"I'll see you tomorrow. I have a meeting at six, and I should be done by eight." I heard the garage door start to close, and I opened the front door. "Meet me in the cafeteria and I'll buy you a cup of coffee."

I practically shoved Peter out the door and closed it quietly as the door from the garage to the kitchen opened. Rolling my eyes at Taffy, I whispered, "Not a word to Josh, understand?"

She wagged her tail, so I took that as a good sign and reached for the bottle of wine. I saw Peter's glass on the coffee table just as Josh walked in. "Hi," I said brightly.

He took in the scene very quickly for a boy and grimaced the way teenagers do when they've caught their parents doing something disgustingly human.

I decided to ignore him, and scooped up the glasses, wine bottle, and plate of canapés as I breezed toward the kitchen. "How'd your day go?"

He followed me into the kitchen and leaned over my shoulder to grab the remaining canapés and shove them into his mouth. "Okay," he mumbled with his mouth full. He opened the refrigerator and took out a gallon of milk and makings for a sandwich, then gave me a hard look. "Heard your day got worse."

"You saw the evening news?"

"Naw, I was gone by then. Heard it on the radio while I was stuck in bridge traffic. Jeez, Mom. I can't believe you let a congressman die in your hospital. That's really going to look bad."

I draped an arm around his shoulder. "Josh, my boy, you have no idea how bad it's going to look."

He slathered mustard and mayo on two large pieces of sourdough French bread, then piled on the roast beef, provolone, sliced tomato, pickles and lettuce. He squeezed the whole thing together so he could get his mouth around it, with the mayo-mustard blend oozing out the sides. I poured him a large glass of milk and signaled for him to sit at the kitchen table.

"Did the radio give any details?"

Josh shook his head. After he swallowed, he said, "They just said he died."

"I was the one who found him." I let the words sink in, then reached under the counter and pulled out the Godiva Chocolates box, the one I kept for really bad days. To be sure, today had been the worst.

Josh shoved back his chair. "No way, Mom. Really? What was it like?"

If I wanted sympathy for the horrific experience I'd been through, it wasn't going to come from Josh. He had a ghoulish interest in every detail, and thought it was "so cool" that it had been murder. At least he showed some concern about Pham being taken in for questioning. Josh had met Pham while working at the hospital during summer vacations and school breaks.

"Why'd they suspect him?" Josh asked as he took his plate to the sink. I gestured for him to put it and his other dirty dishes in the dishwasher. "He wouldn't do anything like that."

"I don't think so either. But the police say he had motive and opportunity."

"If he didn't do it, then who did?" he asked.

I didn't have an answer for him. But, if I firmly believed Detective Pierce had arrested the wrong person tonight, I was left with only one choice. I had to find out who did murder Congressman Hamilton.

CHAPTER 6

The next morning, I slogged through another Pacific Northwest commute, testing a new "shortcut" that turned out to be more trouble than it was worth. By the time I reached the hospital, I was ready to trade in dark, cold, and drippy for sunny, hot, and dry. Our senior snowbirds were already ensconced in Arizona for the winter, while the rest of us scanned the newspaper's travel section and dreamed of escapes to Hawaii. A few days of blue sky: was that too much to ask?

I swung into a parking space and gathered my stuff, including my latté. No wonder Starbucks was such a success here. We had substituted caffeine for serotonin. A number of my friends had invested in full spectrum lights to ward off the mid-winter blahs, or seasonal affective disorder.

Splashing my way across the parking lot, I wasn't surprised at the number of cars that I recognized. I was on time for Will's pre-dawn meeting, but I hated to be the last one to arrive. As it turned out, managers were still streaming past my office toward the conference room. I stopped by my office to drop off my coat, then joined Charley Anderson in the hallway outside the conference room.

He looked as if he had not slept or left the hospital in days. His eyes were bloodshot and worry lines seemed permanently etched into his forehead.

"I don't know how you did it," Charley said.

"Morning to you too." Knowing full well he was referring to

my finding Congressman Hamilton, I changed the subject. "How are things in the ER?"

"Quiet now. But the clinic administrators are insisting on a cut of the billing because their docs were involved. The docs don't care. They get paid for their services wherever they work. But the clinics say this was on 'their' time, and want the administrative overhead normally included in their billings." Charley sighed. "I'm meeting with them this afternoon."

I nodded. "With specialists like the orthopedists, that could be expensive."

"Yeah. What a nightmare."

"And, we aren't done yet. Are you ready for this meeting?" I asked.

"It's too much to hope that Will focuses on how well we followed the disaster plan." Keeping a poker face, Charley cast me a sidelong glance. "Of course, *I'm* not worried. *I'm* not the one who found a dead congressman. Good luck, Rob."

He patted my shoulder as we walked into the room. Everyone fell silent, and I had this sudden churning sensation that I was being served up as the main course.

Many of the twenty-odd people in the room had already taken their seats; the rest clustered around the coffee urn. They started talking again, but their gazes stayed on me as I slid into a chair at the far end of the table from Will. Maybe if Will had to look around others to see me, he wouldn't skewer me with an unobstructed glare throughout the meeting. From the uneasy looks on the faces of those lingering around the coffee, I had chosen well.

Will stood up and everyone took a seat. The room quieted immediately. He towered over those around him, and I didn't have to look up to know he had moved and was staring at me. Damn. I'd counted on him staying seated.

"So, Rob," Will said, drawing out my name. "Do you want to

tell us about your visit to Congressman Hamilton's room yesterday?"

I hated it when he used my nickname. He did it only when he had some point to make, or wanted to act like he was my best buddy—just before he lambasted me. And from the way he was starting the meeting, how well we implemented the disaster plan was low on his agenda.

Then, something inside me rebelled. I hadn't caused that accident on Snoqualmie Pass. It wasn't my fault a congressman was one of the victims. I did not mis-tag him. I did not plan to find him dead, and I did not purposely put Madrona Bay in the media spotlight. I hadn't caused any of these problems. I was involved only because I came in early to work on Will's report. I refused to bear the brunt of his frustration.

"As you know, Will," I said, drawing out his name just a tad, "volunteers visit every new patient. I felt that with a congressman, you would prefer a manager make that visit."

I figured now wasn't the time to mention Hamilton's complaint against me. If Will didn't know about it by now, then Charley and Irene had buried the ridiculous thing under a mountain of paperwork. No point in volunteering for a public flogging.

"I see. What happened when you went into his room?"

I wasn't sure where Will was going with this, unless he was looking for a scapegoat. Did he think I handled it wrong? Perhaps he thought I should have started CPR myself and rung for the nurse and waited for her to arrive, rather than go to the nurses' station and get an immediate response. Everyone hated how he set these landmines. We knew they were there, but we hadn't found a way to avoid being wounded. I glanced around the room and saw compassion mixed with relief on the faces of my co-workers.

"I went into the room. Congressman Hamilton wasn't breathing and I called for help." I don't know what perversity propelled me to open my mouth again. "It wasn't until later, when the police came to my office and took Pham Nguyen in for questioning, that I learned the police suspected the congressman was murdered."

There. I had broken the taboo and said the "m" word. Not only had I said that word, not only had I found the deceased congressman, but I had been on the scene when the suspect was taken in.

The silence was complete. No one shifted position. No one rustled a paper or scratched notes with their pen. From the furious look on Will's face, I knew he had wanted to be the one to make the official announcement, even though the morning news was already reporting it. I hadn't done myself any favors by upstaging him. Oh, well.

Ever since I learned that Hamilton was murdered, I had resisted the idea that someone I worked with was responsible for the congressman's death, but I had vowed to help Pham.

In spite of my belief that the murderer couldn't possibly be someone I knew, I took advantage of the awkward quiet around me to study the people in the room.

Darlene Skaggs, the midwife who calmly delivered a baby in a potentially dangerous situation. Susan Wong, who tried valiantly to revive Congressman Hamilton. She hadn't hesitated to respond, even though she didn't like him. The security chief, Tom Geralding, busy all day trying to keep the curious and the press from interfering with our work. Director of Nursing Brenda Martin had been everywhere, making sure her nurses had whatever supplies they needed to treat the victims. Danny Vincent, the warehouse manager, had worked his tush off to deliver those supplies. Engineering supervisor, Lee Hastings? No way. The man was a teddy bear with a tool belt. Will Slater was difficult to work with sometimes, but I could not see him as a murderer, and I definitely couldn't picture Charley or Irene doing someone in. I sighed with relief, knowing I didn't have to worry about these people.

There were others around the room I did not know as well, and hundreds of employees elsewhere in the building who had the opportunity. Then again, maybe it wasn't someone who worked at Madrona Bay. Dozens of people were here yesterday. Reporters. Congressman Hamilton's staff, including the semi-hysterical Cynthia Martin. Victims and their families. Cancelled surgery patients. People coming and going all day long. Many with opportunity. The task of figuring out who murdered Congressman Hamilton was growing to monumental proportions. What had I committed myself to when I vowed to help Pham?

Maybe if I concentrated on finding a motive it would be easier. Who, among all those hundreds of people, had a motive strong enough to kill? I knew that statistically, most people were murdered by someone they knew. Not a particularly comforting thought as I took another survey of the group seated around the table.

But how many at Madrona Bay would know Congressman Hamilton except by reputation? He wasn't from this area. So much for the obvious personal motive. He didn't represent us in Congress. There went the obvious political motive.

My eye caught Brenda's and she gave me an encouraging smile. I could almost hear her say, "There, there, it will be fine," and I wished I had a boss like her, a boss who cared about her staff and supported them unconditionally. Then, I glanced at Will glaring at a blank space on the wall, lost in his own fury. He twisted the pencil in his hands. It broke, snapping him back to attention.

"Yes. Well," Will said. "Now that the police have a suspect in custody, we'll discuss the disaster, the accident. How well did our plan work?"

Part of me sighed with relief at being off the hot seat, while another part of me wanted to jump up and say, *No, no, you're wrong. They arrested the wrong man.* But, I kept quiet. It was unwise to advertise that I believed Pham was innocent, or that I intended to conduct my own investigation.

The debriefing lasted longer than I'd anticipated, even taking into account how much administrators love meetings. By the time it was over, I was more than ready to leave. No matter what the situation, Will had found opportunities to question my efforts during the disaster. No one came through unscathed, but I felt especially picked on. Will even vetoed my suggestion that we waive the co-pay for the cancelled surgery patients. What a Scrooge. I was fed up enough that for two cents I would've taken the rest of the day off. But with Margie on vacation, that wouldn't be fair to Connie. I glanced at my watch and realized I was late for my appointment with Peter in the cafeteria.

Wanting to escape from everyone, I took the stairs instead of waiting for the elevator.

Peter was seated at a window table that overlooked a patio. In spring and summer, the flowers and greenery were wonderful. Now, it was gloomy and woebegone, despite the landscaper's best efforts. I signaled to Peter and he flashed his Emmy award-winning smile in my direction as I entered the food service area. The pastry tray held one last apple fritter, so freshly made that the sugar glaze hadn't completely hardened. I gazed longingly at it, then breathed deeply, knowing the sugary-yeasty aroma alone was good for five pounds. Instead, I chose scrambled eggs with ham and hurried away before the temptation was too strong.

"Sorry I'm late." I slid into a chair across the small table. I tasted the eggs, then added some salt and pepper. Peter chuckled and I looked up from my plate. "What's so funny?"

"You haven't changed," he said, his mouth quirked with amusement. "You're still the only person I know who always tastes their food before adding stuff to it."

I shrugged and continued eating.

"How did the meeting go?"

I shrugged again, but stabbed viciously at a chunk of ham.

"That bad, huh?" Peter said. "The disaster was a disaster?"

I set the fork down and leaned back in my chair. "No. The disaster plan worked really well. We did everything we were supposed to do. There were no significant recommendations to change the plan except to schedule the next disaster when more employees are here to deal with it."

"So what's got you so hot under the collar? I could see the steam rising when you walked in."

I sighed and thought for a moment. Peter was a reporter; I couldn't forget that. But he was also someone I had cared a great deal for, and he had cared about me. I hoped. "Which are you now, the ace reporter or my friend?"

"Your friend." He smiled and reached for my hand, enveloping it in his large rough hand. "I'd like to be more."

I smiled at the idea, but I wasn't in the right frame of mind to analyze my feelings or the niggling questions about a relationship. Friend was all I would commit to. For now. "Since I was the one who found Congressman Hamilton and was present when the arrest was made, I took a bit of a hit."

"You were there when the police arrested the suspect?"

I glowered at Peter, who looked like a bloodhound on the scent. "You're supposed to be my friend right now, remember?"

He had the decency to look embarrassed. "You're right. So, why are you in trouble? You didn't do anything."

"My thought exactly, but my boss seems to think my visibility is too high right now. I should have gone to the lobby with Connie instead of helping in the ER. I should have stayed away from the congressman, and let only senior administrators pay him a visit. Can you imagine if my boss had found Hamilton?"

I stopped. My voice was no longer a conversational whisper and I was attracting some unwanted attention. I started again in a quieter tone. "You don't know Will. Trust me, he would've flipped out. He's an okay guy, but he's a bean counter, not a healthcare provider." The image of Will finding a dead body brought the first laugh I'd had all day.

"Didn't you help deliver a baby while you were in the ER?"

I looked thoughtfully at Peter. "Yes, I did. Darlene spoke up for me in the meeting, saying she could have done it alone, but it was safer having two of us. Risk is something Will understands because it translates into dollars."

"What're you going to do now?"

I slumped in my chair and sighed. "Go back to my office and get some work done. I'm so far behind that if I work through Christmas, I might be caught up by New Year's."

"Can I meet you for lunch?"

The offer was appealing, but I hesitated. "Thanks, Peter, but I'll be eating at my desk today."

Peter pursed his lips, then said, "I don't know how long I'll be able to stay here."

My stomach clenched. Was he here only to disappear from my life again? "You mean . . . you're going back to the front? Wherever that is now?"

He nodded slowly. "I could take some time off. They owe me, and I can't think of a better way to spend it than with you."

"Oh, Peter," I said, shaking my head. "As much as I'd like to, I can't take off right now. I have a person on vacation, and I can't leave Connie by herself. Dinner tonight?"

"Good. I'll meet you in your office at five o'clock."

"Better make it six o'clock. I'll see you then." I hurried from the cafeteria. Being around Peter distracted me, and I sensed that if I wanted to keep my job, I needed to focus all my attention on the hospital.

I hung up the phone from what had to be the twenty-fifth patient calling to complain about the rescheduled date for his surgery. The accident had lost us only one full day of O.R. time, but it wasn't as if we had a lot of free time slots to plug those patients into. All the surgical specialties were involved, orthopedics, general surgery, GYN, head/neck, and, of course, anesthesia worked with every one of them, as did the surgical and recovery room nurses. Add to that the physicians' clinic schedules, which were also a mess. What we had was a scheduling challenge under the best of circumstances. And this was not the best of circumstances.

Somebody with absolutely no sense of customer service had decided to simply shift these non-urgent patients to the end of the line, which, with the holidays rapidly approaching, was extending their waits. A true recipe for a public-relations nightmare. We needed to make some extra effort to get those people in quicker, certainly before the holidays.

I glanced at my watch and saw I had twenty minutes before my regular meeting with Will. His secretary, Arlene, hadn't called to cancel or postpone it, so I assumed we were still on. Now was as good a time as any to discuss the O.R. backlog and my idea to write-off the co-pays for yesterday's patients. He had vetoed the idea out of hand at the meeting. Maybe he'd be more amenable without an audience to impress.

I wanted to avoid talking about my section of the Quality Committee Report, the data still in haphazard piles on the floor waiting for me to make sense of it. I nudged one of the piles and it slid, threatening to merge with another pile.

I started to separate the stacks when the door opened. A man entered my office and sat down next to my small table. Connie had followed and now stood in the doorway with an exasperated frown. I nodded that it was okay, and she left, shaking her head.

"Hello, Stewart," I said. In an odd way, I was pleased to see him, the rare bit of normalcy in a bizarre week. I sank into my chair, prepared to spend a few minutes.

One of my regulars, Stewart Fromm was in his fifties, but the years had not been good to him. His graying hair was disheveled from constantly running his hands through it, his face deeply lined from myriad anxieties that had plagued him for decades. The polyester pants and jacket were leftovers from the seventies, a leprechaun-green plaid that jolted me every time I saw it. I had the same reaction to the sky-blue leisure suit he wore during the summer.

"It's all the fault of that doctor. If he'd of told my wife to stop smoking, none of this would of happened." Stewart didn't look me in the eye when he spoke, but somewhere off into the glazed distance.

I let him rattle on for a few minutes about all our transgressions over the last thirty years before I interrupted. "What can I do to help you today, Stewart?" My first attempt to focus him.

"If she hadn't of kept drinking, the girls wouldn't of started. It's all that doctor's fault. He told her to have a drink every day for her nerves. Said it was better'n Valium. And he got her started smoking too." He continued to rant about the evils of alcohol and about tobacco addicts.

"I understand, Stewart, but that was over thirty years ago. What can I do to help you today?" Second attempt.

It was as if he never heard me. "They went on to other things, you know. First it's alcohol and tobacco. Then, it's marijuana and who knows what all. Now they just sit around the house and smoke and drink all day."

"I know. Have you talked to your doctor?"

"Yeah. He won't do nothing. Says I can't force 'em to do something they don't wanna do."

"Have you talked to your wife?"

"Yeah, but it never does any good."

"When do you talk to her?"

"When I can't stand tripping over the beer cans no more."

"Can I make a quick phone call?" He nodded, and I punched in the number for the insurance desk. After a brief conversation, I hung up the phone, disappointed with the answers I was given.

"Your doctor's right, Stewart. No one can force someone into treatment." I slid a piece of paper across the desk. He eyed it suspiciously. "Here's the phone number for the alcohol-treatment program. Call them and see what they can offer you. Then talk to your wife before she starts drinking, say after breakfast."

He scowled. "Oughta be something you can do since it's your fault."

I knew better than to take the comment personally. "Call these people, Stewart. Give them a chance to help you."

After I handed him a paper with names and phone numbers, he got up without a word.

Connie came in as soon as he'd left. "He gives me the creeps." She shivered and rubbed her arms.

"He's okay." I smiled sadly. "Well, he's not okay. He's a very troubled man, but he's not dangerous."

"It's weird how he pops in here, then leaves." Her youthful lack of empathy was coming through loud and clear.

"We need compassion for people like him, Connie," I said kindly so as not to make her defensive. "Somewhere along the line, the wires got crossed, and he's never been able to straighten them out again. I don't know why. Maybe something in Vietnam; who knows? But the fact remains, he's a troubled soul who keeps coming to us because we listen and treat him with dignity."

"I suppose." Connie grimaced as she turned to leave. "I'm just glad I don't have to talk to him. I'm going to lunch now. It's Hannah's birthday, so we're taking her to TGIF's."

"Have a good time," I called after her. I was glad the Admin secretaries included Connie in their fun. I picked up my notepad and pen, then followed Connie out the door, locking it behind me.

I was a few minutes early when I walked into the Administration suite for my meeting with Will. All the desks were empty; everyone had gone to the party.

It suddenly dawned on me that this was my first chance to investigate the murder. I could see who had an alibi at the time of the murder. The administrators each had their own secretary who kept their calendars. I approached the first secretary's desk and glanced at the open calendar lying face up, then made my way down the line. After years of reading physicians' scribbles, reading upside-down calendars was no problem.

Howard Knowles, the chief financial officer, was gone for the week. Lucky him. Brenda Martin had been in a meeting with Darlene Skaggs. That gave both of them an alibi. Larry Bridgeway was in a medical staff meeting. When I reached Arlene's desk, I saw that she had nothing written down for Will for that time period. He had no alibi? Too bad he didn't have a motive.

Will's door was open and I leaped away from Arlene's desk as he moved into view. He was walking around his office, talking on his cell phone.

"—with him gone, maybe I have a chance for that appointment now," Will said. He chuckled. "Yeah, couldn't happen to a nicer guy at a better time."

He turned and saw me, and his expression shifted from satisfied to annoyed. "I have to go now. My next appointment's here. The patient rep." He turned away from me again. "Yeah, mine too." The laugh that followed sounded false.

It wasn't hard to guess. He was talking to another hospital administrator who had a patient rep who did her job well. I knew better than to let on that I understood not only his words but the attitude behind them, as well.

I entered Will's office when he waved me in, feeling the usual chill from the sterile room. I found the various pieces of modern art jarring. The desk surface was clear and the bookshelves' contents were perfectly aligned. Aside from some framed diplomas and awards, the room reflected nothing of the person who occupied it. Or, perhaps it did.

We took our usual places, him behind a massive mahogany desk in a high-back leather chair, and me to the side of his desk in what had to be the most uncomfortable chair I had ever sat in.

"Let's make this short, Robyn." Will looked down on me. I wasn't sure if it was because of his height or the height of the chair. "I have a lot of other things on my plate right now."

"That's fine with me. In fact, I have only two urgent matters to discuss with you." I launched into a brief description of the previous day's scene at the check-in desk. "Those people showed up on time, fully prepared for their surgeries. Some came a long distance, and their family members took time off work. I think it would be excellent PR to give them a credit on their co-pays when they come back, say up to fifty dollars."

Will responded immediately. "Get me the exact numbers. Then I'll decide. Next item."

At least he hadn't said "no." It would take time, something I didn't have, but knowing what I did about the rescheduling fiasco, I had at least a week to work out the details.

"The next item also relates to the O.R., rescheduling the patients whose surgeries had to be cancelled."

"We have a joint Admin–Medical Staff meeting next Monday. I'll make sure it's on the agenda." Will started to rise from his chair.

"I'm sorry, Will, but that's not acceptable," I said, letting him hear my disappointment. I kept my expression as bland as possible, holding his gaze, but not in a confrontational way. It was a technique I had perfected over the years dealing with recalcitrant patients, physicians, and administrators. It usually worked.

With an annoyed frown, Will sank back into his chair. "Why not?"

"The accident, our disaster preparedness, and this other situation," I said with a little brush-off wave to acknowledge the murder, "will continue to be in the news. Now, if word gets out that we are making these patients wait, think of the bad press."

"We don't have much choice," Will said.

We had lots of choices; he didn't want to spend the money. I knew it, and he had to know I knew it. "I think we have a couple of choices. We can send the patients to other hospitals."

"Absolutely not. We can't afford to lose the revenues. If that's the best you can come up with." He stood to again signify our meeting was over.

It wasn't. I swallowed the retort that he wanted to bring in as much revenue as possible before the end of the year because it would increase his annual bonus.

I tossed out option number two. "Look, Will, what if we get all the involved departments to agree to put in a couple of extra evening hours and maybe a Saturday shift or two. That way, we keep the revenues in-house *and* demonstrate that we're making a real effort to care for our patients despite this unexpected accident."

"Do you know how much overtime that'll cost?"

I wanted to beat my head against the wall. The man had no vision, except for a narrow tunnel that went straight to the bottom line. I forced myself to remain calm. "So, you tack on a small surcharge for a month or two."

Will stared at me for a moment, and I could almost see the wheels turning. He was figuring how to make this work, and he was irritated I'd thought of it first. It didn't matter to me how it happened, I simply wanted the problem solved so angry people would stop yelling at me. Just because I worked in customer service did not mean I liked getting yelled at.

I knew he would figure out a way to take full credit for this solution. That was okay. Sort of. I'm not a Pollyanna. I like recognition for a job well done as much as the next person, but that isn't why I took this job. It was the intrigue that kept me coming back day after day, the problem-solving. Sometimes, I stuck around if only to see what happened next.

From the Cheshire cat grin crossing Will's face, he'd put the pieces of the puzzle together in his favor. "You may have something there, Robyn. I'll look into it and talk to Larry."

"That's great. Well, I know you're busy, and I am too. I'll see you next week."

I rose from the chair, pleased I could still move after sitting in the torture seat. Will was already flipping through his Rolodex. I made it as far as the door when Will said, "The Quality Report is due today, Robyn."

"It's almost finished," I lied. "I should have a draft on your desk before I leave."

If *I leave today,* I thought. If I started now and did nothing else, I might finish by midnight. My head filled with dark thoughts aimed at administrators who find legal ways to torture their subordinates. Report writing called for another caffeine hit, so I headed for the cafeteria.

I was surprised to find Detective Pierce standing in the

espresso line. The first thing I thought of to say was "you've got the wrong man," but I forced myself to be politely friendly. "Why, Detective, I didn't know you indulged."

He nodded and said, "Even an old gumshoe like me enjoys a good cup of coffee."

"Good coffee in a hospital? Isn't that an oxymoron?"

"Yeah, like all cops love donuts." He chuckled. "I hate donuts."

He picked up his order, and I expected him to leave. Instead, he waited for me. "Have a moment?" He pointed toward a corner table with two chairs.

I hesitated, then figured the Quality Report wasn't going anywhere. I nodded and neither of us said anything until we were seated and had taken a few sips of our lattés. He shifted in his chair as if preparing to say something. Finally he did.

"Ms. Kelly." He sighed. "May I call you Robyn?"

I nodded. Given yesterday's events, we were beyond the formalities, but I had yet to bring myself to call him Matt.

"Robyn, I want to tell you how sorry I am you were there when we picked up Mr. Nguyen."

"Have you charged him?"

Pierce nodded. "Early this morning."

I turned the cup around and around in my hands, then looked at him thoughtfully before saying, "I'm sorry you arrested the wrong man."

Pierce grimaced at me. "You think we weren't careful? You think we don't know what we're doing?"

"What I think is that you're probably a very good detective. But I know there's tremendous pressure on you—"

Pierce snorted. "You can't even begin to imagine the pressure to make an arrest in this case."

"Oh, I bet I can. This wasn't just any murder, this was a congressman."

"Tell me about it." Pierce sank back in his chair and closed his eyes.

For a moment I saw the fatigue, the worry etched in his face. I regretted I had to make life more difficult for him, because he seemed like a decent person. But he made a big mistake when he arrested Pham, and I was going to do all I could to prove he was wrong.

"I guess now that you have the case all wrapped up, you'll be off to investigate some other crime."

"What's the matter? You trying to get rid of me?"

"Not at all, Detective Pierce."

"Matt," he corrected. "I still have hours of interviews to conduct. The prosecutor's office wants an airtight case before we proceed. No slipups on this one."

"I'm sure you'll be thorough. But please, keep an open mind. Pham couldn't have done it."

"You don't know what a man will do when pushed hard enough. Mr. Nguyen thought his family was threatened. Did you know Hamilton was sponsoring a bill that would deny visas for the rest of Mr. Nguyen's family to immigrate to this country? He was the last person Officer Tomlin let into the room before you came and found the body."

What could I say? Pierce had identified motive and opportunity, but I had to defend Pham. "Well, I reserve the right to disagree with your conclusions. Pham has spent hundreds of hours, thousands maybe, in support of refugees. A bill that denied visas to Pham's family would of course make him furious. But Pham was so sincere when he told me he was innocent. I think I'm a reasonably good judge of character, and I've known Pham for several years. He's a compassionate and caring person. To you, he's just an anonymous suspect."

I stood and collected my things. "I'll let you know what I find in *my* investigation."

Pierce caught my wrist. "Don't do that, Robyn. Don't get involved. It's dangerous. Leave it to the police."

"So you can send an innocent man to jail?" I shook my head and gently pulled my arm away from his grip. "I'll be discreet, Detective Pierce. Remember, I'm an investigator myself."

I left him scowling, and although I gave him a bright smile when I left, inside I was scowling too. I had to help Pham. And I had to write that damn report.

CHAPTER 7

Mercifully, my phone was quiet for a few hours. Usually I was interrupted every ten minutes or so, which resulted in my having a ridiculously short attention span. If Connie didn't break in with a question or a phone call, I bounced out of my chair four or five times an hour to retrieve a file, connect with Connie and Margie, or get another cup of coffee.

This afternoon was different. Numb from the last two days' events, I concentrated on the Quality Committee Report without the usual mental distractions. My section of the report boiled down to two essential issues: what patients were complaining about, and how much money my department wrote off in charges. I was confident I could justify every penny.

To my amazement, the information came together faster than I'd expected. Maybe it was because this year we had installed an automated system so the computer crunched the numbers for me. Maybe it was because, after doing it three years in a row, there were few surprises. Maybe it was because I was too tired to be creative. Whatever the reason, I finished before closing time.

"Here it is, Connie." I set a disk on her desk. "I've tortured the data until it confessed."

Connie saved and printed the document on her computer before she hit the exit key and picked up the disk. "What does this year's Quality Report say?"

"Same as last year's," I said with a laugh. "And the year

before that, and the year before that. If doctors and nurses are nice, the patient thinks the medical care is great. If the doctors and nurses are rude, the patient thinks the care was bad. Hospital food is terrible. And they don't want to wait for anything."

"Sounds reasonable to me. I suppose you want me to clean this up and make it pretty." Connie wagged the disk in her hand.

"That would be great. I'm supposed to have a copy of the report on Will's desk this afternoon, but I think he's in Seattle and won't be back tonight."

"We have plenty of time," Connie said. "If you have it on his desk by noon tomorrow, it will be fine."

I looked at her with skepticism. "Are you playing psychic again?"

She hesitated long enough for me to begin wondering. Then she gave me a "gotcha" smile. "Not this time. I had my afternoon break with Arlene and she was saying how relieved she was that Will's out of the building for a while. I guess he's on a tear, yelling at everyone. She said it's even worse than last week when he had a student intern in tears for misfiling a folder."

"Really? Well, I suppose he has reason to be upset. It's not every day an administrator can claim a congressman was murdered in his hospital."

"That goes for the rest of us too," Connie said. "I'm getting E-mails and instant messages from friends and relatives I haven't heard from in months, asking how things are. Real chummy. And then, wanting the scoop on what's really going on."

Knowing I would probably find the same thing when I checked my E-mail, I shook my head. "Don't you just love people?"

Leaning forward, Connie turned serious. "Rob, who do you think did it?"

Her question stopped me cold. "The police arrested Pham," I said, perching on the arm of the couch.

"Somehow I can't see him doing it. But who else could it be?"

"If Pham didn't do it, then maybe someone else in the hospital did. But I find that hard to believe. It was an outsider."

"So, how're we going to find out?"

"We?" I responded with raised eyebrows. I didn't want to lie to Connie, but there was no way I would involve her in this mess. I felt an almost parental urge to protect her, even if it was a case of do-as-I-say-not-do-as-I-do. "It's in police hands. Detective Pierce seems quite capable."

"But—"

"No buts, Connie. This might be the patient-relations nightmare of the decade, but it's outside our jurisdiction. Way outside."

"But—"

"Look, it's one thing for us to be involved when a patient dies because of some accident or oversight. But this was murder. And I don't think Admin or Risk Management or the Chief of Staff or the police or anyone else wants you sticking your nose in this." I smiled to soften my words. "Besides, with Margie on vacation, we have more than enough to do without adding a murder investigation to the list."

"Well, other work never stopped Dr. Mark Sloan or Jessica Fletcher," Connie grumbled as she handed me the document she'd just printed.

"And look at how they almost got killed at the end of every episode," I reminded her. "We're staying out of this, even if your psychic abilities combined with my investigative skills would be an awesome force. Okay?"

Connie pouted as she tugged the clip from her hair and redid her twist. "Okay. If you insist." She handed me a pen. "Sign this, please."

I scanned the printed page and added my signature.

Connie picked up the letter. "Want me to print you a copy of the report now?"

"Might as well. I want to review the numbers at home tonight to be sure I didn't forget anything or transpose some figures. You know some of those committee members. They'll take a fine-toothed comb to the report, looking for errors."

"I'll start formatting now. Philip's running late, so I won't be leaving until six or six-thirty."

"Are you sure you want to wait here?"

"I'd go shopping, but the weather's nasty out there, and, besides, working on this without the phone ringing every two minutes would be heavenly."

"Well, make a note of the extra time so you can take off early some afternoon."

"How about next Wednesday?"

"Next Wednesday? Sure," I said with a shrug. "That's an odd time."

"Rob," she said with a laugh. "It's the day before Thanksgiving."

I froze. "Thanksgiving's next week?" How could I have forgotten?

"Yeah. And dinner's at my house this year. In-laws and everything. Philip thinks I'm a crazy woman. I'm scouring places I've never cleaned before, and making him dig out his den."

"Uh-oh, that is serious. Talk to Larry Bridgeway. I'm sure he can find a prescription to cure you," I joked, glancing at the message slips in the holder on Connie's desk. "Anything I want to know about?"

"Nothing big. Mostly staff calling to report on cases. I noted the gist of their comments so you don't have to call them back."

"Thanks." I flipped quickly through the half dozen or so message forms. "Josh called?"

"That's right. He said to tell you not to worry—"

"Like that'll be the day," I said.

Connie laughed again. "You're not to worry about him tonight. He's going to Chuck's house to work on a project, but he promised to feed Taffy before he goes and he might be late so don't wait up. Who's Chuck?"

"Darned if I know," I said with a heavy sigh. "I used to know all his friends. From preschool on. I even knew the kids who were in his high-school classes. When did I fall so completely out of the loop? What kind of a mother am I?" I said with a sharp pang.

"It's okay, 'Mom,' " Connie reassured. "He's in college now. You can't expect to know everyone anymore."

"At least Chuck is in his engineering program. Someone who understands what he's talking about," I said, somewhat mollified. "Honestly, when Josh starts one of his long explanations, it's all I can do to keep from glazing over. It's as if he's speaking a foreign language."

"He is, just like you speak medicalese. Don't be so hard on yourself. The kid's growing up, that's all."

Mumbling that I wasn't reassured, I returned to my office and shut the door. Connie was right. How could I expect the same involvement in Josh's life at nineteen that I had at nine? Still, it hurt to realize that soon the center of my world would be gone. Of course I wanted him to grow up to be an independent adult, and to someday marry and have a family of his own. I just wished he wouldn't do it quite yet. I wasn't ready to think about life after Josh.

Except for resolving to have a home-cooked dinner with him this weekend, there was little I could do about Josh at the moment. I had no choice but to refocus my attention on work. Before I started, I took a deep breath and stretched. It felt really good to get that report off my to-do list.

The haphazard stack of handwritten notes perched on the corner of my desk was waiting. We documented all the compliments and complaints that came into the office, and sent copies to the department managers. Complaints about physicians went directly to the Chief of Staff's office.

It was a cumbersome system, but we hadn't come up with anything simpler, at least not without spending a gazillion dollars on a customized database management system. And that was not likely to happen anytime soon.

That pile of incoherent notes should be translated to one of our forms soon. I thumbed through the pile, relieved that none of them needed urgent attention.

Now that I had rationalized my way out of writing the case reports, I logged on to the Internet. Despite what I said to Connie about all the reasons why *she* should stay out of the investigation, I still planned to find something to prove Pham Nguyen's innocence. Somehow I convinced myself I was not a hypocrite.

An oddity in Microsoftland, I seldom used the Internet. I have friends who spend hours clicking from one site to another, finding all sorts of incredible things. Me? I have a couple of favorite sites for shopping. It's nice to come home to a "present" on the front porch. But I usually go on the Internet with a specific destination in mind. The concept of blindly "surfing the Net" was a bit intimidating.

Today was different. I had a specific purpose, but would have to search to find what I wanted. I figured I needed to start with motive. Who had a motive to murder Congressman Hamilton? And where should I look? As I reached for the Excedrin bottle, it came to me.

In a hugely popular historical mystery, the detectives figured out who the murderer was by studying the victims. That's what I could do: investigate Congressman Hamilton to find out why someone might want to kill him.

Since he was from eastern Washington, he probably knew few people from around here, so the odds were high that the motive wasn't personal. My best bet was to find information about his congressional activities.

I typed in "Jake Hamilton" and clicked on the "Search" button.

Bingo! Hamilton's Web site was the first site listed, so I clicked on it. His homepage was impressive, with red, white, and blue flashing stars, and a picture of him looking quite the hunk in a white shirt, bolo tie, tan corduroy jacket, and snug jeans while he leaned against a fence post with rolling hills of Palouse wheat country flowing behind him.

Clicking around the site, I learned that I could receive an informational packet about the congressman, including an autographed picture, by keying in my home address. That would keep me on the contributions mailing list forever, I thought.

Or, I could give my E-mail address and receive regular updates from Congressman Hamilton, who would also respond personally to any queries sent to him. My perverse sense of humor wondered how he would respond to "who murdered you?"

The site even had a video of a recent town meeting with his constituents. I watched, so fascinated by the technology that I had to replay the segment. Hamilton was a charismatic politician, no doubt about it. He knew the right words, the right inflections, the right gestures, without seeming the least bit phony. I found it an amazing performance.

I clicked it to replay one more time. That's when it struck me. Whenever Hamilton started to say something that would make him look good, he lifted his chin ever so slightly. It was a mannerism he repeated each time he talked about what he had done for his district. Someone else I knew did that, but who? It probably didn't matter.

It might not be long before the Web master shut down the site, so I decided to print some of the pages for future reference. For the most part, it was a lot of razzle-dazzle and not much substance.

The bio was short, the bare essentials. Born and raised in Walden, Montana, he went to Montana State in Butte and graduated with a degree in public administration. Then, he moved to Spokane, where he became involved in party politics and rose quickly to the top, and was now serving his second term in Congress. Until yesterday, I thought gloomily.

As I read through the Web site, Hamilton's skill at marketing himself fascinated me. He was absolutely committed to saving Social Security, improving education, protecting the environment, promoting business, improving transportation, and, last but not least, cutting taxes. Yet, nowhere did the Web site discuss specifics of how he would do any of this.

Hamilton had more loopholes in his position statements than a medical insurance contract. I'd been around long enough to know that "improve education" could mean anything from a massive federal program to returning all control and monies to local school districts. Save Social Security? For those over sixty? Assumed. But what about us tail-end boomers? What about Josh and his generation?

I realized this site told me nothing as far as why someone would want Hamilton dead, but it certainly gave me a better idea of how polished and professional this man had been.

Were all congressmen this way? I took a few minutes to check on other Washington state representatives. They all had their own Web sites, but most were pretty basic and straightforward compared to Hamilton's.

If the other congressmen failed to use their Web sites' full capabilities to connect electronically with their constituents, why was Congressman Hamilton's Web site so sophisticated? Was the representative from the eastern part of the state actively cultivating supporters from outside his district? It certainly appeared that he was not targeting his farmer, rancher, or logger constituency with this site.

Intrigued, I looked for another Web site that would tell me more about Hamilton's position on some issues. After some false steps, including one that took me to a porno site—oh, I hoped no one monitored this—I found a government site that had the Congressional Record online.

I typed Jake Hamilton's name into the query box, defined a time frame of the last six months and clicked the search button. The number of results astounded me. This wasn't going to be quick. I clicked on the first item and started scrolling my way through the text.

Sometime later, I leaned back in my chair, stunned by what I had read. Last week, a debate had involved a large healthcare funding bill, and in it was a small budget for a new department within Health and Human Services. Congressman Hamilton had spoken adamantly to have the allocation dropped. We did not need another government oversight program, he declared, regardless of what Will Slater, the speculated soon-to-be-appointed head of that new department, had testified.

Will? Testifying in Washington, D.C.? How had I missed that? It made sense, though. Will was an ambitious man, and still fairly young. He made a perfect bureaucrat. Despite our different perspectives of the world, I had to acknowledge Will was an excellent financial manager. However, if he received an appointment such as this, I could only hope there would be people around him who remembered that patients were people, not machines. Healthcare had become so cost-conscious and so high-tech that the personalized high-touch component was too often forgotten.

However, if Hamilton had spoken out against funding a new department, and Will missed a promotion to work in D.C., well, that certainly sounded like a motive to me.

The words I'd heard while standing outside Will's door suddenly flashed into my mind: *maybe I have a chance for that appointment now . . . it couldn't happen to a nicer guy at a better time.*

Then I remembered Connie's comments about Will's anger last week. If he followed the budget debate, he would've known that Hamilton wanted to kill the funding. But would Will murder Hamilton in return? The idea was staggering, and I wasn't much more comfortable with Will being the murderer than I was with Pham.

Did the police know about this motive? Had they bothered to investigate anyone besides Pham? I doubted it. If they knew about Will, they might not have been so hasty to arrest Pham. If Will had a motive this strong, who else around here had an undiscovered reason to dislike Congressman Hamilton?

Still unnerved by the implications of what I had read, I prepared to move on to the next set of congressional testimony when muffled voices filtered through from the front office, Connie's and a man's. I heard them laugh, so I didn't get up. A quick glance at my watch told me it was six o'clock. Realizing whom Connie was probably talking to, I felt a rush of pleasure as I opened the door and stepped from my office.

"Hi, Peter," I said. His dark-brown sweater did wonderful things for his tawny hair and eyes. So did the warm smile that touched his lips.

"How's my timing?"

"I'm impressed." Realizing I probably hadn't done it when Peter had come to the office the previous afternoon, I made quick introductions, then said, "You know, Connie, when I first met Peter, he was always very punctual. He consistently arrived ten minutes after he was supposed to."

"Ah, come on, I wasn't that bad," Peter protested.

"You were too," I responded. "Do you remember the time—"

"Rob," Connie interrupted. "I'll see you tomorrow. Nice to see you again, Mr. Armstrong." Her lingering smile would have raised her husband's jealous hackles if he'd seen it.

Peter nodded while I said, "Good night, Connie. I'll see you in the morning."

The door clicked softly behind her, and I struggled not to laugh out loud. "I see you haven't lost your charm, Mr. Armstrong."

He winced. "She makes me sound so old when she calls me mister."

"Well, you are old to a twenty-five-year-old. You're old enough to be her father." From the pained expression on his face, I'd struck a raw nerve.

"Watch it, Rob. You're old enough to be a grandma."

"Ouch! You really play hardball, don't you?"

His expression softened, and I felt that old shiver run down my spine.

"We better get out of here." His voice was husky.

"Right." I hurried to the storage room to get my coat. Slipping it on, I noticed that Peter already had the door open. As I stepped into the hall, I asked, "What're you in the mood for?"

"How about a candlelit Italian dinner?" He flipped off the light switch and pulled the door closed.

In the bright hallway, I searched his eyes for a reason for his choice. Ah, so he too, remembered. I wasn't sure I wanted to repeat our first date, but my mind was so rattled by his closeness that I couldn't think straight. "I know just the place. I'll drive."

"This once, I'll let you. But only because I don't know my way around."

We didn't talk as we hurried across the parking lot in the pouring rain.

"Don't you people believe in umbrellas?" Peter asked as he jumped into the car.

"Waste of money, most of the time. If you don't forget it someplace, a gust of wind blows it inside out." I turned on the ignition and blasted the heater, then noticed Peter wasn't putting his seatbelt on. "Seatbelt, please," I said.

Peter looked at me with surprise. "I never wear a seatbelt. Never know when I'll have to bail out into a ditch to avoid getting shot."

"This isn't the Middle East; it's Seattle. You won't get shot at here," I said. That wasn't completely true, but the chances of a drive-by shooting in the suburbs were close to nil. "Besides, it's a minimum seventy-five-dollar ticket if you get caught without one."

Peter rolled his eyes, but complied. Once we were on the road, I had to concentrate on my driving. The convoluted routes I used between work and home failed me. Gully-washing rain had turned all the roads into hydroplaning opportunities.

"Good, God," Peter said as I braked for the umpteenth time and he braced himself against the door. "Now I understand why you made me wear the seatbelt. Where did these people learn to drive?"

"That's just it, they didn't." I gritted my teeth to keep from railing about the idiots who whipped in and out of lanes without signaling, and other drivers who inched along as if they didn't have a clue where they were going.

I took him to Giuseppe's, a small neighborhood restaurant halfway between the hospital and my home. The parking lot was almost full, but I hoped we were arriving as the early diners started to leave. We walked in and I sighed with relief; only three other groups waited ahead of us. Giuseppe's didn't take reservations, and so a forty-five-minute wait for a table was not uncommon.

Peter slipped out of his jacket, then helped me with my coat. He whispered in my ear, "If the food's half as good as it smells—"

"It's even better," I whispered back.

We stood quietly for the ten minutes or so it took before a cozy booth was available. A waitress quickly brought a basket of breadsticks and left with our order for a half carafe of Chianti.

I scanned the menu and said, "I haven't had Chianti since. . . ." For two cents I would have taken back the words.

"Since Olivia's?" Peter filled in.

"The clam linguini is great," I said to quickly change the subject. "So's the chicken marsala."

Peter snapped the menu closed and laid it on the table. "I'm in the mood for old-fashioned spaghetti and meatballs."

I nodded. "Good choice." A big plate of pasta, my favorite comfort food, sounded wonderful. But the slacks I was wearing today were snug too. Not as bad as yesterday's, but I had to do something.

The waitress returned and I ordered a chop-chop salad with strips of grilled chicken, figuring I could probably get a bite or two of Peter's spaghetti if I wanted. Realizing I was about to eat my fourth breadstick, I set it gently on the bread plate.

"Tell me about your day." Peter's request was so casual, so . . . so normal, as if we were an ordinary couple with a past. And a future.

I felt a panicky flutter, and took a sip of wine to buy some time. What was I doing here with this man? Why was he trying so hard to be part of my life? True, we had a history, but that had been a long time ago. As for a future? It was too sudden, and too many other things were going on right now. Relationships were not noted for being convenient, but I hesitated, unsure of where I wanted to go with this whole thing.

"Rob? Are you there? It wasn't meant to be a trick question."

I snapped back, unable to believe that I had mentally drifted off for a few moments. I smiled lamely. "Sorry. I guess the last two days have been a little much." That was the understatement of the year. I took another sip of wine.

"Well, how was your day?" Peter asked again.

"Oh, fine. Finished my report, handled a few problems." *Found a motive for murder.* "Just an ordinary day at the hospital," I said with a benign smile.

Peter leaned against the booth and started to drape his arm across the top when he realized it was too high. Annoyance darted across his face, and then he started fiddling with his silverware. "I find that hard to believe. Ordinary and hospital don't seem like they should be in the same sentence."

"To an outsider, probably not. But for those of us who work there, it becomes a routine, just like anywhere else. Cut 'em, stitch 'em, send 'em home." Peter laughed at the description and I remembered how much I'd loved that hearty sound. "Tell me about your day."

"It wasn't my normal aftermath of shoot 'em, stab 'em, leave 'em for dead kind of day," he said, but the bleakness in his eyes betrayed his attempt at humor.

Before I could stop myself, I reached across the table and took his hand, squeezing it gently. "I could never do what you do and stay sane."

His mouth twisted in a crooked smile. "Who says I'm sane?" He looked across the room, but from the pain in his eyes, I sensed he saw not the wall twenty feet away, but one of a hundred battlefields thousands of miles from Seattle.

"I watched some of it on the evening news."

"That didn't even begin to describe it."

He started talking about his experiences, not the gory details, but the conditions and the issues and the participants and the aftermath, so that by the time we finished eating, I had a greater understanding of the rest of the world, and a much deeper appreciation for why some of those issues were spilling over into our own lives.

"Guess I talked your ear off," he said with a deprecating smile as he swirled the last of his wine around the glass.

"Not really." I shook my head. "So much suffering by the innocents. I'm glad you told me about it, though."

Peter nodded as he snagged the bill. After glancing at it, he tossed a credit card on the table. Then he frowned and retrieved it, replacing it with another.

"Guess you can't put me on your expense account."

"What?" He looked startled.

"The credit card, the one you picked up. It had the news service's logo on it."

"Oh, yeah. They're clamping down on expenses, just like everyone else." He slid out of the booth and shoved his wallet into his pants pocket. "I'll pay for this up front."

"I'll leave the tip," I offered. It was the only way I could make a contribution without making a big deal about splitting the bill.

"Fine."

I rummaged through my wallet until I put together the right amount, then went to meet Peter at the front door. We stepped outside to a brisk wind. The rain had died down and the clouds had lifted. We approached my SUV and I clicked the locks. Peter went around to the passenger side.

Decision time. "I still have to work on that report tonight, so I'll take you back to your car," I said to forestall any suggestion that the evening continue.

Peter cast me a sardonic look across the hood of the Explorer. "In a hurry to get rid of me?"

"No." Although that wasn't entirely true. "But I do need some time to sort everything out."

As we climbed into the car, he nodded his understanding. "You've dealt with a lot the last couple of days."

"That's an understatement," I mumbled, shifting into reverse.

Traffic had diminished considerably since we'd entered the restaurant, but the streets were still busy. Didn't anyone stay home anymore? After we reached the hospital parking lot, Peter directed me to his rental car. I stopped behind it and shifted into park.

"Thanks for dinner." I couldn't think of anything more witty to say.

Peter smiled, his teeth gleaming as he moved closer to kiss me. In the limited light, the smile appeared almost feral, but I shook off the absurd notion and leaned into the kiss. It wasn't overpowering like our first one, but there was a poignancy to it that made me look questioningly at him when we parted.

"I'll see you later, okay?" His voice was husky as he slid from the Explorer.

"Sure." I waved as he swung the door closed, and out of habit waited until his car had started before I drove away.

What a night.

What a couple of days.

I exhaled heavily as I rolled my hands over the steering wheel. What I needed was some time off and a trip to a resort where there were sunshine and masseuses, frosty margaritas and good food. And nobody calling with problems for me to solve. What I was going to get was a short night of sleep because of that nagging report and a lot of headaches while I tried to solve Congressman Hamilton's murder.

I was a mile from the hospital when I remembered that I left my briefcase, with the report and all my notes, sitting in my office.

"Well, hell," I muttered. I glanced at my watch. Only eight-thirty. No choice, but to turn around at the next intersection and go back.

Alternately haranguing and forgiving myself for being forgetful, I returned to the hospital. I parked near the front and went in through the main entrance, since the other doors were locked by now.

There's something very soothing about a hospital at night. Many of the lights are dimmed. Carts that rattle through the building all day carrying meals, linens, and supplies are parked for the night. Most of the staff have gone home, leaving a few nurses at each nursing station to monitor patients and complete charts. The ancillary departments such as Radiology and the lab have token crews in case an emergency comes up, but for the most part, the building slumbers.

I walked the silent halls and thought about Jake Hamilton in that final sleep. A part of me believed he wasn't yet at rest, at least not his soul. How could it be after being murdered and after the indignities done to his body in the name of justice? I had never been to an autopsy, but I read enough police procedural mysteries and saw enough episodes of *CSI* to know it was something I could live without. Maybe Hamilton's soul would rest when his murderer was found.

The elevator doors opened on my floor. I stepped out and wondered at myself: choosing to work on a report over spending a long evening with a gorgeous guy. A guy I knew could knock my socks off. It was scary to think I was too tired to consider a night of romance and passion. These days, a good dinner and a couple of glasses of wine, and I was ready for a long night's sleep. With a sigh, I pulled my keys from my coat pocket. Life had a way of catching up with you, I thought as I started to stick the office key in the lock.

But I didn't need my key. At the slight pressure, the door eased open.

CHAPTER 8

I stared at the door. Adrenaline surged through me and my weariness disappeared, replaced by an overwhelming sense of danger. Something was very wrong. Tensed for fight or flight, I considered my next move.

The door is kept unlocked during the day when Connie, Margie, or I are in the office; otherwise, it's secured. Normally, I would've charged right in, indignant that housekeeping had left the door open. But that was before Jake Hamilton's murder in broad daylight. Finding a dead body had turned me more cautious than usual.

Carefully, silently, I reached for the knob and tried to turn it. It didn't move; the door was locked, but for some reason, the latch hadn't caught.

When I let go, the door opened a little more. I listened, my heart pounding in my chest. Nothing. I hesitated, not sure I wanted to know what, or who, might be inside. But I had to find out. I slipped into the dimly lit front office. Everything was as it should be. Standing in the middle of the reception area, I heard a muffled noise.

Hospitals have myriad subdued sounds, even at night, but this sound was distinctive, the muffled clickety-click of a keyboard. Puzzled, I wondered if thieves tested computer equipment before they stole it. I stepped to the left and saw the reflected glow of a computer screen from under my closed office door. *My* office. Somebody was messing with my computer.

Forgetting the need for caution, I stormed forward and slammed open the door.

I stopped, totally off-kilter. "Peter?"

Of all the people I might have expected, he wasn't one of them. "What're you doing?" I looked from him to the computer screen and what I saw left a deep pit of dismay in my stomach the size of the Grand Canyon.

Peter jumped from the chair and tried to hit the Escape key, but it was too late. I had already seen too much.

"Rob." With a dazzling smile, he put his arms out as if to embrace me, then let them fall to his sides as the smile vanished. "I thought you'd gone home." His accusatory tone implied that somehow I was the one in the wrong.

"Obviously. Do you want to explain why you're reading Jake Hamilton's medical records on my computer? Records that are supposed to be confidential?"

"I, ah, I needed something for tomorrow morning's headline and I didn't want to bother you."

His excuse was so outrageous that it took me a moment to respond.

"I've been out of media relations for a long time, Peter, but I know your service has an above-board reputation. They wouldn't report something they had to know was obtained illegally."

The oddest expression crossed Peter's face. If I had blinked, I would have missed it, but now my mind started running through the possibilities. That was easier, less painful, than confronting how I felt about his betrayal of me. Of us. Again.

"This isn't for the cable news, is it, Peter?" I finally asked in a quiet voice.

He hesitated, then pursed his lips and shook his head.

"Want to tell me about it?" I pretended to be calm, belying the fact that I wanted to rip his head off with my bare hands.

His accessing records on my computer could cost me my job, destroy my life. The murderous rage welling up inside me frightened the daylights out of me.

"I don't work for them anymore." His stance shifted, his jaw jutted out slightly, and he crossed his arms over his chest. His whole body language screamed defensiveness.

I was afraid to ask, but I did anyway. "What happened?"

"They found out an interview with some Islamic terrorists was. . . ." He swallowed as if he had a huge lump in his throat and he started breathing hard. He radiated frustration and resentment. "It wasn't a lie. I'd spent enough time there to know that if I'd been able to arrange an interview, what I wrote was what they would've said."

I gasped. "You faked an interview? I, I can't believe—why on earth would you do something stupid like that?" I knew I sounded more like a parent than a lover, former lover, but he'd broken one of the first rules of journalism, to always tell the truth.

"My editor was making noises about bringing me in from the field, that some new guys, young kids, wanted their chance. He said I was. . . ." He wiped his hand over his face, then glared at me. "He said I was getting too old to dodge bullets. I had to prove I still had what it took to be out there, that my age was irrelevant. My experience and my contacts were what really counted."

"So what was this all about?" I waved vaguely at my computer.

"I was at Sea-Tac waiting for a flight to New York when I heard about the car crash. I thought maybe I could scoop the majors. Seems I'm *persona non grata* in the serious news industry. Only the tabloids would take my calls." He laughed humorlessly. "All those years I spent out there, risking my neck to get stories everyone else was too afraid to go for."

"You could've come back and had a fine career with the

network. You didn't have to spend your whole life living an adventure."

"And live *your* idea of a real life? The kind you wanted to trap me into ten years ago? The nine-to-five and Sunday afternoon trips to the zoo with the kids?"

The rancor behind his words was just another blow. I swallowed hard. "So, you didn't want that. Fine. Surely there were other options."

Peter sneered. "You always were so conventional, Rob. Goodhearted, but a little slow. You haven't even asked how I gained access to your computer. Your password's the same as it was ten years ago in New York. Misty. After the cat you had as a child. So predictable, Rob."

The callousness of what he'd done jolted me. I started to shake, angry with him for betraying me, angry with myself for playing the love-struck fool. Again. "Get out of my office," I said. All the hurt and rage bubbled up inside me and spilled out. I screamed at him, "Get out of my office. Now!"

I followed him to the door. He turned to say something. I didn't give him a chance to tell another lie. In a surge of fury, I shoved him hard. It caught him off guard and he stumbled against the doorjamb, then sprawled onto the hall floor.

I slammed the door in his face, but it swung open again. Before I could slam it again, a deep voice from the hallway outside stopped me. "Having a problem, Ms. Kelly?"

I put my fist against my forehead and closed my eyes. My worst nightmare was compounding itself. I opened them again as Detective Pierce stepped into view. A uniformed officer stood behind him, the same officer who'd been guarding Congressman Hamilton's door the day of the murder.

Pierce glanced at Peter, then at me. "What's going on?"

"I found this man in my office accessing confidential medical records," I said dispassionately. The man lying on the floor in front of me was a stranger. Maybe he always had been a stranger and I'd never realized it. The whole time I had known him, he'd been wearing a mask to cover his ambition.

"Did you let him in?" Pierce asked.

I shook my head. "I found the door ajar when I came upstairs a few minutes ago."

By now, Peter was standing up and Officer Tomlin held his arm, blocking his retreat.

Pierce crossed in front of me and ran his hand down the side of the door. "Hmmm," he murmured, then hunkered down to take a closer look. "Tomlin, what do you think?"

The uniformed officer gave Peter a warning look before moving next to Pierce. "Appears the door was taped open, sir."

At his words, I leaned over to see what they were talking about. A piece of silver duct tape covered the latch bolt, which would keep the door from closing and locking. No wonder it had bounced open when I slammed it. No wonder it had pushed open when I started to insert my key. Images flashed in my mind: Peter standing by the open door, Peter closing the door when we left to go to dinner.

Slowly, I straightened and turned to him. His cold-blooded actions of the last two days were more than I could comprehend. "You planned this ahead of time, didn't you?"

He shrugged and looked away as if bored by the whole thing.

"Did he get anything from your computer?" Detective Pierce asked me.

"I don't know. He had maybe fifteen minutes before I caught him."

Pierce looked at me for a moment, and I wasn't sure if it was compassion or pity I saw in his eyes. He went to stand toe-to-toe with Peter. "If it wasn't for the fact that it could get Ms. Kelly in a lot of trouble, I'd haul your sorry ass to jail and charge you with B&E and anything else I could come up with.

Instead, I'm going to have Officer Tomlin take you to the jail and hold you as long as we can legally. Then we'll escort you to the airport and see that you get on the first plane to nowhere with an available seat. And if you reveal what you learned from breaking into her computer to anyone, I'll come after you myself. Got that?"

Peter nodded, and when Officer Tomlin tapped his arm, he started down the hall. Before they rounded the corner, he hesitated and turned to look at me. "If you let them do this, I won't be back, Rob. You'll never find someone like me again."

"I certainly hope not," I spat out as Peter disappeared from sight.

Detective Pierce touched my elbow and I started. I had forgotten he was there. "Here," he said, handing me a linen handkerchief. "You look like you need this."

I didn't know what to say. Or what to think. Or what to feel. I was numb all over, my mind, my body, my heart. He left, and it was then that I realized tears were streaming down my face.

Somehow I found my way into my office, and after sinking into my chair, I did the only thing any normal woman would do under the circumstances. I had a good cry. I cried for Peter's betrayal. I cried for the years I'd lost while waiting for his return. I cried for David's senseless death.

By the time I worked my way down the list and reached the tears for putting on five pounds since the first of the year and Josh having friends I didn't know, I decided the pity party was about over. In addition to Detective Pierce's handkerchief, I'd gone through half a box of tissues usually reserved for distraught patients.

After patting my eyes and blowing my nose one more time, I took a deep breath. It was a ragged breath, but I felt better.

"Are you okay?"

I jumped, startled to find Detective Pierce standing in my

doorway. "How long've you been standing there?"

"Two seconds. I've been out there." He nodded toward the reception area. "Figured you could use some time alone."

"Thanks." I held up his handkerchief. "I'll get this back to you after I wash it."

He grimaced. "You still haven't answered my question."

"Which was?"

"Are you okay?"

"Oh." I had to think about that one for a minute. "I think so. At least I will be later."

"Can you tell if he found anything that could create a problem?"

I'd been so wrapped up in my feelings, I'd forgotten about the computer. I gestured for Pierce to sit down, then I moved the mouse to remove the screensaver from my computer screen. Peter had accessed a system with the best security money could buy. A staff member had to log onto the computer using a department security code, then use their personal password to access the medical records. Employees in most departments could look at only their portion of the records, the lab techs could view lab records, nurses could see records for only their unit.

Because of the nature of my job, I was one of the few people who could access everything about everybody. Even Will didn't have this level of security clearance. My mistake had been to forget to turn my computer off, and to not close and lock my office door myself when I left for dinner with Peter. He hadn't needed the department code to gain access to medical records, just my password. I chided myself for my laxness.

Scrolling up to see what Peter had been looking at, I scanned Jake Hamilton's records for something unusual. Lab reports. Physician notes. Nursing notes. Radiology reports. Finally, I turned to Detective Pierce and said, "Nothing special. Just the usual injuries you'd expect from being in a serious car accident."

Pierce smiled. "Glad to see you haven't lost your sense of humor."

"That's about all I have left, isn't it?" I exited from the medical records. "I can't believe I was such a fool."

"Don't be hard on yourself. You had no way of knowing he wasn't sincere."

I looked sharply at the detective. "Did you know?"

"Not really. You obviously knew each other from a long time ago. He just seemed to be coming on a bit strong. Let's just say my antenna was up." Pierce stared at the bookshelves over my desk, but I could tell he wasn't reading the titles. He was considering very carefully what he was about to say. He looked at his watch, then, from the slight nod, I could tell he had reached a decision.

"I'm off duty now, and it's been a long day. I think we could both use some fresh air. Join me for a walk on the promenade?"

His tone of voice told me this wasn't official business. But he was too good a cop to let his expression reveal what he was thinking. After what had happened with Peter, I wasn't feeling particularly social, but then, I didn't want to be alone either. Josh was at Chuck's, and I wouldn't want Josh to see me like this anyway.

I glanced out the window. "It looks like the rain has stopped."

"Are you afraid you'll melt?"

"No," I said with a chagrined smile. I touched my face. "I must look a fright."

"You look fine, considering all that's happened," he said.

"That bad, huh?"

He smiled and shrugged. "What do I know? I'm just a well-seasoned cop."

I flushed that he remembered my comparison of him to Officer Tomlin. Was that only yesterday? It felt more like a lifetime ago. "Tell you what, give me a few minutes to do something with this face of mine, then we'll go."

He stood to let me pass, and I went down the hall to the restroom. I took one look in the mirror and scared myself. The fluorescent light was most unforgiving, and I doubted I could make myself presentable. Some cold water and a fresh coat of lipstick later, I felt ready to face the world. My eyes weren't quite so puffy, and no one would see my red nose in the dark.

Detective Pierce was standing in the hall when I returned. I went to my office and made sure the computer was off. I glanced at the Quality Report that was supposed to be on Will's desk in the morning. Screw it, I thought. I'd dealt with enough already today. He would simply have to wait.

Feeling better after that minor act of defiance, I strode toward the door and ran my fingers over the latch bolt before shutting the door.

As we walked down the hall, Pierce chuckled at my action. "Don't worry. I removed the tape. We can't have people traipsing in and out of here at all hours of the night."

"That's all I need." I shook my head and pushed the elevator button. "It's bad enough during the daytime."

We didn't talk much, sort of like earlier when I left with Peter. But I felt none of the tension with Detective Pierce that I had with Peter. What I'd thought was sexual awareness sizzling between us had turned out to be the tension of deception. I felt neither with Pierce, and that was okay.

"I'll take my car and meet you there," I said when we reached the front door.

He looked at me for a moment, as if gauging whether I had changed my mind and was looking for a way to escape. He must have decided I wasn't, because he finally nodded. "Good idea. Even though I'm off duty, there's always a chance I'll be paged."

I hesitated to add that this also gave me control of how long I stayed. I hurried to the car, buffeted by the wind every step of the way. Was walking the promenade such a good idea? High above the ground, tree branches cracked, unable to withstand the stress. The trees were a wonderful part of living in the Northwest, but they also meant downed power lines whenever there was a windstorm. The place would be littered with limbs by morning. I hoped I still had power at home.

After navigating my way through the branch-strewn parking lot, I quickly drove to the promenade. The wide, paved path along the edge of Lake Washington was a popular place for joggers, bicyclists, inline skaters, and moms pushing strollers. I'd given up walking there in the summer because of the congestion. It's not relaxing or enjoyable to be constantly on guard for someone running into you from the front or the rear. I was surprised to see how full the parking lot was, even at this hour.

I pulled my athletic shoes and socks from the back seat and opened the car door, relieved to find the wind had died down and it still wasn't raining. I had slipped off my pumps and was tugging on the socks when Pierce approached my car.

"Prepared for anything, are we?"

I caught the teasing in his voice and smiled at him. "You bet. I even have a disaster kit in the back."

He raised an eyebrow. "I'm impressed. Do you change out the food and water every six months?"

I nodded. "Of course." Jerking the last bow tight, I slid from the car and locked it. As we walked across the lot, he quizzed me on the contents of my emergency supplies.

Here I was, on my second date of the evening, one with a deceitful jerk and one with a police detective. Did this mean my social life was picking up? Then I remembered an old saying of my grandmother's: a rogue and a decent man shouldn't be mentioned in the same day. That was out, but I would at least try not to think of them at the same time.

The promenade was well lit, and both directions were busy with lone joggers and walking couples, as if everyone was taking advantage of the momentary lull in the stormy weather. We waited a moment before we could merge into the stream of people. The brisk wind coming off the lake made a susurrus sound through the trees. I pulled my wool neck scarf a little tighter and tucked my hands into my coat pockets.

After we had walked a few minutes in silence, Pierce glanced at me. "You look better."

Tears started to well up, but I took a deep breath and vowed I would not cry. Not here. Not in front of God and everyone. Not again in front of Detective Pierce.

"I guess I am." I thought for a moment, then shook my head. "I feel like such a fool. I mean, how stupid could I be? The man walked out on me ten years ago for a job. He's a world-renowned reporter. And suddenly, he reappears. At the exact moment the biggest news story of the year hits my hospital."

I looked at him before turning my attention back to the asphalt path. "I'm supposed to be a reasonably smart person. A good judge of character. I do it all day long, figuring out who's being straight with me and who's twisting the facts to get something they aren't entitled to. Shouldn't I have seen what was going on from the very beginning?"

In spite of concentrating on where I was going, I stumbled. Pierce caught my arm, then tucked my hand around his arm. I told myself he was trying to avoid the embarrassment of my falling flat on my face.

"Don't beat yourself up, Robyn. It happens to the best of us. He was smooth. Very smooth. It wasn't as if he was a complete stranger pulling a con on you. Obviously you'd had dealings with him before, and they'd been mostly good. You had no way of knowing."

"I don't know." I shuddered to think how close I came to giving in to the yearning for intimacy. "At least he didn't get away with it. I guess I should be grateful for that report I was supposed to turn in today."

"A report?"

As briefly as possible, I explained.

Pierce said, "I'm surprised you put all that in writing. It's discoverable, you know. All that stuff in your office is."

"Always the cop?" I asked.

He looked embarrassed. "Yeah, I guess so. Sorry."

"Don't be. You're right, someone could subpoena our records, but it hasn't happened. If we can't get the patient what they want, we explain everything so clearly, they understand why they aren't getting it. By the time we've worked with them, hardly anyone goes further."

"I bet you're really good at what you do."

The compliment caught me off guard. I smiled, warmed by the recognition. "I guess overall I do okay."

"I wonder if things would have been different if I'd had someone like you working for me a few years ago."

"What do you mean?"

"When my wife was sick." He hesitated, as if considering how much to reveal. Finally, he said, "She had cancer, but no one would do anything. She'd go to the doctor and he'd say nothing was wrong. She wouldn't consider seeing someone else because he'd been her doctor for so long, she felt it would be disloyal. I just watched. Didn't do anything. One night, she collapsed. I brought her to the hospital and a doctor in the Emergency Room . . . the look on his face when he felt her abdomen, it was awful. I knew then it was over. Didn't need X rays or blood tests to tell me it was too late. I've never felt so helpless."

"I'm sorry." Instinctively, I squeezed his arm gently, but I don't think he was aware of my presence. He was staring at the lake, reliving his nightmare.

"She lasted a week, hooked up to tubes and I.V.'s. They wanted to put her on a respirator, but I said no. What was the point? Then she arrested, and they called a Code Blue because she hadn't signed a Living Will. I couldn't believe it. They pounded on her, shocked her, abused her body in ways that were horrible. I kept yelling at them to stop, but they called Security to take me away. Can you imagine that?"

He looked over at me, and I nodded. I had seen it happen before and had never reconciled myself to it.

Pierce shuddered. "It was an awful way to go."

"I'm really sorry," I said again.

"Ah, hell, it wasn't your fault. Wasn't even your hospital."

"I mean, I'm sorry you had to go through all that," I said.

We came to a wagon selling hot drinks. Pierce ordered hot chocolates and we scooted across the promenade to a stone wall overlooking the lake. The drinks were very hot and we stood in silence, waiting for them to cool enough to drink.

Pierce set his cup down on the wall, his face so full of emotion that I watched him with concern as I took a hesitant sip.

"Did you sue the doctor?" I asked.

"Didn't see the point. Would have cost a lot of money, and a lot of time. And it wouldn't have brought Barbara back. I filed a complaint with the county medical society. Heard he retired six months later."

"So you didn't just let it go, you did something."

He picked up the cup again and heaved a heavy sigh. "I did it because everyone expected me to do something, and that was the fastest way to put it behind me."

Baffled by his abrupt response, I slowly sipped the chocolate, feeling it warm me all over. "I guess it would help the grieving process if you don't start something long and involved like a lawsuit."

Pierce laughed, but there was no humor in the sound. "I wanted to put everything behind me. Barbara, my marriage, everything. I sold the house and moved into a condominium."

At his vehemence, I stopped and looked at him in surprise. "But why? Why would you want to erase your life like that?"

"Because," Pierce said quietly, "when I started going through her things, I found cards. Letters. Sexy clothing I'd never seen before. She'd been having an affair. Some guy she met in a night class."

"Oh, I'm so sorry." I had to stop saying that, but I didn't know what else to say.

He shook his head. "Mostly my fault, I guess. I'd been working swing shift for a long time, and she got bored being alone every evening. After I found out, I started to wonder if perhaps she saw the cancer as her punishment for adultery, or maybe she was too tired to keep up the pretenses any longer and so she didn't fight it. I don't know."

I didn't know either. I never would have expected such a story from Pierce. He seemed like a nice guy, someone who would take all his responsibilities seriously. But then, my ability to judge character was rather suspect at the moment.

Lost in thought, we stared at the lake in silence. Clouds scudded towards us from the west bringing the next storm with them. Across the lake, the tops of Seattle's skyscrapers shone like beacons. Homes and apartments dotted the hills and shoreline. In a few weeks, people would be lined up in this very spot to watch the Christmas ships parade.

I dragged my thoughts back to the present and tried to figure out how I could have been so wrong about Peter. Was it because David had been so incredible that I assumed the next important man in my life would be wonderful? Or had I seen what Peter wanted me to see, and hadn't bothered to look further? Or maybe, deep down, I had known that Peter would leave me.

Eventually my meandering mental processes wound around to the events that had led me to be standing next to a stone wall with a police detective. I glanced up and saw him looking sheepishly at me.

"Guess I made a fool of myself," he said.

"Not at all. You went through a horrendous ordeal. Two actually. The loss of your wife to illness, and then . . . the other thing," I finished lamely.

"Never told anyone before." He finished his drink in a few gulps and tossed the cup into the trash. "It was a long time ago."

"It's not something you easily forget."

"No, it's not. At least I don't think about it all day like I did at first."

It was time to change this morbid subject, and I knew just what I wanted to talk about instead. "So, Detective Pierce—"

"Matt."

"Pierce. What's the latest with the investigation?"

"Now, Ms. Kelly—"

"Robyn." I smiled sweetly and secured my scarf against a freshening wind.

"Ms. Kelly, that's confidential information. Our investigation is still underway, and we don't want to say or do anything that would—"

"—compromise the investigation," I finished for him.

He chuckled. "You watch too many cop shows."

"No, I watch too much local news and that's what your spokespeople are always saying. It's as much a part of the vernacular as 'you have the right to remain silent.'"

With a shrug, he said, "I guess it's okay to say that we know the accident on Snoqualmie Pass was simply that, an accident. The congressman just happened to be in the wrong place at the wrong time."

"And?"

He eyed me for a moment before turning back to face the lake. "The M.E.'s report came back. Hamilton was definitely murdered. Smothered, in fact. There's not much more I can tell you. He was alive when that nursing director left his room, and he was dead when you went in. Pham Nguyen was the only person who entered the room in between you. We've officially arrested him and the case is building."

"He wouldn't do something like that," I insisted. "Have you looked at his activities? All the work he's done for the Southeast Asian refugee community? I've known him for years, and he's the gentlest man I've ever met."

"Gentle men can be pushed too far, like anyone else."

"But he's worked so hard and he's fiercely proud of his family. All the kids did well in school, and they're all successes."

"It's that family loyalty that pushed him over the edge."

"So he didn't like Congressman Hamilton's bill. A lot of people hate legislation that's pushed through. But that doesn't mean they murder the sponsors. A man like Pham would work through the system."

"Robyn, we have him dead to rights," Pierce said in an exasperated tone. He held up his hand and raised his index finger. "He had motive. Hamilton sponsored legislation that would prevent any more of Nguyen's family from immigrating to this country."

He raised a second finger. "He had opportunity. He was the last person allowed in the room before you found Hamilton's body."

He raised a third finger. "And he had the means. Given Hamilton's weakened condition, it was easy for a small but sinewy man like Nguyen to suffocate the congressman with a pillow, especially if he was enraged."

Weighing each of those factors, I tried to find a hole in

Pierce's logic, and kept coming back to opportunity. It was too obvious. Something must have happened between Nguyen leaving and my arrival. Someone else went into that room.

In my mind, I repeated what had transpired when I went to Hamilton's room. Something flitted through my memory, something that did not fit. It had to do with . . . Officer Tomlin. That was it.

Trying hard not to smile smugly, I said, "I think I've found a gaping hole in your case, Detective Pierce."

He scowled, whether at my use of his formal title or at my insistence in trying to prove he arrested the wrong man, I wasn't sure. It didn't matter. I knew I was onto something important.

"And are you planning to enlighten me?"

"First, tell me if Officer Tomlin has a problem with sweaty palms."

"A problem with what?" Pierce looked at me like I'd lost my mind.

"Does he have a problem with sweaty palms?" I repeated. "It's a treatable medical condition for those who have a serious problem."

"How the hell would I know? And even if he did, what difference would it make?"

I leaned against the stone wall and stared hard at Pierce. "When I went to see Congressman Hamilton, I introduced myself to Officer Tomlin, and I remember being surprised that his hand was damp. Now, if he doesn't have hyperhidrosis, sweaty palms, then that means he'd just washed his hands. And he couldn't have done it without leaving his post in front of Hamilton's door. Someone could have snuck into the room without anyone seeing. And whoever it was didn't come in to say hello. They came in to commit murder."

Pierce opened his mouth, then snapped it shut. His expression may have been frozen, but the mental gears turned and shifted as he considered the ramifications of what I had just told him. Then, he swore quietly under his breath. Taking my arm, he swung me onto the path and we double-timed it back to our cars.

CHAPTER 9

Pierce looked mad enough to chew nails. Choosing discretion, I said nothing as he gripped my arm and hustled me to my car. But as I climbed into the Explorer, I gave him another expression I had worked on over the years, this one a combination of expectancy and encouragement to share information.

He didn't disappointment me. "I'll call dispatch to track down Tomlin."

"Will you let me know what happens?"

Pierce scowled at me. "Don't push your luck, Robyn." He slammed the car door to cut off further probing. By the time I had the key turned in the ignition and the window lowered, he was halfway across the parking lot, talking on his cell phone and gesturing with his free hand.

I watched him thoughtfully. Here was a man who wasn't afraid to admit he had made a mistake. For a moment, I considered Pierce-the-man, not Pierce-the-cop. We had both lost spouses we loved, but how different our responses and the way we had led our lives since then. How sad that he felt driven to rid himself of everything that reminded him of his wife, her deception overriding any good memories. All he had now was his work.

I considered his initial gruffness, and how annoyed I was when I first met him. Then I reflected on his kindness, his gentleness when I fell apart. Like everyone else, he was a complex person. Yet, if I had to define him in only one word, it would have to be "honorable." I decided that perhaps I was fortunate to know someone like him.

A sudden gust of wind reminded me the window was still open. I started the engine and headed for home.

It wasn't every day a girl discovered her former lover was really a cad, capable of deliberately ruining her life for his own gain. I felt better now than I had a couple of hours earlier when I first discovered Peter's duplicity. Taping the door latch. Remembering my old password. Those were the kinds of tricks one read about or saw in movies. I'd never expected to experience them in real life.

At some level, I suppose I always knew Peter wasn't right for me. But then, probably no one was. No one could live up to the memories of my six years with David. Maybe if he had lived longer, if he had refused to help around the house, or left his wet towels and dirty underwear on the bathroom floor, or insisted on spending weekends in front of the television watching game after game instead of going on family outings. Maybe then the sterling silver image would have been tarnished and pitted. As it was, we'd been idyllically happy and deeply in love, and no one could take his place.

I looked at the gold claddagh ring I still wore. The crowned heart between two hands was an Irish symbol for love, friendship, and loyalty. It had been David's mother's, and her mother's before her. He had given it to me as an engagement ring, and I moved it to my right hand when he replaced it with a wedding band. Even after all these years, I hadn't been able to bring myself to turn it crown inwards, signifying my heart was available.

Maybe that was why I'd been attracted to Peter. Maybe I had known, deep down inside, it wouldn't work out. In the last day and a half, I had held back, reluctant to believe this reunion was for real. Now I knew my gut instincts had been correct. My little voice had warned me, protected me from a second broken heart. It did hurt, a lot, that he played me for a fool, even if it hadn't been a total disaster.

But, it was over. Really over. Perhaps I was coming to a better understanding of myself and my self-imposed single status and I was comfortable with it. Like so many others, I wore different masks, pretending, even if only to myself, to be something I wasn't. It didn't mean I would change my life, just that I was aware of the whys.

With the distraction of Peter gone, I could concentrate on my efforts to clear Pham as a murder suspect. I sighed as I contemplated the direction that was taking me. It wasn't every day I learned my boss had a motive for murder. Tracking Will's activities or interests had never been high on my list. The image of us discussing hospital problems over a drink after work was laughable. We weren't likely to become friends. Even though his predecessor had hired me, Will had more important things to worry about than replacing me with someone he could control better.

But simply because we weren't simpatico didn't mean I could readily point an accusatory finger at him. That was a big leap in logic, from disagreeing with Will over killing programs for financial reasons to judging him capable of killing people. Still, with what I'd learned from my search on the Internet about Will's possible federal appointment and Congressman Hamilton's opposition, and the tail end of Will's telephone conversation I overheard, it, well, it was definitely enough to make me wonder.

I turned the Explorer into the driveway and pulled into the garage. I could hear Taffy jumping against the door in greeting. I'd had enough excitement and disappointment for one day. A glass of wine and a little cuddle time with my dog—that was all I wanted for the rest of the evening. I entered the house determined not to worry about anything more until morning.

Distracted and a bit overwhelmed by the events of the last two days, I forgot to set the alarm when I went to bed. Given the hours I'd been putting in lately, I rationalized oversleeping and my late arrival to work. However, I wasn't prepared for the furor that greeted me.

Reporters hovered around the front door and the employee entrances. As I ran the gauntlet, three of them pounced on me, demanding to know if I had an opinion as to who murdered Congressman Hamilton. I was relieved that Peter was nowhere to be seen. Detective Pierce must have followed through with the threat to hold him as long as legally possible.

When I finally made it to my office, I said, "Quick, Connie. Bolt the doors. They're coming to get us."

"Do you believe it? The police are interviewing everyone all over again. Do you think it means they decided Pham isn't guilty?"

I hoped that was exactly what it meant, but it was too soon to say anything.

"Tom is probably going nuts," Connie said, wide-eyed. "Do you think the police will let Pham go? I wonder what changed their minds?"

"Must have picked up some new information." I walked past her desk toward my office.

"Rob. You know something." Connie was out from behind her desk in a flash, following me like a hound on a fox scent.

"I've always believed Pham was innocent," I said.

"You know something," Connie repeated.

"Using your psychic abilities again?"

"No. I see that little twinkle in your eyes. The one that says, 'I know something you don't know.' "

"Well, perhaps I was able to point out some little detail that the police missed."

"When?" Connie threw up her hands in exasperation. "How did you have time? Last I saw, you were leaving for dinner with Peter."

I sat in my chair and flipped on the computer with a grimace. "Yes, well. That's over and done with. We won't be seeing him anymore."

Connie sank into the extra chair. "Rob, what happened?"

My plan had been to not say a word about the fiasco with Peter. But that plan went out the window when Connie put her hand on my shoulder and looked at me with apprehension in her eyes. I told her what had happened. It was either that, or start to bawl all over again, and I was finished with tears.

I gave her a highly sanitized overview, however, with just enough details so she understood. I held back the fact that Peter had actually accessed Hamilton's medical records. I liked Connie a lot, but she was young and new, and I shuddered to think of the whole story inadvertently becoming fodder during the secretaries' coffee-break conversation, and then filtering its way to my boss. Especially the part about Peter accessing the records because I forgot to turn my computer off and he remembered my old password. It was one thing for the story to spread of how the famous reporter had been caught trying to pull a fast one; it was another for anyone to know he'd partially succeeded.

"Oh, Rob, I'm so sorry." Connie gave me a hug. "He seemed so nice and acted like he was really pleased to see you again."

I forced myself to smile. "That's why he was very successful at what he did. He could charm anyone into telling him anything he wanted to know."

The outer door opened and closed. "Hello, anybody here?" a familiar voice called out.

Connie and I both stepped from my office. I remained in the

doorway while Connie scooted back to her desk.

"Melanie. What brings you here?" As if I couldn't guess. It had to be only a matter of time before all the reporters found my office.

Looking sharp and sophisticated in another plaid jacket, this one red and black, over a silky black top and slacks, Melanie Cole smiled in a friendly way. After my experience with Peter, I was more suspicious than I'd been two days before, and had no interest in becoming any reporter's buddy.

"I wondered if you have a few minutes. With the new developments, I need some help with today's story."

"What happened?"

"The police released Pham Nguyen and are interviewing everyone again."

"PR should have what you need. Can I call them to check for you?" Even though I was stonewalling, I could at least appear helpful.

Melanie waved some papers. "I've got that already. There's nothing really useful, just generic stuff about the hospital and the parent corporation. I was hoping you could tell me something that would give this story more of a human-interest twist."

I had yet to prove that Pham was, in fact, innocent, but at least he was no longer the sole focus of the police investigation. We still had a murderer on the loose, and there was always the possibility that Melanie knew something that might help.

Deciding it might not hurt to talk, I said, "I don't know if there's anything I can add, but come on in." I signaled for Connie to bring her some coffee, then gestured for Melanie to come into my office and take a seat.

After we were settled, Melanie glanced quickly around my office. Her gaze hesitated at the collage of pictures of Josh, the association awards, the picture postcards of Ireland. Then she took out her notepad and flipped it open to a blank page.

"So, tell me a little about you," she started.

I obliged, giving my name, rank, and serial number, and a brief overview of the Patient Relations department, adding that most hospitals had something similar.

"Hmmm. I had no idea hospitals paid that much attention to complaints. Mind if I mention this to our consumer-affairs person? She might want to do a segment on you."

"Only if she agrees to include my counterparts from other hospitals."

Melanie nodded as she scribbled on her pad. Now was the time for me to ask a few questions.

"I've always been intrigued how someone ends up in front of the camera. Did you plan this or did it happen by accident?"

The question seemed to catch her by surprise. Maybe she wasn't accustomed to having the interview tables turned, or maybe it was the question itself that caught her off guard. Whichever it was, when she looked up, I caught a ferocity in her eyes that she quickly banked.

"I've wanted to do this for as long as I can remember." It sounded like a throw-away answer. Too automatic. Too pat.

"I grew up in Colorado, outside a small town, and didn't have a clue what I wanted to be when I grew up," I offered. "All I wanted was to move to a big city where things were happening."

"Ranch girl, huh? Me too, except I'm from Montana."

"Really? What a coincidence," I said, surprised that she was responding so easily to my prompts. "I started in media relations for a New York City hospital, then moved out here. New York wasn't the best place to raise a child." I shuddered. "Too much crime. We never had any problems when I was growing up in Colorado."

"I can't say the same for Montana." That ferocity flashed in her eyes again. "I've seen it everywhere, Robyn, and it's been happening forever. It's just that now we talk about it. People need to know what really goes on."

I didn't think she had any idea how revealing she was. Something had happened in her small town, something that no one talked about. Something had set a fire in her belly that still burned.

"You're right," I said.

Suddenly, Melanie smiled, her intensity softening so quickly it was as if she flipped an internal switch. "We're getting off the track here. Let's see. . . ." She flipped through her pad. "What do you know about the suspect, Pham Nguyen?"

"I'm glad the police seem to be considering other possibilities."

"Really? Why?" The question had a sharpness, a biting edge that surprised me. This woman's moods changed as rapidly as a chameleon's colors. Did she have a personality disorder?

"I've known Pham for years. He's always been a kind, gentle man and very proud of his family." I told her about the last time he'd shown me pictures of his son's college graduation. "I just can't reconcile the man I know with a murderer."

"Sometimes people snap," Melanie said. Her words reminded me of Detective Pierce's assumption.

I shook my head. "Not Pham. He's come too far, and he's such a hard worker. I can't imagine him jeopardizing his family's honor by murdering someone."

"What can you tell me about Congressman Hamilton?" she asked quickly, as if by rushing me on to the next topic she could get me to say something I shouldn't.

"Such as?" I asked.

"Oh, what kind of treatment he was getting, test results, that sort of thing."

"I think PR put all that in the press release." I knew full well what she was fishing for; she was simply more straightforward than Peter in her attempts to acquire confidential medical information.

She looked resigned and flipped her notepad closed. "Well, I didn't think I could get you to slip, but it was worth a try. Guess I'll see if someone in Administration is available." She stood up, then hesitated. "I don't suppose you have any ideas about why the police are re-interviewing everyone?"

I reminded myself that she was a reporter, not my friend. This wasn't the time to share confidences and theories. "Haven't a clue."

"Didn't think so. Here's my card." She pulled a business card from her jacket pocket and handed it to me. "It's got everything on there, cell phone, pager, E-mail. If you find out something, call me, okay?"

"Sure thing." I stuck the card into my Rolodex.

I followed her to the hall and said good-bye, then shut the door and turned to face Connie.

"Well? What'd she say?" Connie asked.

"Nothing. She wanted to find out what I knew."

"Did you tell her anything?" She reminded me of Josh. Her excited eagerness somehow overlooked the fact that this wasn't fantasy, it was reality. A real person had died, murdered by another real person who might well be still walking the halls of this hospital.

"There wasn't anything to tell."

"Not even why the police are back?"

I laughed. "What makes you think I know?"

"Because of the way you sidetracked me before Melanie Cole came in. So, what gives?"

"I really don't know anything, Connie. I simply observed something that gives the situation a different twist than the police considered before. I shouldn't say anything until they finish their investigation."

Before Connie could badger me anymore, I returned to my office and shut the door. I wanted to avoid Connie's questions, and I also wanted to avoid interruptions for a few minutes because I needed to think. Melanie Cole was a driven woman. It might not be an obsession, but it was more than a passion for journalistic truth. Something she'd said kept ricocheting around my brain like a pinball looking to fall into a high-scoring hole. What was it . . . ?

Bingo! It hit me. Well, okay, I mixed my metaphors, but I thought just maybe I had something. Clicking the computer to the Internet, I waited impatiently to check my theory. Before the connection was completed, someone knocked on my door.

"What?" I called impatiently.

Connie opened the door and whispered, "Mrs. Flanders is here."

My mind went blank. "Who?"

"Mrs. Flanders. The surgery patient."

It came to me then. The cool breeze lady. "What does she want?"

"She wants to see you."

"Now?" I couldn't believe this was happening, right when I was so close to proving, well, I wasn't sure what I was close to proving. Nevertheless, the patient came first. With a sigh, I clicked to end the Internet connection and followed Connie to the front.

"Mrs. Flanders? I'm Robyn Kelly." I extended my hand. She was what I had pictured during our phone call. Soft and pink and round. "And this is my assistant, Connie Wagner."

Mrs. Flanders nodded at us both. "Oh, my, Miss Kelly. Thank you for helping me yesterday," she said in a breathy voice.

I gestured for her to take a seat on the couch. Normally, I take a patient into my office to talk, but I didn't think privacy was an issue if she'd come by to thank me. "It was my pleasure. I hope everything went well with Dr. Davisson."

"Oh, my, yes. He was so nice, so reassuring, even though I'm quite certain he thought I was a bit dotty," she said ruefully.

I swallowed a smile and glanced at Connie. That was probably an accurate assessment on Mrs. Flanders' part. "So, what brings you here?"

"Why to see Dr. Davisson, of course." She looked momentarily puzzled, then brightened. "Oh, my, yes. And I wanted to say thank you in person and bring you something."

She reached into her oversized purse and I winced, then relaxed when she pulled out a flat, round tin and popped it open. Fresh baked cookies.

So my first assessment of her had been right again. "Mrs. Flanders, you shouldn't have," I said as Connie approached to accept the tissue-lined tin.

Connie held the cookies close and took a deep sniff. "They smell divine. Thank you."

Mrs. Flanders made a fluttery gesture. "Oh, my, it was no trouble. When I'm off my porridge, I bake. And then I don't know what to do with it all. I'm trying to keep my girlish figure, you know."

This time I smiled openly. "I know what you mean, Mrs. Flanders." I started to stand up, expecting her to follow suit. She didn't, and so I sank back down. "Is there something else I can help you with?"

"Oh, my, I don't know how to ask this." She looked so helpless. Then her eyes sharpened and she said, "What was it like to find the body?"

Caught off guard, I said, "Excuse me?"

"The body," she snapped. "Congressman Hamilton's body. What happened when you found him?"

I almost laughed out loud at her audacity. "I'm sorry, Mrs.

Flanders. I'm not allowed to talk about it." Leaning forward, I whispered, "Police orders, you know," then pulled away and raised my eyebrows knowingly. I stood up again.

"Oh, I see." She pursed her lips as if annoyed that her ploy hadn't worked. "Well, I won't take up any more of your time."

She hefted herself from the couch and eyed the cookie tin in Connie's hands. I could almost see the wheels turning: should she or shouldn't she take them back? She must have decided she might need our services in the future, because she sailed out the door without another word.

Connie stared at me. "Do you believe—"

"Oh, my," I mimicked. "Believe it. I keep telling you, after you've been here awhile, nothing will surprise you anymore. Now, I have things to do." I started toward my office.

"Don't you want a cookie first?"

I thought about it for a moment. With a sigh, I capitulated. "Sure. Let's see what she brought."

We were delighted to find iced raisin oatmeal, rationalizing that the nutritional value of the raisins and oatmeal offset the sugar and butter. After sharing a cookie and fresh cup of coffee with Connie, I took one more cookie into my office and shut the door, determined to finish what I'd started before Mrs. Flanders came to call.

Drumming my fingers with impatience, I waited for the Internet connection to go through, then I typed in Channel Eight's Web address. As I'd hoped, they featured profiles of the key reporters. A couple of clicks later and I was opening Melanie Cole's bio.

Montana isn't a heavily populated state, with a whole lot fewer people than greater Seattle, and miles of wide open space in between. The chances of Melanie Cole and Congressman Hamilton knowing each other were pretty slim, but it was still a possibility.

The screen changed and I started reading. There it was. Born and raised in Walden, Montana. Stunned, I slumped in my chair. They had grown up together. Not just the same county, but the very same small town. And something had happened there that still drove Melanie. Could it have involved Jake Hamilton? If so, was it a motive for murder some fifteen years later?

I groaned at the leaps my imagination was taking and clicked off the Web site. Not for the first time, I wished Margie was back from vacation. She was the closest thing I had to a best friend at work. My outside-of-work best friend, Andrea, was out of town this week on business. We talked about everything. I sighed with frustration. They weren't here and so I had to muddle through by myself.

Finding a link between Melanie and Congressman Hamilton was more than I'd ever thought possible. Of course, what was the probability that Will and Hamilton would have a connection, or Pham and Hamilton either, for that matter? If Will and Pham had bad experiences with Hamilton, what were the odds that Melanie's were positive? The whole thing was giving me a headache. It seemed that everyone had a history with Hamilton.

The plaguing question was what I should do with this information. After the fiasco with Peter, I still didn't trust my judgment, and I didn't want to implicate either my boss or a highly respected local reporter simply because I was eager to give the police someone else to focus on.

From what I had learned about Pham and Will, Congressman Hamilton had not been the wholesome all-American boy he pretended to be. He seemed to have had a mean streak, something that usually appeared long before adulthood. It may well have been visible when he was growing up.

Which put me right back where I started, wondering what to do with all this unearthed information. My original goal had been to prove Pham innocent. If I failed to prove that, then at least I could help the police keep an open mind. I wouldn't come right out and tell Pierce I suspected Melanie. Instead, I would suggest he check the police records in Walden about the time Hamilton would have been there.

Pierce could draw his own conclusions.

CHAPTER 10

If I hurried, which seemed to be the only way I functioned anymore, I could grab a sandwich in the cafeteria and take a fresh latté upstairs with me to the nurse managers' meeting. As I paid for the sandwich, I noticed Darlene Skaggs and Kate Connolly sitting at a large corner table, surrounded by notebooks and laughing at a paper in Kate's hand. In need of a good chuckle, I started toward them.

"Rob," Darlene said. "Have you seen the new Bloomingdale's?" Still laughing, Kate waved for me to sit down.

Two years before, someone inside the organization had created the Bloomingdale family as a way to zap Admin and the physician leadership. Every now and then, a "Bloomingdale" wrote a letter and circulated copies throughout the building so the letters couldn't be kept a secret. Despite everyone's best efforts, the identity of the real writer hadn't been uncovered.

"I didn't know there was one." I slid into an empty chair as Kate handed me the letter.

"I don't know who's behind these, but they really know how to make a point," Kate said.

The first thing I did was check the sender, and breathed a sigh of relief. Sometimes, the letters were from "Patti R. Bloomingdale, Patient Relations", another source of friction with Will, even though he knew it wasn't really from me.

This one was addressed to Will from "Ena G. Bloomingdale," Madrona Bay Public Utility Department, chastising Will for disregarding the district-wide effort to reduce power consumption.

Last summer, we did a major remodel of the maternity unit on the fourth floor. The solid concrete north wall and part of the roof had been removed and replaced with green glass to create a spacious solarium, complete with a garden, benches for resting, and a small waterfall. Instead of the traditional labor/delivery rooms, with separate postpartum rooms, we'd put in deluxe suites, complete with whirlpool tubs.

The remodel was a marketing success, and the OB department was inundated with new patients. But despite the energy-efficiency claims, the new unit had increased our use of electricity and water.

In her letter to Will, "Ena G." went on to describe several very creative ways he could reclaim and recycle the whirlpool tub water, and suggested window coverings for the solarium to reduce heat loss through the glass.

The letter was funny, and guaranteed to give Will fits, especially since he'd made such a big deal about being one of the first community leaders to sign the "We Will Reduce" pledge.

"Has everyone seen this?" I asked.

"Just about. Even my docs are laughing," Kate said, referring to the physicians in the OB/GYN clinic. "And they are the biggest beneficiaries of the remodel."

"It's been wild." Darlene shook her head. "I don't know what happened last February, but we have a bumper crop of new babies this month."

"It was that big windstorm," Kate said. "Remember? The power was out for three days on the Sammamish Plateau."

"That's it." Darlene nodded toward Kate. "This is the first meeting I've made it to since you and I delivered that baby in the ER, Rob, and that's only because Kate dragged me down here. Everyone was so busy absorbing that surge of patients from the accident that we cancelled everything on our calendars that day."

"Speaking of the new mom, how are Linda and her baby?" I asked.

Darlene beamed. "She's fine. They both are. She came to the clinic this morning so we could see the baby again before her husband took them home to Ellensburg." She rolled her eyes. "Boy, that could've been a real mess."

"We were so lucky," I said, glancing at the wall clock. "Uh-oh. I'm due at Brenda's meeting. See you guys later." Darlene and Kate were part of the OB/GYN clinic, not the hospital, so they didn't have to attend Brenda's meeting.

I didn't have time to get a latté, so I hurried to my office and grabbed what I needed for my presentation. Dropping papers and overhead projector transparencies into a box, I sprinted to the conference room. The weekly hospital nurse managers' meeting was already in progress with Charley leading a discussion about a new system to track patients' belongings from the ER to the inpatient unit. Charley was running overtime, as usual, so I winked at him and quietly took a seat off to the side to wait my turn.

The routineness of this meeting was at such odds with the chaos that had filled the hospital the last couple of days. I sat back, prepared to concentrate on the discussion, but my mind soon drifted to the realities outside this room.

The first, of course, was finding Congressman Hamilton's body. I would never forget that eerie, chilled silence until the day I died. And I never wanted to repeat the experience.

Mentally, I listed the possible murder suspects I had identified so far. It was all very puzzling. I planned to call Detective Pierce after I finished this meeting. He was probably still annoyed with me for spoiling his case against Pham. Giving him some other leads would annoy him even more.

"Robyn? Are you ready?" Brenda's crisp voice broke through my thoughts.

I looked around. Charley was gone and the women seated around the table were looking at me with some amusement.

"Go easy on her, Brenda. She's had a rough week. It isn't every day our patient rep delivers a baby," quipped Nancy Mancuso, the postpartum manager. The twenty or so other nurse managers laughed.

"It's not every day she finds a dead body, either," added Irene, who had faced the reporters with me the morning the accident victims inundated the hospital. "At least it wasn't our fault." The murmured agreement was more subdued.

Picking up my box, I carted it to the head of the table and plopped it down, then sighed heavily. "I really wish they'd sent more of those accident victims to somebody else's hospital." There was another, louder, murmur of agreement.

"I'll say," said Judy Francis, the new O.R. manager. "It'll be weeks before our schedule's back on track. My satisfaction numbers for this year are ruined." She had a good point.

"We'll figure out something, Judy," I said. "Now, let's talk about the numbers."

I handed out copies of the report that included the overall hospital nursing data and the data for each manager's respective unit. Turning on the overhead projector, I laid the first transparency on the lighted screen and started talking. It pleased me to report that the number of compliments to the staff continued to far outweigh the complaints.

When I finished the formal presentation, Brenda turned to me. "Robyn, thank you for coming. We appreciate the information."

She led the discussion for another half hour, then asked, "Do I have some volunteers to look at the noise issue?" She nodded as three hands were raised. "Good. I'd like to see us make some improvement on this."

She glanced at the institutional wall clock and stood up. "Time to go. If anyone has something to add to next week's agenda, call me."

I put leftover copies of my report into the box and chatted with the managers as they slowly filed from the room. When I finished, I turned to see Brenda collecting her papers.

"I hope that went as you planned," I said.

She nodded. "Sometimes it's hard to hear that some of the patients aren't happy, but we need to know. And I value the fact that you present it in a way that doesn't cast blame."

Brenda thumbed through her copy of the report. "I'm not looking forward to discussing this with Will. He wants to identify the precise nurse who's responsible for the complaints and fire her." She glowered with indignation.

Alarmed, I said, "The report's not supposed to be used like that."

"Of course not. It's a learning tool. But he keeps cutting our budgets, which means I don't have the staff I used to, and then he wonders why it takes longer for the nurses to respond to call lights. Sometimes I'd like to make him a nurse, or at least have him spend a half day on each unit to see how busy we are. It's a wonder we get any compliments at all."

"From what I hear from patient reps at other hospitals, we're not unique," I said.

"I know. I hear the same thing from my colleagues too. But that doesn't make it easier."

I didn't have an answer for her. Many of us in the business were concerned about the dwindling resources to care for patients. It wasn't a problem that was going to be solved soon.

"I was thinking about what Judy said. She's right," I said. "The way we track this data over time, we'll be explaining this O.R. backlog for several years."

"Absolutely not," Brenda said, her mouth drawn in a hard line. "I am not about to have to justify the O.R. every year for something we had no control of. I don't want any more reminders of that . . . accident."

I sensed she'd been about to say something else, but had no idea what. "I agree."

Brenda's commitment to her nurses was commendable. She was a mother bear protecting her cubs. But I didn't envy her having to explain a spike in complaints over and over and over again for the next five years.

A solution suddenly occurred to me. "Brenda, how about this? I'll keep a separate manual tally of the O.R.'s complaints that are directly attributable to the accident victims bumping scheduled patients, and include them as a footnote. They won't show up at all after this quarter."

Brenda's expression relaxed. "That would be perfect. This whole thing's been such a nightmare. By the way, I heard that Pham is no longer the primary suspect."

I was relieved that Brenda had brought up the subject. She was a good administrator, one of the few who really cared about the people she worked with. I could talk to her, and know that whatever I said would go no further.

"That's right." I smiled. "Before I went into Hamilton's room, I introduced myself to the police officer and we shook hands. I noticed his hands were damp, and I mentioned that to the police detective investigating the murder. It turns out the officer left his post for a few minutes to use the bathroom so someone else could have slipped into the room and murdered Hamilton without anyone seeing him."

Brenda's eyes widened. "That's very clever of you, Rob. Are you adding murder investigations to your repertoire of skills?"

I laughed. "No, not really. I have learned some interesting things about Congressman Hamilton. He wasn't always what he seemed to be."

"Really?" she said, straightening the chairs around the table. "He seemed very pleasant when I visited with him."

"You must have caught him at a good time."

"He wasn't in pain, but he was uncomfortable. I think he appreciated the extra attention. When I left, I told him to be sure to call me if he needed anything." She failed to mention Hamilton's complaint against me, for which I was grateful. Maybe she hadn't heard about it.

I realized I probably shouldn't say anything more until I talked to Detective Pierce. Changing the subject, I asked, "How's your daughter doing?"

Brenda looked startled and clutched the silver cross she wore every day. "Cynthia? She's upset, of course. But, she's doing better."

"I'm glad to hear that. When I saw her yesterday, she was still so distressed. Is she planning to return to D.C.?"

Brenda's mouth softened with maternal pride. "No. She's decided to move home. She'll work for my husband's furniture company. He always needs good sales people. It was hard on the family, having her so far away. I don't think we'll let her do something like that again."

I nodded, understanding that after losing her boss, Cynthia would need all her family's support, especially since she'd been so distraught after the accident and Hamilton's death. But, she struck me as being old enough to decide for herself what she wanted to do with her life. Maybe I had misjudged her age. "Was she working for Congressman Hamilton as a college intern?"

"Oh, no. She graduated from the University of Washington two years ago and finished her master's in public administration last spring."

I didn't want to say anything, but Cynthia seemed qualified

to be much more than a sales rep for the family furniture business. But then, it wasn't my place to comment. I certainly didn't know how I would react when the time came for Josh to launch out on his own. The thought was troubling. "You have a son too, don't you?"

"Yes. Curtis. He's still at the university. In business. He'll take over the company when my husband's ready to retire."

"Sounds like you're keeping it all in the family."

"A family business is the best way to show your children what your true values are. Honesty, integrity, family. It's God's plan."

"Mmmm." I said as noncommittally as I could. This wasn't the time to point out that she herself worked for a huge organization, or that small businesses were struggling to compete against megastores and Internet sales.

She glanced at her wristwatch and scooped up her coat. Slipping into it, she said dryly, "I'm supposed to be in Seattle for a meeting in thirty minutes. Do you think I can make it in time?"

Her question surprised me. It was the nearest thing to humor I had ever heard from her. "Only if the 520 Bridge is wide open and you find a parking place right out front." I followed her from the room as she flipped off the lights. "I'll see you later, Brenda."

Walking toward my office, I wasn't sure what God's plan was these days. Maybe Brenda had a reason to be worried enough about Cynthia to want to keep her close to home for a while. The girl had obviously been an emotional wreck when she arrived at the hospital, on the verge of a breakdown right there in the lobby.

She wouldn't be the first young woman to fall in love with her employer, but from what I'd been learning about Jake Hamilton, I doubted he would have risked his political future for a fling with a subordinate. He seemed too calculating for a misstep like that.

How would I feel if I were in Brenda's shoes, and Josh was the one involved with a sophisticated older woman? I wouldn't like it one bit. I'd haul him home for his own protection too. Or send him to my dad's Colorado ranch where he could mend his broken heart in splendid solitude. I smiled, thinking how that kind of banishment would appeal to an adolescent prone to occasional theatrics. Josh might be studying engineering, but he had the typical young man's mood swings and could be as dramatic as the next when it came to expressing his wounded feelings.

Counting my blessings that I wasn't the consoling parent in Cynthia's case, I fumbled to open my office door. As I stepped in, Detective Pierce turned around. He was standing in front of Connie's desk, eating one of Mrs. Flanders' cookies and looking very pleased with himself.

"Hello, Detective," I said and shut the door with my foot.

He looked at the box in my arms. "Need some help?"

"Where were you an hour ago when I couldn't see over the top of this thing?"

"Trying to put my case back together and explain to my superiors and the DA that I wasn't a complete screw-up," he said with only a hint of sarcasm.

I winced. "Sorry." I proceeded to my office where I dropped the box onto the desk.

Pierce followed me. "It's not your fault," he said heavily. "I made the mistake of going with the obvious suspect."

"It's not like there was no pressure on you," I said. "Everyone was screaming for an arrest."

"Tell me about it." Pierce slumped into my extra chair. He was wearing the same tweed jacket he'd worn the night before, and judging from the wrinkles, probably the same white shirt. His brown eyes were so weary I wouldn't have been surprised if he fell asleep sitting there.

"I haven't released Mr. Nguyen yet," he said. "But his family hired a bulldog attorney. Nguyen still swears Hamilton was asleep when he went in to clean the room. He claims he only cleaned the bathroom so he wouldn't disturb the congressman. My case against him isn't strong enough for an indictment anymore."

He didn't add "thanks to you," for which I was grateful. "I hear you've been interviewing everyone again." I sat down in my chair and kicked off my shoes.

Pierce shook his head. "It's a nightmare. Do you know how many people were on and off that unit?"

"A lot?"

"More than a lot," he said with a grimace. "Why can't this place be like the tech companies where you need a security card every time you go in and out of an area? Then we could prove beyond a doubt who was there when."

"It'd be a nightmare for us. Besides, what would we be securing ourselves from? There's nothing of real value to steal on the units. Except for the drug cabinet, and only a few people have access to that."

"I suppose from your perspective it makes perfect sense to have everything wide open. For me to prove who dunnit? A nightmare."

I smiled and said, "How did you like the cookies?"

"Those were great. Connie told me how you came by them." He shook his head again and chuckled. "People. I suppose you see all kinds too."

"That's for sure. Most are only brief telephone encounters, and others we get so involved with, it seems like we should be spending holidays together. If they were all like Mrs. Flanders, I'd be a complete cynic by now."

"As it is, you're only a partial cynic?"

I grinned at him. "Yeah, only a partial cynic." I turned serious, but couldn't look him in the eye. I wasn't sure if I was about to do the right thing or not. Guilt over messing up his case swung the decision to confessing all. Still, it wasn't going to be easy. I fidgeted with my pen and said, "I might've found something interesting for you."

His eyes narrowed. "What do you mean?"

"I've been checking a few things, and—"

"Dammit, Robyn, this is a police matter." Pierce was no longer slumped in the chair. He was sitting upright, alert with an eagle sharpness in his eyes. "You're not to get involved."

"And I suppose I wasn't to get involved when I told you about Officer Tomlin's wet hands?" I said indignantly.

"That's different."

"How?"

"You were conveying information as a witness, not playing detective."

"Was I right?" I asked. "Did Officer Tomlin leave his post to use the bathroom?"

"Yes, you were right," he snapped.

I crossed my arms over my chest. "So. I guess you don't want to know what I've learned."

Pierce glowered at me. Finally, he said, "Okay, spill it."

"Well, since you asked so politely," I said to needle him. When he looked away and scowled as he shifted in his seat, I almost laughed.

"Ms. Kelly, would you be so kind as to share with this overworked and underpaid civil servant what you've learned, please, ma'am," he said finally, still scowling.

"Why, thank you, Detective. I thought you'd never ask." I shared what I had discovered about Congressman Hamilton's efforts to keep Will from a federal job and how Melanie must have known Hamilton, growing up in the same town.

At first, Pierce tried to appear disinterested, but after a few moments, he took out his notepad and jotted down everything I said. When I finished, he pursed his lips and tapped the notebook with the end of his pen.

"You found all this on the Internet?"

I nodded. "I just wanted to show that Nguyen couldn't have murdered Hamilton. I had no way to prove it, so I tried to find other people who had a motive and opportunity. I can't imagine my boss or a respected reporter like Melanie Cole killing Congressman Hamilton any more than I believed Pham did. But, I had no idea it would be so easy to find other suspects."

"Neither did I." Pierce sighed heavily. "Damn. The guy doesn't even live here or represent this district, and there's three possible suspects. Now we have to check out the background of every single person who had access to that room during the two or three minutes Officer Tomlin left it unguarded."

"Surely some people can vouch for each other that they were together."

"During that narrow a window?" Pierce snorted. "Not likely. Take the nurses. They can say they were together from one o'clock until two o'clock, after one returned from lunch and before the other went on break, but if one of them ducked into a supply room for even a few minutes, that left the other unaccounted for."

"Hmmm. I see what you mean." When he said it like that, even Susan Wong, one of my favorite nurse managers, had the opportunity. Fortunately, I couldn't imagine her killing anyone unless he was threatening one of her four kids. But even she had complained about the congressman. Should I add her to my growing list?

I didn't know what else to suggest to Pierce. I'd dealt with a lot of complicated "he said, she said" investigations in the past, but nothing on this scale, and certainly not involving a murder.

I didn't envy Detective Pierce his job.

"By the way, we put Armstrong on a plane to Juneau this morning," he said with a wide grin.

I felt the heatwave surge through my body, and I hoped my face wasn't flushed a beet red. "I see."

Pierce chuckled softly and his eyes were lit up as if he was quite proud of himself. "Yeah, he was one unhappy camper." He must have seen my embarrassment, because he sobered immediately. "Sorry, Robyn."

I brushed aside his apology. "You have nothing to be sorry about. I'm the one who fell for his line."

"Not completely," Pierce asserted. "You're too smart for that. He was a really good reporter at one time, though. I checked him out through some of my sources. He really blew it with that faked interview, didn't he?"

"I can't believe he was that stupid. Or desperate." I looked at Pierce. "I guess some of us accept the fact that we're no longer twenty-five better than others do."

"Hell, I don't think I was ever twenty-five," Pierce said with a shrug. "I've always been a crusty old fart."

"Oh, I don't know," I said, relieved that the topic of Peter was now over. "I imagine you were quite the dashing street cop at one time."

Pierce rolled his eyes. "I live in constant fear I'll have to attend some official function that requires my uniform. I don't think they make them in my size anymore."

This was a side of Pierce I hadn't seen before, the dry sense of humor. He had shown me the tough-cop, the compassionate-cop, and the efficient-cop aspects of his personality, but not this one. I found it very appealing.

"They must make uniforms your size."

"Yeah, they do," he said wiping his hand over his face. "And then, they report the purchase to a commanding officer who makes you have a physical, and you know what happens then."

"No more cookies?"

He shook his head. "No more cookies."

"Almost not worth living anymore," I said with a mock sigh.

"My sentiments exactly."

"Would you like another of Mrs. Flanders' homemade, loaded with butter and sugar, cookies?"

"Absolutely."

We both laughed as I brushed past him and went to Connie's desk.

"Make it two," he called from my office. "One for the road."

"Having fun?" The gleam in Connie's eyes said she thought there was more than official business going on in my office.

"I'm trying to distract him from how much extra work I've created for him." I plucked a handful of cookies from the tin. At Connie's dropped jaw, I patted my hip and said, "Better him than us."

"You're right." But her gaze lingered hungrily on the cookies.

I popped the top back on the tin and returned to my office where I pulled a tissue from the box and laid it on the table for the cookies.

"Is this the best you can do?" Pierce asked. "Where's the good china? The linen napkins?"

"I wasn't expecting company," I quipped.

After we'd munched silently for a few minutes, I asked, "So where do we go from here?"

"*We? We* don't go anywhere."

"But, I helped you. I gave you information you didn't have," I protested.

"I know, Robyn. I appreciate what you've done, but this is a police matter."

I heard the exasperation in his voice, but I didn't like being brushed off. "You're just annoyed because I found some other possible suspects," I grumbled.

"Suspects you don't think could have done it any more than you think Pham did it. You can't keep coming up with people and motives, and think none of them could possibly have murdered Hamilton." Pierce's voice rose.

"Sorry," I said, my voice rising too. "Next time I find a viable suspect with a strong motive and opportunity, I won't bother telling you so you won't have your case muddled up."

"There won't be a next time," he said, his voice louder, "because you're not poking your nose into this any further."

"What are you going to do, arrest me?" I said, louder still.

"Don't be ridiculous." He picked up a cookie and waved it at me. "I'll say it again. I appreciate what you've done. But this is a high-profile case. I have to be very careful about how I get each piece of evidence. I have to build my case, brick by brick. I'll get to the truth, but I have to do it my way. In accordance with the law. *Comprendez?*"

I nodded. When he put it that way, I understood. Still, it seemed a shame to reject my help. I did my own form of investigation in this hospital every day. Everyone knew me and would talk to me a lot more freely than they would talk to a police detective.

At my nod, Pierce visibly relaxed. "Good. I'm glad we've got that settled." He took a big bite from his cookie.

"So, what are you going to do next?"

He scowled at me, but after he swallowed, he said, "I'm going to call Walden, Montana, and see what I can find out. It's a long shot, but you never know."

"I'd hate to think Melanie's mixed up in something like this."

Pierce shot me a patronizing look. "Robyn, you don't want anyone to be guilty. But someone has to be. Congressman Hamilton is dead, and he didn't die from natural causes."

"I know. It's just that I find it hard to believe anyone I know would do something like that."

"Anyone is capable of murder if the motive is strong enough. Trust me, Robyn. Anyone. And that means the guilty person will take whatever steps are necessary to keep from being revealed." He paused for a moment, then gave me a hard look. "Do you understand what I'm saying?"

He meant the murderer would be willing to murder again if it meant protecting himself.

A shiver raced down my spine. Pierce was warning me that I could become the next victim.

CHAPTER 11

While I drove to work the next day, I tried to take Detective Pierce's warning to heart. With Margie on vacation, we were short-handed, so I really had no time to investigate a murder. But as I worked, scenarios of who might have killed Congressman Hamilton drifted through my mind. Some possible, some ridiculous. None that I could prove.

The first thing I did when I reached my office, though, was sequester myself for half an hour to proofread my section of the Quality Report. I had given it back to Connie to print and deliver to Will when the phone rang. "Robyn Kelly."

"My office. Now." Click.

I had to laugh. Dr. Weiser always assumed I knew it was him. His deep voice with a hint of accent made him easy to identify, still even a brief comment about what I was dropping everything for would be nice.

The only case I had pending with him was the Stone case from the Insurance Commissioner, so I grabbed the file, a pad of paper, and a pen. "I'm going to Weiser's office," I told Connie as I sailed out the door.

When I reached OB/GYN, the receptionist nodded as I passed her desk on my way to the back. I saw Darlene and gave her a quick wave before knocking on Dr. Weiser's office door.

"Enter." A tall, wiry man, Gunther Weiser exuded energy. With his salt-and-pepper hair, still thick and wavy, and his pewter-gray eyes keen with interest, he had earned the nickname, "the gray fox." Impatient with administrators and purposeless meetings, he listened attentively when it was important, picking up what was spoken and what was left unsaid. No wonder his patients fell in love with him. "Ah, good. I like that you are prompt."

I took my usual seat across from his desk, but didn't open my file.

Dr. Weiser handed me a stack of pictures. "These are from my trip to Indonesia." He proceeded to entertain me with anecdotes about a pirate ambush, hiking through the rain forests, and delivering a village chieftain's son, a breech birth that would have left the child brain-damaged and the mother hemorrhaging to death if he had not happened by at the right time. The chieftain, in his gratitude, offered Dr. Weiser a choice between three goats or his twelve-year-old daughter.

"I did not, of course, want either," he said. "But it is not wise to anger the tribal leader, so I chose the goats."

I looked up from the picture of him holding the animals on tethers and laughed. "How did you explain them to Customs when you came home?"

"Do not be silly. I sold them at the next market and put the money in an account for the child."

How like him, I thought as I handed the pictures back.

"Now, this case. What do we know?" He was all business, this time in his teacher role.

I wasn't prepared for a case review, and silently wished that for today, he would just give me the answer. Opening the file, I glanced at him and saw kindness in his eyes.

"This has been a difficult week for you."

It was not a question. "Yes, it has."

"Okay, we will walk through it together."

"I'd like that."

Fortunately, the case turned out to be very straightforward.

Mrs. Stone had enrolled with Health Assurance through her job, and the medical-insurance coverage began April first. She saw our Dr. Kyler the end of April for menopausal problems. He prescribed hormone replacement and told her to return in six weeks. Instead, she saw Dr. Chin, who was not affiliated with Health Assurance, the first week of May and had a hysterectomy a week later.

Dr. Weiser tsked. "The uterus is the most maligned and abused organ in the body."

I didn't contradict him, but from flipping through Dr. Chin's records prior to Mrs. Stone seeing Dr. Kyler, it appeared she'd had problems for a long time.

"I think if you check, you will find she failed to fill Dr. Kyler's prescription," Dr. Weiser said.

"It looks like she changed insurances without checking first to see if Dr. Chin was on the provider list."

"Can you read that first line on the May appointment?"

I squinted and turned the page at an angle. "I think it says 'pre-surg exam'."

"Ah! How did you do that? I could not make sense of it."

A physician complaining about the legibility of another physician's handwriting? I didn't laugh. "It comes from reading so many different records."

"Good. Okay. So what does this tell us?"

"It sounds to me that she had already discussed the hyst with Dr. Chin." I looked at his notes from the previous appointment. "Yes, here it is, from March twenty-second. 'Discussed options with patient. She is changing insurance for lower deductible and will schedule surgery after April first.' "

Dr. Weiser leaned back in his chair. "So the doctor knows she is changing insurance, but he fails to mention his services are not covered by the new insurance." He tsked again. "From our perspective, this is not a question of medical care, Robyn. It is strictly insurance coverage. Now, Dr. Chin was negligent by not informing her, but that is not something we can affect."

"It looks that way to me too. She probably realized what happened when she received the letter rejecting the bills. Blaming Stan Kyler is a ruse. I'll write the letter, but since she stated her complaint as quality of care, I have to run it by you before sending it out."

"That is fine." Dr. Weiser scribbled on his pink sheet that there was no physician error and that it was an insurance coverage disagreement, and signed it.

I returned to my office and started organizing the case to write the letter after calling the pharmacy to confirm Mrs. Stone had not, in fact, filled Dr. Kyler's prescription. I had all of five minutes, just long enough to be totally immersed. I jumped when the phone rang. "Robyn Kelly."

"Hi, Mom."

"Josh." I glanced at my watch. "Is everything okay? Shouldn't you be at school?"

Josh laughed. "Everything's fine. I'm on my way to physics. But I was wondering, can I invite Chuck for Thanksgiving?"

Thanksgiving?

I flipped open my calendar. Oh, lordy, that's right. It was next week. Even with Connie's prompt, I'd forgotten to give a thought to my own dinner plans. I hesitated. "Sure. That would be fine," I said more positively than I felt.

"I knew you wouldn't mind. And Mom? Do you know how to fix baked yams?"

"Baked yams."

"Yeah, you know, the kind with marshmallows melted on top."

I pulled the receiver away from my ear and stared at it. This couldn't be my son. Some alien had taken over his body.

"Mom? You still there?"

I set the receiver back against my ear. "I'm here. You want baked yams this year."

"Uh-huh."

"I probably have a recipe for it somewhere."

"That'd be great. Chuck's from the south and it's kind of a tradition there."

"Okay. I'll see what I can do." I started jotting a shopping list. Yams and marshmallows. Turkey, bread, celery. After all these years, I had it pretty well memorized, but if I didn't write it down, I'd forget something small, but critical, like cranberries.

"What time?"

"Dinner at two with plenty of things to nibble during the football games?"

"Thanks, Mom. You're terrific."

Definitely an alien takeover. "I'm glad you noticed."

Josh laughed. "Gotta go. See you tonight."

"Bye." By then I was speaking into a dead connection.

I hung up the phone and sighed. Thanksgiving had always been quiet for Josh and me. That was the day David had died, and since then, we'd always spent the day alone together. We watched football, played games, and ate turkey, but it was a day we saved for each other.

With mixed feelings, I acknowledged that this year marked the change of that tradition. I had known it would come someday, and I was pleased Josh had reached out to a classmate who otherwise would be alone. At least Josh would be home and not going off to someone else's house. That was something. But what about next year?

He was growing up and soon he'd leave home. I had to start thinking seriously about that. Most of my life had been focused on Josh and work. I had other interests, of course, but I'd wanted to be there for Josh, and I had been. The reality was, he didn't have ball games for me to attend anymore. I hadn't been able to help him with his homework for a long time. All that physics and math numbed my brain.

But, he still needed me to buy his clothes. I smiled smugly. On that happy note, I set the Thanksgiving grocery list aside and went back to the letter.

Five minutes later, I became aware of the smell of fresh coffee. Looking up, I saw Connie standing in the doorway with a fresh latté in each hand.

"Here, Boss. Thought you might need this."

After clicking to save the letter I was working on, I reached for the steaming cup. "Thanks." I took a sip and sighed with contentment.

Connie nodded and slipped into the extra chair. A worried frown replaced her usual cheery expression.

Setting my cup down, I turned to face her. "Connie? What's wrong?"

She pursed her lips as if not sure what to say. Finally, she took a deep breath, then burst out, "I'm worried about you."

That was the last thing I expected her to say. I gave a short laugh. "Me? Why on earth would you be worried about me?"

"I overheard your discussion with Detective Pierce. I wasn't eavesdropping, but I couldn't help overhearing. And now . . . It's . . . it's this feeling I have. That something's going to happen to you."

I gave her a reassuring pat on the shoulder. "After the last couple of days, I'm sure it won't be anything I can't handle."

"No, Rob. This is different." She grabbed my hand. "I'm afraid something bad's going to happen to you because you're trying to solve Congressman Hamilton's murder."

I smiled and eased my hand from her grip. "Are you practicing your psychic abilities again?"

She looked at me, then her gaze shifted over my shoulder to

the window, but not before I caught the haunted look in her eyes. "I don't understand it, Rob," she whispered. She glanced at me, then back to the window. "Just before I reached your door, I felt this overwhelming sense of something bad. This . . . this invisible cloud, menacing. The hairs on the back of my neck stood straight up. Then the feeling was gone. But I know it was intended for you."

Now, I'm not a superstitious person, but that gave me pause. I'd heard other people describe similar experiences, and found it disturbing to find it applied to me. Leaning back in my chair, I considered her words before I said slowly, "I suppose there's always an element of risk in a situation like this, but I'm being very careful."

"I know, but someone's going to figure out you're the one feeding the police information."

"Oh, I think Detective Pierce is more subtle than that. I'm sure he's doing his own research. He wouldn't act on my say-so alone."

Connie still looked worried and skeptical, so I added, "But if it makes you feel any better, I'll be extra careful from now on."

She nodded and returned to her desk. What else could she do? She was in no position to forbid me to continue looking for suspects any more than Detective Pierce was.

I tried to pick up the letter where I'd left off, but I was distracted. I kept thinking about what Connie had said, and was more unnerved than I wanted to admit. First Detective Pierce, and now Connie warning me.

There was a murderer out there, someone with a strong interest in staying undiscovered. Was that motive enough to kill again? I had to admit it was, yet I still found it difficult to accept that someone I knew, someone I worked with every day, could do something that cold-blooded. Will Slater? I couldn't see it. Melanie Cole? I couldn't see that either. Susan Wong?

She didn't even make the list.

Rather than work myself into an emotional frenzy, I forced everything else from my mind and returned to the letter. That worked for about five more minutes, when Connie approached my office again and rapped lightly on the doorjamb.

"Melanie Cole's here," she said.

"She is?" I felt a twinge of dread and guilt. "What does she want?"

"She says it's about the patient-rep group you mentioned to her."

It took me a moment, but then I remembered our earlier conversation. "Send her in," I said, then grumbled to myself as I saved and closed the computer file, "I didn't want to finish this letter before Christmas anyway."

When Melanie appeared, I gestured for her to sit down. "How's the news business today?"

She bobbed her head from side to side. "So-so. No new big stories and nothing breaking on the old ones." She raised one eyebrow. "You don't have anything new on the Hamilton murder, do you?"

"I'm sure I know less than you do," I said, although I suspected that wasn't completely true. And what I knew would probably surprise the daylights out of her, especially that she was on my list of possible suspects. "What brings you here?"

"I told Ashley Volstrom, our consumer-affairs reporter, about you, or rather, your program, and that other hospitals have the same kind of thing. She's thinking about doing a feature and wanted to know if there's an organization."

Nodding, I pulled open a desk drawer and reached for a file folder. "Here's the current roster. I'll make a copy for you."

"Thanks. I'll give it to Ashley when I get back to the station."

I walked Melanie to the outer office and quickly made the copy. "Here you go." I handed the roster to her. "The current president is Sharon Forbes at Hillsbrook Memorial. She's probably the best person to start with."

Melanie made a small checkmark by Sharon's name and dropped the paper into her bag. "You never know when one of these consumer-affairs stories will turn into something big and be transferred to a news reporter." She grinned. "I want to be the reporter Ashley thinks of first."

"Cooperation is the name of most games," I said.

"Well, thanks again, Robyn." She gathered her coat and bag and headed out the door.

"Drop in anytime," I said.

After she left, I wondered why Melanie had come by personally when a phone call from this Ashley would have sufficed. Was it paranoia from Connie's warning? I finally brushed it off as guilt over mentioning Melanie's name to Detective Pierce.

Speaking of the detective, I realized it had been twenty-four hours since I'd seen him. That wasn't a bad thing, but he'd become a fixture in my life the last couple of days, and it seemed odd for him not to be there. I was sure he would show up again to harass me about something, so I shrugged it off and reviewed where I had left off with the letter.

"Rob!" Connie called from the front.

"What?" I couldn't keep exasperation from my voice.

"You have that meeting!"

"I got it. I got it." Thoroughly frustrated at my inability to get anything done, I scooped up a pad, a pen I wouldn't feel bad about losing, and my coffee, which was now cool enough to slurp with abandon.

"I'll be back," I said as I left the office and hurried down the hall. I wasn't looking forward to this. Corporate had a bee in its bonnet about the latest "new way" to do business, and the consultant was here to give us the sales pitch on how this would change our lives, improve everything, and reduce costs. I am not a total cynic, but yeah, right.

I hurried into the conference room and set my notepad and coffee on the table between Judy Francis and Susan Wong.

"Hello, ladies," I said as I sat down.

"Hi, Rob," Susan said, while Judy only gave a token wave, her attention focused on a report.

Will and Brenda were huddled in a corner talking to a man I didn't recognize, but I assumed he was our guest speaker. Melanie stood off to the side as if waiting to catch Will's eye. What was that about? She was holding a pocket calendar, so maybe she wanted to schedule an interview with him.

Most of the other people were still talking and helping themselves to the giant cookies and the cans of pop on the cart delivered by Dietary. It's a little known fact that hospitals run on caffeine in the morning and sugar in the afternoon.

I started to say something to Susan when I saw Cynthia Martin standing in the doorway. The young woman didn't look well as she scanned the crowded room. Her agitated gaze rested on me for a moment, her eyes narrowed in recognition, and her whole body stiffened. Then, with a subtle lift of her chin, she continued her search, calm crossing her face when she spotted her mother.

I watched as Cynthia made her way to Brenda, who broke away from Will and the consultant to talk to her daughter. I wondered for a moment why Cynthia had appeared wary when she saw me. I'd only met her twice and had been nice to her both times. Maybe it was because I'd been the one who found her precious employer, or maybe because I told her about the autopsy. Whatever her anxiety was about, it wasn't my problem.

Melanie was now talking to Will, and from his expression, Will wasn't happy. But then, he seldom was.

With a few minutes left before the meeting was scheduled to start, I scanned the agenda. "I'm glad I don't have to perform this time," I said to Judy.

"This consultant better have the best idea since sliced bread," she replied. "I left a scheduling nightmare to come to this thing, and it better not be a waste of time."

"Tell me about it." Susan leaned forward to look around me at Nancy. "Do you know how hard it is to explain to patients and their families that it's perfectly safe to be here, even if a guarded congressman was murdered just a few rooms away?"

"You must both be doing a good job, because no one's called my office to complain," I said.

"I'm thinking about hypnotizing them to think it happened at Hillsbrook Memorial," Susan said with a sigh.

"Hey, if hypnosis works, let me know," Judy said. "I have some things I'd like my staff to forget."

As we laughed, I looked around the room again and spotted Connie in the doorway. She beckoned for me to join her.

"What's up?" I asked as we stepped into the hall.

"Dr. Lieffer's on the phone. He needs to talk to you now."

I followed her to our office. The chief of the Kenmore clinic wouldn't be calling unless it was important. As it turned out, it wasn't serious, just a procedural question he needed answered while he had a patient in his office.

By the time I returned to the conference room, Brenda had called the meeting to order and had darkened the room for the slide projector. Will must have already given his two cents' worth because he was gone. But the chairs and tables had been re-arranged classroom-style.

After my eyes adjusted, I spotted my things on an extra chair against the wall. I slipped into my seat and started taking notes. I took a big swallow from my latté and grimaced. After all this time, it was barely lukewarm, and bitter. I took only a few more sips.

I had been right. The consultant was here to give a detailed presentation on how his version of the "new way" was better than anyone else's. He went into minute detail, quickly flipping through slides. After a while, I started to feel woozy.

I stopped looking at the screen and tried to concentrate on his words, but that didn't make me feel any better. Then my heart started pounding. Slowly at first, then faster. I'd never felt anything like this before. The nausea worsened and my head pounded as if a dozen jackhammers were working inside my brain.

Panic set in.

I had to get out of there.

Fumbling, I gripped my notepad and cup and stood. I fought the dizziness as I walked toward the door. One step. Then another. I concentrated on reaching the door.

I had to escape.

I groped for the doorknob and opened the door just enough to stagger into the hall. I squinted as the bright lights hurt my eyes. Everything looked yellow. What was wrong with me?

Leaning against the wall for balance, I made my way toward my office. I had to get there before . . . before . . . Everything was worse, the pounding in my head, the nausea. Something was terribly wrong.

At last, I reached my office. I pushed the door open and stumbled in. Connie was at her desk. She looked up. I opened my mouth to speak, but nothing came out.

Blackness.

"Where is she?"

Josh's voice filtered through the heavy blanket of unconsciousness. Shrill. Filled with fear. I pushed myself to concentrate.

I had to reach him, had to comfort him. But I could not get beyond . . . beyond . . . I did not know what it was I had to get beyond.

Then I heard another voice. Deep, familiar. Soothing.

"It's okay, son. She's going to be okay," Larry Bridgeway said with a physician's practiced reassurance.

"You're sure?" The panic in Josh's voice changed to wariness.

"I wouldn't lie to you."

"Okay. If you're sure." Josh was calm again. He did not need my help.

Tired from the effort, I let go and sank into peaceful oblivion.

"Robyn. Wake up."

I stirred at the sharp command. Tired. Still so very, very tired.

"Come on, girl. Look at me."

With a groan, I slowly opened my eyes, then closed them again. "Too bright," I croaked.

Fingers snapped and the light dimmed. I opened my eyes again and blinked several times. Larry Bridgeway's ebony face hovered over me. An ICU nurse stood on the other side of the bed, her gaze focused on the monitors stationed behind me.

I wanted to sit up, but my body wouldn't cooperate. My mouth tasted gritty. "Water," I whispered.

Larry held my head up so I could drink from a straw.

"Just a few sips now," he cautioned.

That was fine with me. The effort exhausted me and I was happy to sink against the pillow again. He handed the cup back to the nurse, then took my pulse and blood pressure.

While he did that, I tried to make sense of what was happening. Gradually, I remembered the meeting and not feeling well. Trying to make it back to my office.

"What happened?"

Larry glanced at the nurse, then back at me. His expression revealed nothing. He took my hand. "Don't you worry about a thing, Rob. You're going to be fine."

"Why am I in ICU?"

"You're getting the VIP treatment, of course. Only the best for our favorite patient rep." Larry smiled, but it didn't reach his eyes, and his jocular tone sounded false.

I felt myself growing more alert, and more concerned.

"Level with me, Larry," I said in a stronger voice. "What's going on?"

He sighed before nodding to the nurse. She stepped across the room, opened the door partway, and spoke quietly to someone on the other side. Then she stepped back, opening the door wider. Josh, his face pinched with fear, and Detective Pierce, whose expression was as masked as Larry's, stepped in.

"Mom." Josh stumbled toward me and buried his face in my shoulder. I laid my arm across his back and patted him gently. His sobbing broke my heart.

"It's okay, Josh. I'm going to be fine. Right, Larry?"

Larry nodded once, curtly. I wanted to ask more questions, but right now, Josh needed my attention. I spoke quietly to him and finally he lifted his head. He sat up, but held my hand tightly.

"What happened?" I asked again, glancing from Larry to Detective Pierce.

Larry signaled for the nurse to take Josh out and she moved toward him.

"I'm not leaving my mother." His jaw jutted out and he looked so much like his father. He held my hand all the more fiercely.

Larry glanced at Pierce, who shrugged. "You're very lucky, Rob."

I sighed. "No clinical mumbo-jumbo, Larry. Just give me the bottom line."

Larry glanced at Pierce again. The detective stepped forward.

"The bottom line is you were poisoned."

"Poisoned! But how?"

Larry and Pierce exchanged looks again.

"Someone tried to kill you." Pierce's words were flat, unemotional, but the effect on me was electrifying.

"Someone tried to what—?" I fumbled for the bed controls and pushed the button to raise the top. When I was finally sitting up, I tried to laugh it off. "You've been watching too much television, Detective Pierce."

"He's not kidding, Rob," Larry said. "You got a dose of digoxin. Not enough to be lethal, but enough to make you very sick."

Now I was more confused than ever. "Digoxin! That's a heart medication. I don't take that," I said.

Detective Pierce moved closer. "We found the remains of several capsules in the bottom of your coffee cup. It's lucky you didn't finish that latté. That's probably what saved you."

Stunned by his revelation, I slumped against the pillow. "After it got cold, it didn't taste good," I murmured.

By this time, Josh was squeezing my hand so tight that it hurt. I wriggled my fingers and he loosened his grip, but his expression was still an intense frown. I didn't like him hearing that someone had almost left him an orphan. I wasn't particularly happy about it, either.

"Dr. Bridgeway, would you mind if I spoke with Robyn alone?"

Larry gave me a visual once-over, then nodded. "But only for a few minutes, Detective. I don't want her tired out."

"You too, son," Pierce said gently to Josh. "I need to ask you to leave."

"But—"

"It's okay, Josh. I'll be fine," I said with more spirit than I really felt. "You go with Dr. Bridgeway and find out when I can come home."

Reluctantly, Josh nodded and followed Larry from the room. Pierce and I watched the door swing shut behind them, then turned to face each other.

"Who—"

"Who—"

Detective Pierce and I obviously had the same question. "I haven't a clue who could have done it," I said.

"Let's start with who had opportunity."

Despite the seriousness of the situation, I couldn't help but quirk a grim smile. Opportunity was what attracted the police to arrest Pham, and that had led to my looking for other possible suspects.

"Connie brought me the coffee, but—"

"She's the one who found what was left of the capsules in your cup."

The closeness of my close call was beginning to sink in. "Did she tell you—"

"That she warned you about getting hurt?" Pierce interrupted again. It was getting to be an annoying habit. "Yes, she told me. Did the coffee taste okay when she gave it to you?"

I looked at him sharply. Connie was a suspect? No, not possible. "It tasted fine," I said truthfully.

"So, who else had a chance to drop something into your cup?"

"Melanie Cole stopped by the office."

"Did she—"

"Not there," I said with a sigh. "She was never alone with the coffee in my office, but she was in the meeting room talking to Will Slater when Connie called me out. But she wouldn't want to hurt me."

Pierce hoisted himself up on the edge of the bed. "Remember that little tidbit you picked up about her growing up in the same town as Hamilton? Well, I did some checking."

"Really?" I was inordinately pleased that he'd taken me seriously and followed up on my clue.

"I had to pull more than a few strings to get some sealed records unsealed." He paused to let the suspense build. It worked.

"And?" I prompted.

"And your hunch was right. Seems young Jake Hamilton had a real wild streak as a boy. When he was a senior in high school, he cornered Melanie under the bleachers at a football game."

"Did he . . . did he rape her?" I dreaded his answer.

Pierce nodded. "The local judge wrote it off as a boys-will-be-boys thing, because Hamilton testified she was asking for it, then changed her mind too late. She said he'd assaulted other girls, but none of them came forward. Probably too ashamed or didn't want to be the subject of gossip. The judge ordered the records sealed so Hamilton's record would be clean. He had excellent grades, was the track star. And Hamilton's adoptive father was the judge's cousin by marriage."

"I see. So Melanie is emotionally scarred and Hamilton goes on to national glory. Doesn't seem right, does it?"

"No, but you know as well as I do, Robyn, that justice isn't always served. However, it does give Melanie Cole a motive to commit murder. And if she realized later that she'd revealed too much of herself to you, well. . . ." His expression told me he thought I'd brought it on myself.

"She's not the only one who had opportunity." I told Pierce about leaving my coffee unattended and how the room had been rearranged and was dark when I returned five or so minutes later.

Pierce threw up his hands. "Why don't you just tape a bull's-eye to your chest and hand out rifles?"

As I'd told the story, I started to feel incredibly stupid. Pierce's reaction didn't help any. "I didn't think—"

"That's right," he snapped. "You didn't think. Do you know how close you —" Pierce slid off the bed and paced the room as if trying to get his temper under control. "Okay. Who was at the meeting?"

I rattled off a half dozen names before he raised his hand to stop me.

"In other words, half the hospital," he snarled.

That was an exaggeration, but I didn't think this was the time to point that out. "So, Detective," I said as brightly as possible. "Where do we start?"

"We?" He gave me a long, hard look. "You're not going to do anything. It's your unwillingness to leave the investigation alone that put you in this position. Now back off."

Feeling thoroughly chastised and contrite, I nodded.

"Good," Pierce said. "Let me do my job. I'll start by looking for the person with the most to lose if you live."

That seemed as good a place as any.

CHAPTER 12

I woke up groggy and disoriented. Where was I? Then, I remembered. The hospital. I was a patient.

Someone had poisoned me.

After wiggling my toes, I tested my hands and arms, then cautiously rolled my head from side to side. Relieved that everything still worked, I still wasn't ready to try sitting up.

I gradually became aware of the heated discussion going on outside my room.

"I want to take my mother home." Josh's low voice was controlled, but fiercely intense.

"That's not advisable." Larry sounded just as direct, but not unkind. I knew he was shaking his head and wearing his "serious physician" expression.

"Why not? You said she's okay. Her heart rate's stable."

"She is stable, Josh. For now. But if there's a problem, she's better off right here."

"There's something you're overlooking, Doc," said a third voice. So, Pierce was still here.

I breathed a sigh of relief. His presence felt like a safety net. The hospital, on the other hand, was no longer a friendly place.

"Someone poisoned her," he said. "The longer she's here, the greater the chance they'll try again."

I heard only grim silence. Pierce had spoken the inconceivable.

It was one thing to have a stranger murdered in our hospital.

In an odd way, we had emotionally detached ourselves from the crime. We'd focused on the murder's effect on the hospital's reputation, and speculated on who did it as if it were a mystery dinner theater.

This afternoon was different, shocking me into reality. One of *us* had deliberately tried to murder *me*. From Larry's silence, he must have felt the same way. Dismay. Horror. Disbelief. Not *here* at Madrona Bay. Not *our* staff. We knew each other. We laughed and complained together, shared birthday lunches and budget woes. We were all good people, caring and compassionate.

Now we faced the chilling reality that someone we considered a friend and colleague had committed one murder and had attempted a second one.

A wave of nausea swept through me and I swallowed hard. It finally sank in how close I had come to dying. Connie and Detective Pierce had both warned me to mind my own business, to let the police conduct the investigation. But no, I'd thought I knew more and could do better than the professionals.

The three somber-faced men entered my room, three people I knew I could count on. I glanced at Larry, and, for a moment, my confidence wavered. Could I really trust him? Then, I remembered he hadn't been at that meeting. He couldn't have poisoned my coffee. But the momentary doubt brought a sense of loss. I shuddered, knowing I must be on guard with everyone in the hospital until the murderer was identified.

Larry looked at me, and his dark-brown eyes burned with an intensity I'd never seen before. He must have caught that brief questioning in my expression, and no matter how much he might understand, his feelings were hurt.

"Sorry." I reached out.

He took my hand, giving it a reassuring squeeze. "It's okay. I understand."

I shook my head. It was not okay and we both knew it. But there was nothing we could do about it now.

"I'm taking you home," Josh said.

Larry opened his mouth as if to say something, then snapped it shut. Instead, he scribbled away on a clipboard, pulled off a piece of paper, and handed it to Josh. "Here are the discharge instructions."

He turned and pointed his finger at me. "Rob, you are to rest through the weekend. No stopping by your office to pick up work. No calling Connie for messages. Go home and do nothing. It'll take a day or two before the digoxin is completely out of your system."

I rolled my eyes and glanced at Pierce in search of support from him. Instead, he gave me that don't-you-dare look and shook his head.

Resigned to my helpless damsel fate, I asked, "Anything else?"

Larry looked at Josh again. "If she so much as shivers, I want her in here."

"There's a fire station two blocks from us. I'll call them," Josh said. Then he grinned. "Unless Detective Pierce wants to loan me a siren so I can race Mom back here myself."

Pierce clapped Josh on the shoulder. "Call the aid car, son. Don't go playing Richard Petty on my streets."

The relaxed camaraderie between them surprised me. Josh was usually reserved around strangers. But then, I suspected Pierce had a way with distraught family members. I remembered how I'd felt consoled by his solidness after finding Hamilton's body.

While Larry reviewed the discharge instructions with Josh, Pierce approached my bed. "I'll feel a lot better once we get you out of here," he said quietly.

The anger behind his words caught me off guard. His professional detachment had slipped, and I was comforted that he might have a personal interest in my well-being. I nodded as he returned to listen to Larry and ask a few more questions.

They left so I could dress with the help of a nurse's aide, then returned with Larry pushing a wheelchair.

"Oh, no," I said. "I'm walking out of here."

"Hospital rules," Larry insisted.

"And I'm the one who breaks the rules, remember?" The last thing I wanted was to look like a victim as I left the building. The grapevine would have already reported my collapse, but I couldn't bear the concern or speculation on my colleagues' faces. Besides, if I came across the poisoner, I wanted to look him straight in the eye. Maybe I would recognize his disappointment and identify him from that. Wishful thinking? Probably.

"Get in the wheelchair, Rob," Larry said again.

"We'll take the service elevator," Pierce said. "If there're any reporters hanging around, I don't want them to see us."

I hadn't even thought of that. Dear God, had I made the evening news again? I didn't want to know. "The service elevator would be fine."

We rode down in silence before I realized I couldn't leave yet. "I don't have my purse," I said. "It's in my office."

"I'll get it," Josh said.

"We'll do it later," Pierce countered.

"But I need it now," I insisted.

Pierce scowled at me. "What could possibly be in there that's so important?"

Exasperated, I said, "My keys and wallet."

Pierce laughed shortly. "You can survive without them."

"Then how am I going to drive home?"

The elevator doors opened, but no one moved. Josh and Pierce stared at me as if I had lost my mind.

"You are not driving, Mom."

Josh startled me. He'd used the same no-nonsense tone I used with him when I denied a request and made it clear the discussion was over. When had he assumed the mantle of a responsible adult? He was not my little boy anymore.

We left the building, and Pierce stayed with me on the loading dock while Josh went for his pick-up truck.

"I don't want to be stranded at home," I grumbled.

"You won't be stranded," Pierce said. "You're not supposed to leave the house anyway. We'll get your car and your purse later."

I muttered to myself at being at the mercy of these two concerned tyrants.

Josh pulled up and Pierce helped me into Josh's truck, then added, "Stay home and rest, Robyn. Let me handle this."

I nodded reluctantly.

"Call me if she gives you any trouble, Josh." He slammed the door before I could give him a piece of my mind. In a short time, they had bonded and were now ganging up on me.

We bounced and jostled our way home in silence. My bones felt like they needed a chiropractic adjustment by the time we reached our driveway, and I would've given Josh money to buy new shock absorbers that night. If I'd had my purse.

From the garage, we entered the kitchen and after Taffy greeted us with her boundless enthusiasm, I absorbed the safety of being home. I never comprehended before how helpless patients are in the hospital; strange and stark surroundings, clothes taken away, and dependent on strangers for even the most basic of needs. The bright colors in the kitchen cheered me. The lack of an antiseptic smell was as welcoming as the fragrance of fresh baked bread.

All the stress of the week exploded, draining my remaining energy for anything more strenuous than a hot shower and climbing into bed, too tired even for a comforting cup of tea. In a daze, I kissed Josh on the cheek and said good night. He hugged me then, a bone-crushing hug that told me how scared he really was.

I patted his back. "Worried about your old mom?"

He nodded.

"I'm okay," I said.

He lifted his head and I saw tears welling in his eyes. "Someone almost killed you, Mom."

Despite his grown-up façade, he sounded as vulnerable as a five-year-old. I reached up and smoothed his hair into place.

"But they didn't, did they? I'm all right, Josh."

The phone rang.

"I'll get it." Josh reached across the counter, picked up the phone, and checked the number before answering it. "Hi, Granddad. Yeah, she's here."

I took the offered phone. "Hi, Da."

"Robyn Anne, are you all right?"

"Yes, Da, I'm fine." I wasn't really, but I would not give him something more to worry about.

"Don't lie to me. I called your office this afternoon and talked to that Connie who works for you. Been calling the house for hours. You were poisoned!"

When he said it like that, I winced. "The important thing is, I'm okay now. Really."

"Humph. Do you want me to come?"

"No, Da. I'll be fine, really," I repeated. "Josh is here and the doctor thought I was well enough to come home." I didn't add that a murderer still running loose in the hospital was the best reason for getting me out of there.

After several more reassurances, and promising that Josh and I were coming for Christmas, we hung up.

I looked at Josh. "I wish he hadn't heard."

Josh shrugged. "He was going to find out sometime. Think how mad he'd be if we'd deliberately kept it from him."

"I suppose. Okay, you should probably do what you need to for school tomorrow."

"But Dr. Bridgeway said—"

"Larry is a very conscientious physician. I'll be fine. You don't need to stand watch tonight or tomorrow. If something happens, I'll call you."

"But—"

"No buts. I'm going to the shower."

He nodded, but I felt his troubled gaze follow me from the room.

He had come close to being an orphan today. On a practical level, I'd made all the necessary arrangements years ago: a will, life insurance to pay off the mortgage and provide an income, a trustee to manage things until Josh was twenty-one. He wouldn't be homeless and he'd have funds to finish his education without burdening my father. But, he wouldn't have a mom or dad. Of all the things that had almost happened today, that scared me the most.

I pushed from my mind the somber thoughts of what might have been. Instead, when I reached the bathroom, I debated between a long soaking bath or a quick shower. The shower won only because I didn't think I could stay awake long enough to fill the tub. I shed my clothes and dropped them into the hamper, then stepped under the pounding spray of hot water.

For once, I didn't even consider conserving water. I let it beat on me, warming me to the core. My mind drifted, a meditative trance, until I realized I was falling asleep. I dried off and pulled on my comfort pajamas, white flannel with pink teddy bears, and toddled off to bed. Slipping between Egyptian cotton sheets and fluffing the floral duvet dispelled the remnants of my hospital stay.

If I had expected to fall asleep immediately, however, I was sorely disappointed. I lay on my back, covers up to my chin. I curled into a fetal ball, covers over my ears. I tried the same position, opposite side. A quick glance at the clock told me only thirty minutes had passed.

Sitting up, I flipped on the table lamp and picked up my current book. I usually chose my bedtime reading based on its sleep-inducing potential. This book, an acclaimed literary novel, had been outstanding, putting me to sleep every night for the last two weeks in no more than four pages.

Tonight, it failed. I couldn't focus on the angst-filled characters who continued to do nothing to solve their own problems. Instead, my mind drifted back to the hospital and to a subject guaranteed to ruin a good night's sleep.

Who wanted me dead?

I put the book down, turned off the light, and slid back under the covers to stare at the dark ceiling. Again, I asked myself, who wanted me dead? It only made sense that it was the same person who killed Congressman Hamilton. We didn't have two murderers running loose in the building. And why me? Because I was getting too close to the truth was the obvious reason.

True, I'd been sleuthing, but I'd been subtle, or at least I had thought so. Was someone tracking my Internet searches? No, that couldn't be it. No one I worked with was that computer literate. And I hadn't talked to anyone about my suspicions except Detective Pierce, and he wasn't about to leak information.

That line of thought wasn't helping, so I switched to who had the opportunity. A mind-numbing list of people had access to Hamilton. The list of possible poisoners was considerably smaller, but more distressing. No wonder Pierce was so annoyed with me. It had been dumb to leave my coffee cup unattended, but who would've thought I'd be in danger among my colleagues? The only drugs we used at meetings were caffeine and sugar.

Larry wanted me to stay home tomorrow and rest through the weekend. Pierce wanted me to leave the case alone. Both reasonable pieces of advice, given the circumstances.

The problem was, despite it all, I wasn't ready to stop. This attempt on my life had happened because I'd come too close to the truth. If that was the case, then the murderer wouldn't believe I'd been scared away. It was awful to accept the idea that a co-worker was the murderer. But, whoever poisoned my coffee had to know I wasn't the kind of person who backed off. As a patient rep, I worked within the system, but was persistent, looking for different ways to reach the best result for everyone involved. Why would the murderer expect me to behave any differently in this case?

I sighed as another thought came to me. Maybe I was wrong to be this way. Maybe what I considered to be the best solution wasn't viewed the same way by others involved. Was I wrong to push so hard for my vision of "justice"? Was I actually as arrogant with my convictions as some of the people who annoyed me with theirs? It troubled me that I might be considered difficult to work with. Probably not difficult enough to motivate murder, but enough that some people chose to avoid me.

Even if this was true, I thought as I fluffed my pillows, now might not be the best time to change. I could already have the clues needed to solve the case and just not know it. Had I been looking at the clues the wrong way, or in the wrong combination or sequence? I needed to find the connection to tie it all together.

Well, I decided, I would play the game. I would lay low for a while, take a break to sort through what I knew, then begin again, more subtly this time. I would figure out who murdered Congressman Hamilton and who tried to murder me. Before they tried again.

The knocking on my bedroom door finally broke through the layers of unconsciousness, dragging me to awareness. I wasn't happy about it. My alarm clock said seven-thirty. At least an hour before the sun came up. I closed my eyes again.

The door opened with a painful groan. I winced at the noise. I'd been meaning to take some WD-40 to that hinge.

"Mom?" Josh whispered. "Are you awake?"

Taffy brushed past him and landed on top of me.

"I am now." I shoved Taffy to the other side of the bed and propped myself up on my elbow.

Josh stepped into the room, carrying a potted azalea covered with hot-pink blossoms. He set it on the nightstand, then turned to face me.

I fingered the leaves. "That's pretty. Where'd it come from?"

He looked different. I couldn't put my finger on what it was exactly. Tidier, maybe?

"Chuck brought it and wants to say hi," he said.

"Chuck? Your friend from school?"

He nodded. This was very strange, but then, the whole week had been bizarre. I wasn't sure about entertaining a guest while wearing pajamas, but it wasn't as if I was wearing something frilly or see-through. Actually, it was rather sweet of him to want to wish me well, so I decided not to make a big deal about it.

"I'm not exactly dressed to receive company. Give me a minute to freshen up."

Josh nodded again, then disappeared. I made my way to the bathroom and brushed my teeth, washed my face, and ran a quick comb through my hair. I climbed back into bed and propped myself up with pillows.

When Josh returned, he said, "Mom, this is Chuck."

I gawked. This was Chuck?

Petite, blond, and cute as the dickens, the girl standing next to Josh was the furthest thing from a Chuck I could have imagined. She wore the college uniform, faded jeans and a UW Husky sweatshirt. Her skin had the fresh bloom of youth, and, as she approached, I saw that her make-up had been applied with a light touch, accentuating her cornflower-blue eyes.

"Hi, Miz Kelly. I sure am sorry to hear you're doing poorly."

Her drawl was soft and gentle on the ear. I glanced at Josh and from the heated look in his eyes, it was obvious he was smitten. Was I ready for this?

"Thank you, Chuck. I'm glad to say I'm feeling better than I was yesterday." I wondered just how much Josh had told her.

"Food poisoning's a mighty dangerous thing," Chuck said. I appreciated Josh's spin on my near-death experience. "I remember my granny warning me all the time about not canning properly and not leaving potato salad in the sun. She was always careful about what she served to folks. Do you know what it was that made you sick?"

I wanted to say, *Yes, it was digoxin-laced coffee.* Instead, I shook my head and changed the subject. "So, tell me, how come you're called Chuck?"

She laughed, a twinkle lighting her eyes as she glanced at Josh, and I could see why he was captivated. "Oh, Miz Kelly. I'll bet you thought I was a boy, didn't you?" She turned to Josh. "Shame on you, letting your mama think that."

Josh frowned in puzzlement. "I never said you were a boy."

"But you didn't tell her I was a girl, either." Chuck laughed again and squeezed his hand. I noticed he didn't let go. "My real name is Charlene. Daddy calls me Charlie, and somehow my friends changed it to Chuck."

"I can understand that. My first name is Robyn, but my friends call me Rob."

"I like that." Chuck glanced at her watch. "Oh, wow, look at the time. That bridge traffic is going to be backed up something awful if I don't leave right now."

"I'm staying home today to keep an eye on my mom," Josh said. "Can I borrow your notes this weekend?"

"Why, of course, sugar. I'll call you when I get home." Chuck stood on tiptoes and pecked Josh's cheek before she dashed off.

Josh glanced at me, then mumbled something incoherent as he followed her out.

I smiled broadly. If Chuck was in the engineering program, she was smart, and she had charm and good looks. If she set her sights on Josh, he wouldn't stand a chance. I wasn't ready to turn my baby boy over to another woman, but unless Chuck was hiding some deep, dark secret, Josh could do a lot worse.

"Taffy, old girl, looks like you and I are going to be spending a lot of evenings alone." I patted her on the head and she rolled over so I could rub her tummy.

Before I could turn completely morose, the phone rang. I leaned across Taffy to reach it. "Hello?"

"Robyn? Matt Pierce. Is Josh there?"

"Yes, he's saying good-bye to his girlfriend."

"I thought I'd swing by and pick him up so we can get your car. Can he be ready in fifteen minutes?"

"He's ready now." I hung up the phone and clambered out of bed. From the bedroom door, I hollered, "Josh! Josh!"

Josh sprinted down the hall. "What? Are you okay?" He stopped and held out his arms as if expecting me to collapse.

"I'm fine. Detective Pierce just called. He's picking you up in fifteen minutes to get my car."

"Are you sure you'll be all right by yourself? I mean Dr. Bridgeway said—"

"I'm fine," I repeated. "In fact, after you get my car, go on to school. I'll hang around here with Taffy."

"We'll talk about that later." From his tone, he was not into compromise.

"I'm going to take a shower."

Josh opened his mouth to argue about that too, so I shut my bedroom door on him. I took a hasty shower and was dressed and made up by the time Pierce rang the doorbell.

I started to answer it, but Josh barreled past. I sank onto the couch and waited for the detective to come in.

It's a funny thing about our homes; we get so accustomed to our things that it takes someone new coming into the house for us to see it from a fresh perspective. In his line of work, Pierce had to see all kinds of homes.

What would he see here? Furniture upholstered in warm earth tones, designed more for durability than for fashion. Hardwood floors with large area rugs. A few knick-knacks scattered on the mantle over the used-brick fireplace, items that showed a touch of whimsy or were family heirlooms. *House Beautiful* it wasn't, but it was comfortable, and it was mine.

I watched Pierce's quick survey of the room, the slight stretch of his neck to confirm the layout of the rest of the house, before his gaze rested on me.

"Do I pass?"

He glanced away as if embarrassed to be caught. "You look a helluva lot better than you did yesterday."

"Thanks. Would you like some coffee?"

"If it's made."

"It'll only take a few minutes."

"That's okay. I'm on duty so I shouldn't stay." He perched on the arm of the sofa.

A wild idea struck me, and for once, I acted on impulse. Pretending to be totally engrossed in a stray thread on a sofa pillow, I said, "Pierce, I was thinking. If you're not working next Thursday, and if you don't have other plans, would you like to join us for Thanksgiving dinner?"

The silence was so loud and lasted so long that I finally looked up. He had the nicest smile on his face. It changed my impression of him again.

"You're inviting me for Thanksgiving?"

I shrugged and gave up on the loose thread. "Josh has invited his girl friend. I'm a reasonably good cook, and we have all the usual turkey day fare. Plus baked yams with melted marshmallows on top."

"Yams? Really?"

I nodded and he thought for a moment.

"What kind of pie?"

I struggled not to laugh. "I'm not sure yet. Does it make a difference?"

"Not really," he said, looking sheepish. "I'd like to come. Thank you."

"Good. Come around two or whenever the ballgames start." Pleased with how that went, I put the pillow in its place and looked straight at him. "So, have you figured out who tried to kill me?"

"Robyn, it's not even nine o'clock in the morning."

"The detectives on TV would've solved it last night." Despite my teasing, my stomach clenched with fear. "Someone out there wants me dead, and I have to say, Pierce, that's a bit unsettling."

"As long as you stay home and don't let anyone in, you're safe."

"I have to go back to work on Monday. Will it be safe then?" I snapped.

He gave me a hard stare.

"Look Pierce, I have a job to do. I have a son to support. I have one person out on vacation and my assistant is alone in the office. You have to solve this thing, and quickly. I don't have time to wait." *And the longer it takes, the more terrified I am.*

He sighed in exasperation. "Doc Bridgeway said to stay home and do nothing this weekend. Now I'm adding, don't worry about it. I'm doing the best I can. You have to trust me. Now, back off and be a good girl."

Josh returned before I came up with a flippant response. I watched them go, knowing I had behaved peevishly, but I didn't care. I hated the restriction. I loved my house, but I wanted it to be my choice to stay home, not forced imprisonment.

Still fuming, I went to the kitchen, Taffy close on my heels. It took a few minutes, but I finally found the discharge instructions Larry had given Josh. Nothing about limiting what I ate, and I was hungry. I fixed myself a cup of tea, decaf just in case, and made a batch of scones. I tried to convince myself that the routine of mixing and lightly kneading the dough was reassuringly normal, but I wasn't successful. With the scones in the oven, I whipped up an omelette. While it finished cooking, I flipped on the TV and checked all three national affiliates for local news, but found nothing except weather inserts. Wet and drippy. What else was new?

Zipping through the non-English channels, an image flashed by. Stunned, I backed up until I found it again.

Peter? On a French-Canadian cable station? I watched for a few minutes, not understanding a word he said, but recognizing the familiar backdrop of war in a Third World country.

I shook my head. How like him to land on his feet. Within a year, the major stations would forget his breach of journalistic ethics and he'd again be on top.

I was pleased with how I was reacting, the same degree of detachment I'd feel for a movie star. Nothing personal, good or bad. To paraphrase my grandmother, I had mistaken a goat's beard for a fine stallion's tail.

Satisfied that I was truly over Peter, I sat down to eat and watched television until Josh came home.

"Take that coat back out," I said when he came in through the garage. "You're dripping all over the floor."

He seemed distracted and looked surprised at the amount of water on his raincoat. "Sorry." He left to hang it on the clothesline we'd strung up in the garage for just that purpose, and returned with Taffy's foot-wiping towel to sop up the excess water.

"Are you hungry?" I asked, knowing full well what the answer would be.

He perked up. "Sure."

"Breakfast, coming right up!" I cracked three eggs into a non-stick frying pan and felt a twinge. How many more mornings did I have to fix meals for him? I had to pay more attention, treasure the time we still had.

Josh set the table for himself and poured a glass of orange juice. "We got your car okay."

"Thank you." I put three scones on his plate. "What about my purse?"

He didn't look over, but I saw his face and neck turn red.

"Sorry, Mom. We forgot it," he mumbled.

Something about the way he refused to look up led me to think they'd done it on purpose, that if I didn't have my keys and wallet, I really would be confined to home while Josh was at school.

I slid his eggs onto the plate and handed it to him. Leaning against the counter, I watched him wolf down his breakfast, despite years of telling him to eat slower.

After cleaning up the kitchen, I took his dirty dishes and said, "Go to school."

"But—"

"I'm fine." The phrase was becoming my mantra. I placed the dishes into the dishwasher and turned to face him. "Really."

"But Dr. Bridgeway said—"

"Larry said the first twelve hours were the most critical. It's been that long, and nothing's happened. I'm okay."

"What will you do?"

"Josh. Dear." I draped my arm around his shoulder. "I have been known to entertain myself. I don't need you to keep me from getting bored." *Or worrying.*

He looked at me with a suspicious frown. "I don't know."

"Look. I've had a shower, I'm dressed, I fixed my breakfast, I fixed your breakfast. I cleaned up the dirty dishes. And nothing's happened. Go to school." He still didn't look convinced, so I used my last resort. "Won't the other boys work real hard to be sure Chuck doesn't miss you?"

"Oh, Mom, I can't believe you said that," he said with a tinge of disgust. "That's so high school."

There it was again, signs he was growing up. "Sorry. But really, I'm fine. I don't need you to hover over me. Go. Please."

He stood there, my big strapping son, looking torn between duties, between his work and his family, the adult dilemma.

I patted him on the back and said nothing more. In a few minutes, he was out the door.

After making my bed and tidying up, I felt at loose ends. I always brought something home from the office to work on, but obviously not this time. I picked up a book, a hot new bestseller; it didn't hold my attention. The TV was all talk shows and real judges and soap operas and news. Except for the formats, it was hard to tell the difference.

Restless, I stood at the window and watched sheets of rain scrub the street. It took all of five minutes to choose what I wanted to plant in a bare corner of the yard, bulbs that would bloom from early spring through the fall. I thought about taking a nap, but I wasn't the least bit tired, despite tossing and turning all night. I considered cleaning a closet, finally deciding I would save that for a snowstorm.

By noon, Taffy was the only one happy with my restriction, but a person can bond with their dog for only so long. I had no ill effects from yesterday, no symptoms, expected or unexpected. I basically felt fine, no worse than if I had a mild cold. I was well enough to dig out the spare car key and go to work for a couple of hours.

The problem though, the real reason I would follow Larry's directive to stay home, was simple: I was too terrified to go back.

CHAPTER 13

The weekend dragged by in half-hour increments. I called out-of-town friends to catch up, never mentioning "the incident," as Josh and I referred to it. I cleaned out my personal E-mail in-box, a chore I'd been meaning to do for months, but never seemed to get around to.

On Saturday night, Josh stayed home, something he had rarely done since he obtained his driver's license. He went to the video store and rented some of my favorite movies. We watched and ate popcorn, saying little, but clutching the memories of happier times.

During the marathon of Sunday football games, I organized boxes of pictures, labeling them as to who, when, and where. It struck me that this was a task people finally got around to doing when they knew "the end" was near. Whenever my mind drifted to how close I had come to my own end, I pushed the thought aside and refocused on the pictures scattered across the table.

Underlying all the busyness was unspoken fear.

At last—or too soon—Monday morning came. Josh had picked up my purse and keys on Friday on his way home. I waited for him to leave for school, something I rarely did, then found odd chores that needed to be done *now*. Critically important things like changing the sheets and starting a load of laundry. Emptying the dishwasher. Sorting the recycles.

By early afternoon, I admitted I was dragging my feet, that I was too emotionally paralyzed to leave the house.

It bothered me to acknowledge the fear gnawing at me, and I didn't like the dread that held me captive. The longer I waited to return to the hospital, the harder it would be.

Finally, I resisted the temptation to do one more thing, the task that would last long enough to say it was too late to go at all.

I had to return. I needed to go back today, before the events of last week scared me away forever.

It felt strange when I pulled into the parking lot and looked at the building where I had worked for the last ten years. After all that had happened the past week, I felt detached from this place. I didn't know it anymore. Maybe I never had.

Grasping for a reason to leave the security of a locked car, I thought about the work waiting for me. I sighed with relief; the State Insurance Commissioner case was sitting on my desk. The response letter was due in Olympia today, and I had yet to draft it, let alone have Dr. Weiser review it. Focusing on work was good. Maybe it would help me to avoid intensive psychotherapy in the future.

Despite my attempt to be logical and rational, my thoughts were still jumbled as I slid from the car and approached the rear entrance. People were coming and going; it was shift change. It all looked so normal.

Not wanting to see anyone yet, I took the service elevator and arrived undetected at my office door, noting how easy it was to move around in broad daylight without being seen.

How easy to find the private minute or two necessary to end a life.

Shaken, I entered my office. "Hi, Connie."

"Rob!" Connie jumped from her chair. "Thank God, you're back. I was so worried, but I didn't want to call, in case you weren't feeling well."

I was not about to tell her the truth, that physically I was doing okay, but emotionally I was a wreck. Instead, I smiled wryly and said, "Staying home isn't near as much fun as we thought."

Connie came from behind her desk. I'm not really old enough to be Connie's mother, but I am her first real boss, and she hugged me with a desperation that reminded me of Josh when he brought me home.

"I'm okay, Connie."

Like Josh, she nodded against my shoulder, and I wasn't surprised to see tears when she pulled away.

"Detective Pierce came by earlier," she said with a sniff and a quick swipe at her eyes. "I haven't heard if he's found anything."

"What's the talk around here?" I asked.

"That's just it. No one's talking." She grimaced as she shook her head. "Everyone's so appalled by what happened to you. I mean, it didn't take five minutes for it to get out that you'd been poisoned. It was okay if you'd fainted, but that. . . ." She shuddered.

"So everyone knows it was deliberate?"

Connie nodded. "Uh-huh. And since it had to be someone at that meeting, everyone's gone totally weird. All of this week's meetings are cancelled. The excuse is that it's a short week and a lot of people have taken off early for the holiday. That doesn't explain why no one wants to take a break together. And at lunch, a few people sit alone in the cafeteria, but mostly, they grab a tray and leave. Everyone's afraid."

Something she said niggled at my brain, but I couldn't put my finger on it. "You can't blame them, though. It's frightening to realize that one of us is a murderer."

"That's just it. No one wants to think about it, so they're avoiding everyone."

It made sense. As I walked to my office, I called over my shoulder to Connie. "How's it been in here?"

"Not too bad," Connie said. "I've referred most of the stuff that's come in. I took some messages for you and Margie, ordered medical records, that sort of thing."

"I better be careful. Pretty soon you'll be running this place so smoothly you won't need me anymore."

"Don't kid yourself, Rob," Connie groused from her desk. "I want nothing to do with those big messy cases you and Margie love."

I plopped into my own chair, closing my eyes for a moment, glad that Connie couldn't see me now. Despite how rested I'd felt when I left home, I was exhausted.

Resisting the urge to put my head down and take a nap, I started looking for the Insurance Commissioner case file, sifting through the bits and pieces of paper and folders on my desk: a hodge-podge of phone messages, hand-written notes, half-completed report forms, letters from patients and medical records. What a mess. I should come in over the long Thanksgiving weekend and clean it up.

The phone rang as I found the file. I picked up the receiver, noting that the call was on my direct line, not a transfer from Connie. "Hi, this is Robyn."

There was a pause, then, "Oh, you finally showed up." So much for Will's sympathetic response to my ordeal. There was another brief pause, before he said, "Come down to my office. Immediately." The phone slammed down.

I stared at the receiver. "Yes, Will. I'm feeling much better, Will. Thank you so much for asking." I dropped the receiver into its cradle. How like him. I'd never seen him show the slightest concern for any of his staff. Whether it was an accident, illness, or a death in the family, it all occurred below his radar and remained unacknowledged.

I sighed heavily. Okay, so Will was upset about something. I really regretted answering that phone. Why did he need to talk with me now? Maybe it was nothing important; maybe he wanted to delegate something so he could be done with it. I could always hope.

I shrugged out of my coat and took a moment to run a comb through my hair and to add some lipstick. If I was going to be seen in the building, I wanted to look good. At least I'd worn my gray suit, which added to a professional demeanor.

During the short elevator ride, my anxiety increased. I tried to figure out if he was upset with me personally, but except for finding Congressman Hamilton's body and being poisoned myself, I couldn't come up with anything. Okay, so maybe that was more than enough to send even the most reasonable of bosses over the edge.

Feeling an affinity with Anne Boleyn on her way to the executioner's ax, I walked into the administrative-office suite.

Arlene, Will's secretary, looked up. "Oh, am I glad you're here."

That caught me by surprise. "You are?"

"He's just been on a tear all afternoon," she whispered. "Of course, he was already upset, what with the murder, and . . . and then the thing with you. By the way, how are you feeling?"

So, they'd sanitized the poisoning to "the thing with you."
"I'm doing okay. Is he upset with me?"

"Oh, it's probably the whole thing," she said with a brush-off wave. "But now a hospital board member's called and the police were here questioning him again."

I saw a glimmer of hope. Maybe I'd been paranoid for no reason. "Why does he want to see me?"

"I don't know for sure, but—"

She stopped as Will flung his door open and stepped out.

"Robyn." He turned and disappeared back into his office.

I looked at Arlene. We both shrugged and rolled our eyes, then I walked around her desk and into Will's office.

"Shut the door." He was already seated. The normally sterile desk was overflowing with papers. His usually perfectly styled hair was a mess, as if he'd repeatedly run his fingers through it. His eyes lacked their typical hardness, and his anxious gaze darted around the room. What surprised me most was that Will called me, of all people, in an apparent moment of panic.

I pretended not to notice the chaos. "What's up?"

He picked up a copy of the Quality Report and tossed it at me. It was a fumble, but I caught it before it hit the ground.

"Is there a problem with my part of the report?" I asked.

"What's there is okay, but the chairwoman of the Quality Committee called. Samantha Duke. She wants more information."

I relaxed. It wasn't an unusual request. "That's fine. What does she want?"

"She wants specifics. Names. Details, like what kind of medical problems these patients had. Plus demographics. Are we discriminating against a particular patient group. That sort of thing."

The request stunned me. "I can put together the demographics, but she can't have names and diagnoses. We never release those. The committee knows that. That's all part of the patient's right to confidentiality. It's—"

Will raised his hand to stop me. "That's the past. This is the new chairwoman and she doesn't care. She's convinced the report is a whitewash."

"A whitewash! Are you kidding? That report gives them everything. Tables of numbers, qualitative summary, corrective actions taken." I ticked off the items with my fingers.

My earlier fear was gone; I was back in the saddle again. The new chairwoman obviously needed an orientation to the federal patient-confidentiality laws as well as the purpose of the report. "Don't worry about it. I'll talk to her."

I wasn't sure what the penalty was for patient reps who were found in contempt of oversight committees, but I had no choice. It went with the badge.

Will leaned back in his chair and said, "Apparently she has some basis for concern."

Warning bells clanged in my brain. "What do you mean?" I asked cautiously.

"It seems her sister-in-law filed a complaint with your department, and the family's consensus is that you covered up a physician's gross negligence with a lot of nice words."

"So based on that she questions the veracity of everything coming out of my office?"

Will nodded. He tented his fingers and looked at me with speculation.

"What was the patient's name?"

"Emma Jamison."

I laughed out loud. "You're kidding? That woman—"

I caught myself before going any farther. I couldn't tell Will anything. He wasn't part of the medical staff review. I couldn't reveal that the woman was certifiable and under a psychiatrist's care, without violating her right to privacy. Her complaint had been groundless. What she claimed could not possibly have happened.

But I was stuck. Just as I wouldn't reveal specifics to the Quality Committee chair, I couldn't discuss a mental-health case with Will.

"I've been thinking about this situation, Robyn. This and other incidents that have occurred. In fact, I had a call from corporate this morning." He had that this-hurts-me-more-than-it-hurts-you look.

"What do you mean?" I was nervous now. I didn't like the "gotcha" gleam in his eyes. An icy cold wave followed by searing hot dread swept through me. I doubted it had anything to do with the digoxin overdose.

"It happens sometimes. Even to good managers." His tone implied I was not one of those good managers.

"What happens?"

"Oh, they get set in their ways. Resist new approaches." He looked at me with feigned sorrow. "What I'm trying to say, Robyn, is that maybe it's time you found a different position."

If he had made a pass at me, I wouldn't have been more surprised. "You're firing me?"

"No, no, of course not. I'm merely suggesting you look for another job more . . . more stimulating. Something different. We're part of a large organization. I'm sure you can find something by . . . let's say by the first of the year?"

I choked. "You're giving me five weeks during the holiday season to find a management position?" The cold-hearted bastard.

"I'm sure you'll do just fine." Will stood and walked to the door. He turned to me with a glazed smile. "I'm glad we could reach an agreement on this."

Shocked, I left Will's office, thankful that Arlene was busy on the phone. I gave a token wave and strode from the Admin suite. Holding myself together, I took the elevator to the third floor, but couldn't bring myself to return to my office. Instead, I went down the hall to a conference room. Not the one where I had been poisoned, but the one next door.

It was empty. Leaving the lights off, I approached the window and stared at the trees swaying in the wind. Rain pounded against the glass, blurring the bleak view that matched my beaten spirit.

Cold seeped through from the outside, chilling me. Or maybe it was the cold inside my heart that made me shiver. So much to deal with. Hamilton's murder. Peter. The poisoning. And now this.

Will's words had left me numb. And hurt. He made it sound as if I deliberately went out of my way to make his job harder by finding the dead congressman and being poisoned myself. How could he continue to have so little comprehension of who I was or what I did?

Then, I started to get angry. He said he received a call from corporate, but he got those calls every day. He didn't say the call had been about me. He'd only inferred it, the slimy bastard. But what if it had been about me? He said we'd reached an agreement. What agreement? What a euphemism! We hadn't reached an agreement. He had issued an ultimatum.

The reality was that Will could simply fire me. The threat hung over every middle manager. We had no union, no mandatory disciplinary process. If an administrator didn't like someone, he could strongly encourage them to pursue their career goals elsewhere, and if they resisted, he made life impossible. It happened all the time.

He was right about one thing: Madrona Bay was part of a much larger organization. But the job options for someone like me were not terrific. I was not a trained and licensed provider, so the clinical jobs were out. There were always openings for billing clerks and claims processors, but management positions that required my skills and experience were rare.

If I wanted to stay with the company, I could either take a disastrous cut in pay or relocate to another state. Neither appealed to me. Besides, applying for management positions took months, much longer than Will's end of the year deadline.

But I didn't want to leave. I loved my job, and I was good at what I did. I liked Madrona Bay and the people I worked with. Except for the one who tried to murder me, of course.

For the sake of argument, for a moment I would assume Will wasn't the murderer. The bottom line was Will didn't like aggravation, and I had been a nuisance since he became administrator five years ago. After last week, he probably viewed me as trouble with a capital "T." Will considered this problem with the new committee chairwoman as the last straw. Somehow, in his mangled little accountant brain, he had rationalized that if I disappeared, so would all his problems with corporate, the press, and who knew who else. Simplistic, yes, but understandable given the week he'd had and the pressure of applying for a federal position and hoping no one at corporate noticed.

I had two choices.

I could give in quietly and slink away, try to find a new job within the company which would not disrupt my entire life and endanger everything I'd worked hard for.

Or, I could fight. I could talk to someone in Human Resources and make a nuisance of myself by insisting on a formal process. Make Will identify in writing what I was doing wrong, and meet with me on a weekly basis to review my progress. Nothing aggressive, just calmly assertive.

There was no guarantee he wouldn't fire me at the end of the process, but maybe it would buy me some time. He might get that federal job, or transfer to another hospital, or simply get bored and the whole thing would become moot. It was time to advocate for myself the way I championed a patient's cause.

I felt much better. Outside, the wind and rain had abated, leaving small branches and leaves strewn across the parking lot.

As I turned to leave, I had another thought. I could talk to Larry about the Jamison case. She'd been a nightmare patient for everyone involved. Maybe Larry could say something to Will without violating her confidentiality. Will had to believe it wasn't my fault if Larry told him, right? Eternal optimist, that's me.

When I returned to my office, I told Connie that Will's thing had been no big deal. No point in worrying her. In fact, I decided to say nothing to anyone until after I talked to Human Resources. I looked up Sarah's number in the directory and called. The phone rang a few times, then went to voice mail.

"Sarah, this is Robyn Kelly. It's Monday afternoon. I need to talk to you soon. It's important. Thanks."

I hung up and wondered if there was something else I should do. I couldn't think of anything at the moment. My watch said it was almost five o'clock. Where had the time gone?

I called home. "Hi, honey," I said when Josh answered.

"Mom? Where are you?" He sounded so angry, so worried, that I winced.

"I'm at work."

"You should've left a note." Yes, he was definitely overreacting.

"Perhaps, but you knew I was coming in."

"Are you okay? You were supposed to leave right after me, but I could tell you were here for lunch. That's why I was worried. I thought you got sick or something."

"Of course, I'm okay," I lied. I hesitated. We'd had several long talks over the weekend, and he had surprised me with his perceptions. I'd come away with a new awareness that I really should be treating him as an adult, and be honest about what I was thinking. I took a deep breath and said, "I was afraid."

After a moment's pause, Josh said, "I think I understand. But I wish you'd've told me. I'd have gone in with you."

The sweet sincerity of his offer brought tears to my eyes. "That's very thoughtful, Josh, but I needed to do this alone."

"I guess. Call me when you decide to come home, okay?"

Warmed by his efforts to keep track of me, I said, "I'll do that. See you later."

I smiled as I hung up the phone, but the smile faded quickly as I faced the threatening future.

If someone at the corporate office was asking for my head because of Hamilton and the poisoning, then the surest way to redeem myself was to find the murderer. I went over Connie's earlier comments, but still couldn't grasp what had to be a most important clue.

Hoping it would come to me—and wanting to avoid a complaint from the Insurance Commissioner about my handling of that case—I picked up the Stone file and started the letter. The format was very straightforward, outlining the basics of Mrs. Stone's complaint and then the results of my investigation. As Dr. Weiser had said, the problem had been primarily a matter of what had not been said. The patient had been given the wrong impression, not only that her surgery was covered by the new insurance, but that Dr. Chin had her best interests at heart.

The letter went quickly, and after spell-checking and rereading it one more time, I gave it to Connie to print and prepare for mailing. Dr Weiser had to review it first, so I would drop it off at the Medical Staff offices on my way home.

I went back to my office and stared out the window.

What was not said. Giving the wrong impression.

Was that what this was really all about? Since I still couldn't figure it out, I pulled out a pad of paper. If I wrote down everything I knew, maybe the elusive answer would come to me.

The easy part was narrowing the list of suspects. The murderer was at last week's meeting. I hesitated. Did I really want to do this? The answer was a resounding "YES!" By sleuthing on my own, I had helped prove Pham Nguyen's innocence. When I was poisoned, it became deeply personal. I didn't want to live with this fear any longer, and I didn't want my friends to live with it either.

I took a deep breath, then another, and forced myself to think logically. This was just like any of my other investigations. I frowned. Sure it was, only the stakes were much higher.

I quickly jotted down the names of everyone I could remember being in the room when Connie had called me away from the meeting. I tore that page off the pad and started with a fresh page for the first suspect.

It was, of course, Will.

Chapter 14

Will's name leaped off the page as a suspect. He had both motive and opportunity. Congressman Hamilton had thwarted Will's attempt at a federal job, which gave him plenty of motive. He also had an open calendar at the time of the murder, giving him opportunity. He could easily have slipped the pills into my coffee. I wrote in the margin: *does Will have a Rx for digoxin?* When Will failed to kill me, he'd tried another way to get rid of me.

I stopped writing. If Will wanted to get rid of me, he could have fired me to begin with. Why bother with the poison? *Note to self: to be on the safe side, do not go to any meetings where he will be.* The thought nagged that maybe I was seeking a way to avenge his shabby treatment of me, but I honestly didn't think so because it all fit, it all made sense. Besides, proving Will was the murderer would be karmic justice for his being a jerk.

As satisfying as that would be, Will's whereabouts at the time of the murder had probably been thoroughly dissected by Pierce. I flipped to a fresh page to consider another suspect.

Melanie had a strong motive to kill Hamilton, and she had followed me into the meeting room, ostensibly to arrange an interview with Will for later that day, giving her ample opportunity to drug my coffee. Were the two in cahoots?

I shook my head, doubting this was a conspiracy. Murderers usually worked alone. Besides, the idea that more than one person might be involved was beyond the pale.

Furthermore, everyone knew Melanie was a reporter. She'd stick out like a sore thumb around the patient rooms, and be quickly escorted off the unit.

I flipped to the next empty page and started over.

Cynthia Martin. I knew she'd been on the unit, but she had caused such a ruckus that she was ejected from the area and told not to come back. If she'd tried to sneak into Hamilton's room, Susan and her nurses would have caught her. She'd reacted frantically at the idea of an autopsy, but she was the dramatic type, and she was young and in love.

New page.

Susan had opportunity to kill Hamilton too, but I couldn't think of her motive. We didn't go around killing patients just because they annoyed us. Besides, Susan had been my friend for a long time, and I simply couldn't picture her holding a pillow over a helpless patient's face until he died.

I shivered at the thought. From what I'd learned, Congressman Hamilton had gone out of his way to be obnoxious to anyone who couldn't vote for him. He championed funding cuts for some unlikely groups. If his youthful behavior with Melanie was any indication of his character, he'd probably left a string of unhappy women around the country. It surprised me that he hadn't been nailed with sexual harassment allegations. But then again, Cynthia adored him, and he presumably used that same charismatic charm on all women.

It had taken someone with cold determination to see the job through to the end, someone willing to risk discovery to accomplish the task. Someone desperate enough to kill again when they thought I was too close to identifying them. After scanning the list, I went back and stopped at each name. Who fit those criteria?

I studied the list again, finally stopping at one name, and I knew who the killer was. At least I thought I knew. Karmic justice aside, it had to be Will. His disheveled appearance and erratic behavior were signs of a guilty conscience. But how in the world was I going to prove it? I didn't think Pierce would take my word for it. And no matter how much sense it made, I had no proof.

What I needed was to find a bottle of digoxin capsules in Will's office. Maybe a lab could compare what remained in my coffee with the ones in the bottle to see if they were from the same lot. I didn't know if they could do that, but it sounded good.

Soon, everyone would be gone for the evening and I'd have my chance. Now was the time for patience.

"Here it is." Interrupting my thoughts, Connie came into my office and dropped the printed letter to the Insurance Commissioner on my desk. "I'm leaving now."

I skimmed over the letter and checked to be sure she had attached an extra copy for the Medical Staff files. "Thanks," I called after her. "I'll take it downstairs for Dr. Weiser to sign." Setting the pad upside down on my desk, I picked up the letter and tapped it against my hand.

Pierce had told me to stay out of it, but I had to share what I knew rather than wait for him to discover it on his own. He would be annoyed for a variety of reasons, but it couldn't be helped. I refused to stay on the sidelines when my life was at stake. I knew I was putting myself at risk, but I didn't like the fear that was becoming my constant companion. I'd be careful, I promised myself. I wouldn't take any unnecessary chances.

Picking up the phone, I dialed Pierce's cell phone number. Annoyed when his voicemail answered, I left a detailed message as instructed. Maybe his exasperation with me would be diminished before he called back.

Stiff with tension, I rolled my chair away from the desk and stood up to stretch. It felt so good. In fact, it felt good simply to be alive.

For my own sanity, I needed to resolve this tonight. If I found any evidence, I would leave it where it was and call Pierce again and tell him to bring a search warrant. He'd probably be even more annoyed with me, but I couldn't wait for him to work his methodical way, hampered by rules I didn't have to abide by.

Taking one last deep breath, I glanced at the clock. It was time. I turned off my computer, knowing it was secure with the new password I had chosen. If Peter somehow found his way into my office again, it would take a million years for him to figure it out: *Slime.* I would change it again, but for now, it was a grim reminder of what people can do to someone they claim to care about.

I slipped on my coat and picked up the letter and my purse. Checking to be sure I hadn't forgotten anything, I flipped light switches off as I made my way from my office to the door. Before stepping into the hall, I glanced around the suite and felt an incredible sadness that everything I had worked for could be ruined by one jerky boss. The sadness was not only for myself, but for all of us. Having a murderer in our midst had changed everything. Would we ever regain that special camaraderie we'd had?

I decided the best approach to the Admin suite was the least trafficked. To avoid evening visitors, I walked the long way towards the clinic, my steps echoing in the empty hallway, and then took the elevator to the first floor. When I stepped off the elevator, the specialists'-clinic doors were closed and their check-in desk area dark.

I passed other departments, also closed and darkened. The front reception desk where Nicole sat during the day was occupied by a security guard I didn't know. From the uniform, he looked like a temp. He didn't bother to glance up from his

Sports Illustrated.

Across the hall from the Admin suite stood a janitorial cart. The men's room door was propped open. I wondered if Pham had been released and when he would be back, if he wanted to come back here. Trying to prove his innocence was what had involved me in the first place. His arrest in my office seemed years ago, not just a week.

I stepped quietly to the Admin suite door and tested it. The knob turned in my hand. I opened the door and slipped inside, closing the door gently behind me. All the office doors were closed, and no light shone underneath. A quick peek at the usually overflowing recycled-paper bin told me this area had already been cleaned. Good; I shouldn't be interrupted.

I crossed the darkened reception area and moved toward Will's office. When no one answered my knock, I opened the door and slipped into his office. I didn't want to turn on the lights, so I raised the blinds. A nearby parking-lot light illuminated the room.

The top of the desk was still a mess, and I doubted Will would leave evidence there. I started searching his drawers, disappointed, but not surprised, to find them full of folders bulging with paper.

I opened the last drawer on the bottom and saw it. A prescription bottle. But I couldn't read the label without holding it up to the light. Remembering all the detective shows I've seen, I pulled a tissue from my pocket and carefully lifted the bottle from the drawer, holding it by the edges. It felt as if it was almost empty. I turned it toward the light and read the label.

Digoxin. Will took digoxin.

Now I had proof. Now I could call Pierce and give him the evidence he needed to make an arrest. I bent down to replace the bottle where I'd found it.

Suddenly, the office door opened and the lights came on.

I froze.

"Robyn?" Brenda stood in the doorway, a stunned expression on her face.

"Ah, Brenda. Hello."

"But . . . but I . . . Wh—"

I held up the letter and smiled brightly. "I'm dropping this off for Dr. Weiser to sign."

Brenda raised a skeptical eyebrow, then she stared hard. "Robyn, his mailbox is not in Will's office."

That was the downside of working with smart people. It's really tough to put something over on them.

Shaken by what I'd found, evidence that proved beyond a doubt that Will was the murderer, I sighed heavily. "I know. I came looking for this." I held up the bottle of digoxin, making sure I touched only the tissue to keep my fingerprints off.

Her eyes narrowed. "What is it?"

"I . . . it means that Will is the one who tried to kill me. I think he killed Congressman Hamilton too."

If Brenda had looked stunned when she first entered the office and saw me, now I could have knocked her over with a feather. "Will? You think Will's the murderer?"

I nodded. "He had motive and opportunity to murder Congressman Hamilton and to kill me. And this bottle could prove that he poisoned my coffee last week. I have to call Detective Pierce."

"Yes, I see." Brenda's expression softened. "Come into my office. You can call from there."

I set the bottle back exactly as I'd found it and closed the drawer.

"I'm surprised to see you so soon after what happened last week," Brenda said as she held the door open for me to pass. She turned out the light and started toward her office. "How're you feeling?"

"Better."

"That was a terrible thing," she said, shaking her head. "What a shock for you. You should've taken more time off. Catch your breath. I'll make us some tea, then we'll call the police."

"Sounds good." I appreciated Brenda's mother-hen fussing over me.

I followed her into her office. The overhead lights were off. No wonder I'd thought the Administration suite was vacant when I hadn't seen light from under her door. Only a green-shaded banker's desk lamp illuminated the room. I took the chair between a small round table and the desk while Brenda fussed with a hot pot and tea bags.

The tightness in my shoulders started to ease, tension I hadn't even been aware of. Soon it would all be over. I rubbed my hands over my face.

"Are you okay?" Brenda's voice was filled with concern.

"I'm just tired," I said. "It was hard to come back, and it hasn't exactly been an easy day."

She nodded. "I imagine not." She returned to fixing the tea.

For a moment, I felt safe. Brenda was the protector, the staunch advocate for her nurses' safety and well-being. Now that I was convinced it had been Will who'd poisoned me, I could trust Brenda. Nothing could happen as long as I was with her.

As I began to relax, I absorbed the calmness of the room. I'd always liked Brenda's office. She had decorated it with some small impressionist prints that added pink splashes of color to the walls. A planter filled with peach-pink silk flowers sat on the wide windowsill. A Bible sat next to the ceramic planter. The feminine touches had always seemed at odds with her no-nonsense clothing and hairstyle, revealing a side of her that was otherwise shrouded.

Like my office, the work area was cluttered with the ubiquitous stacks of papers and journals and myriad manuals covering everything from hospital policies to OSHA regulations to clinical nursing topics. Her dark wood desk was immaculate, in sharp contrast to the rest of her workspace.

"Sugar?"

When I shook my head, Brenda brought two cups and set one in front of me before sitting in her chair behind the desk. I picked up the cup and pretended to take a sip. Even though I knew Will was the murderer, several days of suspicion were hard to forget.

"So, let's talk about what's been going on," Brenda said. "Why do you think Will murdered Congressman Hamilton and tried to murder you? A lot of people take digoxin." She leaned back in her executive-style chair, her hands resting gently on leather-covered arms.

I set the tea cup on the table and took a deep breath, then told her everything, a rehearsal for what I'd tell the police—from my search for Will's motive to murder Congressman Hamilton, to checking his calendar for opportunity, and finally, to the attempt on my life. I concluded by saying, "And when that didn't work, he told me to find a new job by New Year's."

Brenda's eyes widened. "You're kidding."

"I wish I was," I said with a heavy sigh. "I never expected that someone I worked for could be a murderer."

"I'm sure you didn't."

"I just hope when this is all over I'll still have my job," I said, noticing a brass picture frame on the corner of the desk. It was a recent photograph of Brenda and Cynthia, both laughing into the camera.

"She's a beautiful girl." I picked it up to take a closer look.

"Thank you," Brenda said with a slight lift of her chin.

"She looks a lot like you, especially around the eyes." I set the frame back on the desk.

Brenda smiled softly with maternal pride. Absently, I glanced at the newspaper lying on top of the paper recycling box next to her desk. *Rep. Hamilton Murdered in Local Hospital,* the headlines screamed. I pointed to it and said, "I can see it now, the next time a patient complains about the care they received, they'll throw in that everybody knows we murder our patients."

A colored picture of Hamilton at a recent rally was splashed across the middle of the page. Hamilton was smiling and waving. Behind him, beaming with happiness, was Cynthia.

I picked up the newspaper and shifted closer to the desk lamp so I could see the picture better. I looked at Hamilton, then at Cynthia, then at Hamilton again. I'd never seen the two of them together before. Then I remembered the video I'd watched repeatedly on Hamilton's website.

And suddenly, I knew. It all fell into place. Darlene had said the meeting I had seen on Brenda's calendar, the reason I never considered her as a suspect, had been canceled.

She was the last person to see Hamilton alive. She had access to my coffee cup. And, besides Pierce, she was the only person who knew I was investigating the murder.

Jake Hamilton had a mannerism of lifting his chin. So did Cynthia. And so did Brenda.

Brenda was related to Jake Hamilton.

I had been so smart, thinking I had figured out who the murderer was, sending Pierce off on a wild-goose chase. But I'd been wrong, terribly, terribly wrong. Will wasn't the murderer after all. And now, I was alone with this woman who had murdered once and had tried a second time.

A cold swirl of dread seeped into my bones. Afraid of what I might see, but unable to stop, I slowly looked up at Brenda. It was the eyes. The eyes, and the lifting of the chin, that innocuous gesture.

I had to get out of there. Could I fool Brenda? Could I leave without her knowing that I knew?

I casually tossed the newspaper back into the recycle box and stood up. "Thanks for the tea, Brenda. It was really nice to have someone to talk to."

Brenda stood up. "Do you have to leave so soon?"

"Josh is waiting for me at home. I called before I left my office and told him I was on my way." If she thought he was expecting me, would she let me go? I forced a smile. "It's interesting to see him worry about me for a change."

I walked from her office, desperately trying to appear casual. I remembered to put Dr. Weiser's letter in his mailbox; surely that had to look unconcerned. I turned to see Brenda had followed me and was standing outside her office. "I'll walk you out."

In my years of dealing with the public, I had faced a lot of moods and attitudes. Frantic, distraught, angry—I had worked through them all. I didn't worry about my safety when a person was ranting and raving because there were techniques for bringing them around. I became uneasy, though, when a person spoke calmly, when they had nothing to lose. I heard that calmness in Brenda's voice. If she knew I'd figured out the truth, then I was in big trouble.

I should have known better than to trust Brenda. It was just common sense: when a murderer was loose—and it was probably someone you knew—you didn't hang out with anyone when no one else was around. I should have thought of that earlier, but I'd been so sure the murderer was Will that I'd never considered Brenda.

Wordlessly, we walked to the elevators. The elevator signs displayed "4," meaning both cars were on the top floor. Fear welled up inside me.

I had to get away from her. I started for the stairwell door and pushed the door open. "Well, good night, Brenda. I'll see you in the morning."

To my dismay, Brenda continued to follow me through the door and down the stairs. Now I was really worried. Did she know? Was she planning to follow me all the way to my car? I forced myself to walk at a normal pace, holding onto the railing. My heart was pounding, and I prayed it was from anxiety, not from the digoxin that might still be in my system.

We reached the landing and I glanced at her as I reached for the exit door. I was going to make it.

She shoved me. I went flying down the stairs, grabbing for the metal railing, but missed. I bounced on the hard concrete steps, banging my head.

Brenda followed me down, kicking and screeching about devil spawn and cursing me for revealing her secret. The stairwell echoed with her voice, the words repeated over and over. None of it made sense as I tried to escape her attack. I twisted away from her kick and landed awkwardly on the next step. Something snapped and white hot agony seared down my leg.

I couldn't stop my descent, couldn't protect my head, let alone my broken leg. I landed in a heap on the landing, fighting the pain and the blackness that threatened to overwhelm me.

Would she leave me now? If I played dead, would she be like a bear and go away?

I wasn't that lucky. Brenda continued down the stairs toward me. ". . . cursed from the moment he was born, but I did nothing," she ranted. "Now, we all must pay."

She bent down and rolled me and pushed me toward the next set of stairs. I knew I wouldn't survive another fall. I was on the edge of the landing now. This was it, the end. She put her hands down to push one last time. I reached out and grabbed her collar, pulling her over. She stumbled, then fell headfirst down the stairs.

Silence filled my ears. Had I blacked out? I looked down to

the bottom of the stairs. Brenda lay still.

I couldn't worry about her; I had to get myself out of here. It was a holiday week; a lot of people had taken vacation. It was evening; the usual hustle and bustle was over until tomorrow morning. I could lie there for hours before someone came into the stairwell.

Panic bubbled through me. Taking deep breaths, I fought for control. Hysteria wouldn't help; calm assessment would. My head hurt, but my vision was okay. I could breathe through my nose, so it wasn't broken. I ran my tongue around my mouth and all my teeth were in place. That was good.

I wiggled my arms and hands, pleased with the movement. My left leg was okay, but my right leg throbbed. That was a good sign, but with a bone sticking through the skin, I had a compound fracture. It needed treatment soon, before infection set in. I didn't want to think about what could happen then. No need to borrow more trouble than I was already in.

I had to save myself.

Blackness closed in, and I put my head down on the cold concrete. It felt good, so easy to just let go. . . .

No! I struggled to stay conscious. And to not let terror take over. I had to breathe, and think my way out of this.

I grimaced. The same way I had figured out Will was the murderer.

Leave it to the professionals.

Pierce's voice came through loud and clear. I vowed to do that next time. But right now, I had to get out of here.

Where was my cell phone? My purse was six steps up, but it might as well have been ten miles. I wouldn't have a signal anyway.

I had to do something. Even if it meant losing my leg in the end. I shoved that thought away. Escaping was most important. Slipping out of my rain coat, I wrapped it around my leg and tied it together with the belt. At least it would keep all the pieces together, although a splint would have been better.

Lying on my left side, I held the raincoat sleeves to keep my leg stable, and hitched myself toward the stairs. I lifted my rear onto the bottom step, and nearly passed out from the pain. The raincoat didn't support my leg as well as I had hoped.

I had no choice but to continue.

Inching my way up, I reached my purse and pulled out the cell phone. I was right: no signal down here.

A few inchworm steps later, I glanced toward my goal: the door that led to the cafeteria and the parking lot, a heavy metal fire door. Even if I reached it, I might not be able to pull it open. And if I did, there might not be anyone around.

Three steps later, I was ready to lie down and die. Anything to stop the pain.

But, I couldn't stop. Someone had to tell Pierce about Brenda. I wasn't finished raising Josh. I convinced myself that people needed me, that I would be letting them down if I gave up now.

Then I saw the little red box on the wall next to the door. The fire alarm. All I had to do was reach that box and I would be saved.

Five more steps, and I was underneath the little red box. Struggling not to fall again, I held onto the metal railing and drew myself up, stretching until my fingertips curled over the little handle. I pulled it down.

The alarm ricocheted around the concrete stairwell. I sank to the floor and covered my ears. Help had to be on the way.

It seemed like forever, but finally the alarm bell stopped. The fire department had to be in the hospital lobby. Someone would come soon, as soon as they identified which alarm was pulled.

At last, the stairwell door one flight up banged open.

"No smoke here," said a male voice.

"Help me," I called out.

"Hold on, there's someone down there." Several sets of feet hurried down the stairs.

"Robyn?" Pierce's voice. "Are you okay?" The fireman who'd come with him was calling for a paramedic.

"I am now," I said, closing my eyes. My last thought before losing consciousness was of Thanksgiving dinner.

And candied yams.

EPILOGUE

I sank against the cushions, my tummy full of turkey and all the trimmings and just enough wine to feel mellow. My leg ached, so I shifted position and listened to the debate going on around me.

"It goes like this, son," Pierce said with a deadpan expression. "Guests bring a contribution to the meal, and the family cleans up afterwards."

Josh roared with laughter. "You think one can of cranberry sauce and a bottle of wine saves you from dishes?" Josh eyed Pierce with a mischievous grin. "Consider this, Matt. Would you want to eat here again knowing that *I* had washed the dishes? My idea of clean is to let Taffy lick the plates."

From my perch, I groaned silently, but vowed to stay out of this discussion. After all, I still had one leg in a cast. Supervising from a distance was all I was good for.

"I'll help you, sugar," said Chuck.

Josh squeezed her hand. "The point is," he said to her, "Matt's been here so much the last couple of days that I think he's shifted from the honored guest category to the like-family category."

Pierce's face reddened, but he didn't look displeased. "Okay. Chuck, you scrape and stack. Josh, you load the dishwasher. I'll wash the other stuff."

"Deal."

The kids trooped off to the dining room to get started. Pierce stayed behind.

"How did the investigation go?" I asked. This was the first time I'd had both the time and the inclination to hear the rest of the story.

"I managed to talk to Brenda before she died. She wanted to confess her sins and she hoped her family would forgive her. Her husband knew a lot more than she thought he did."

Pierce shook his head. "It was a real mess. She got pregnant in high school, back in the times when that was still a disgrace. To complicate matters, her parents were extremely religious, and they shipped her off to her aunt's place in Montana. The aunt wasn't much better. I guess she harangued her all the time about being a sinner and disgracing herself in God's eyes. It was the aunt who arranged for a local farmer and his wife to adopt the baby."

I remembered something I read while investigating Hamilton on the Internet. "Wasn't Hamilton involved with some bill that caused them to lose their farm?"

"I wouldn't be surprised. He was a real piece of work." Pierce shrugged. "Have to wonder, though, if he wasn't a victim too. After you told me that he and the reporter were from the same town, I had several conversations with the local sheriff back then. He told me the adoptive parents were interested only in cheap labor. They'd adopt a new child every two years as the oldest graduated from high school and left. They gave the kids enough food to stay healthy, and clothes and schooling to keep the authorities from getting suspicious, but Hamilton and the rest worked hard for their keep."

I let his words sink in. How awful for Hamilton. I had grown up on a ranch, and was expected to work hard, but I knew my parents loved me. "Others have it tough and turn out okay."

"But some are born with a mean streak, and he sure turned out to be one of them. Brenda went to visit him partly because of her administrative position and partly because her daughter worked for him and was obviously falling for him. When she glanced at his chart and saw his date and place of birth, she knew immediately he was her son."

"So she said something about him and Cynthia."

Pierce nodded. "After she realized he was Cynthia's half-brother, she told him who she was. It wasn't a joyous reunion. He told Brenda that seducing Cynthia would be his revenge for being abandoned. Brenda panicked. She left, then doubled back and waited in the stairwell for Officer Tomlin to take a break. That's when she slipped into Hamilton's room and smothered him."

"And she couldn't warn Cynthia to stay away from him because that would mean exposing her mistake," I added. "That poor woman, murdering one child to protect the other."

Dismayed, I shook my head. I could understand why she felt she had to kill Hamilton. He wasn't a nice person. If he'd know-ingly planned to seduce his half-sister, then he was more than not nice; he was evil.

It was more difficult to rationalize her two attempts to murder me, so I set that aside. Maybe later I could forgive her in my heart.

"Her poor family," I said, feeling compassion for them that I couldn't feel for Brenda.

"Yeah. Her husband, he's taking this hard. And from what he's said, the daughter's going to need some psychiatric help. She was on the edge anyway, and this pushed her over."

Pierce helped me resettle the pillows supporting my leg, then said, "Explain to me why you thought Will Slater did it."

"He had motive and opportunity. When I first started in-vesti—"

"—snoop—"

"—investigating to clear Pham, I checked all the calendars

when I was in Admin. Will's time was the only one that was unaccounted for at the time of the murder. I looked at Brenda's calendar and scratched her as a possible suspect because it showed she had a meeting with Darlene."

Pierce nodded. "We saw that too, but hadn't gotten around to cross-checking it with Darlene."

"Two days later, Darlene said she hadn't had a meeting all week. I didn't put it together and Brenda certainly didn't say anything to correct the misperception that she was someplace else at the time of the murder."

"Next time you think you've figured it out, call me and stay in a locked room alone. Don't go off with someone until the case is really solved."

"Believe me, there's not going to be a next time," I vowed.

"Hey, Matt," Josh called from the kitchen doorway. "You going to help or sit there with Mom all night?"

"I'm coming, I'm coming." Pierce heaved himself off the sofa. "Pushy kid. Just like his mom," he mumbled as he headed toward the kitchen.

Alone, I thought about how much I had to be thankful for. I still woke in the middle of the night in a cold sweat, but I was alive.

I had other things to be thankful for. Sarah, from Human Resources, had called to say my job was secure. Will had been offered the federal job, and he said nothing to her before he left for the holidays. She figured he'd be too busy with other things in the few weeks before he moved to D.C. to fuss with me.

Laughter erupted from the kitchen, reminding me how thankful I was for family and friends who were as honest as anyone could be. Josh and I were talking more openly, less like parent and child. There was no masquerading between Pierce and me. He knew about David. I knew about his wife. He knew about Peter. No secrets that could cause problems later.

Josh slid onto the couch next to me and draped his arm over my shoulders, searching my face for signs that I was tiring. "You okay, Mom?"

"The best I've been all week."

He rolled his eyes. "That's not saying much."

"Guess you're right," I said with a quiet laugh. Then I gave him a hard look. "This was a very different Thanksgiving for us, Josh."

"Yeah, but it felt . . . right." He thought for a moment before saying more. "I think it's okay to remember Dad without being sad every year."

"I agree," I said over the lump forming in my throat. I patted his hand. "You better get in there and help Pierce."

He left me alone then, alone with my thoughts. He was right. We'd kept Thanksgiving frozen in time in David's memory. I had frozen that part of my life for too many years. I'd refused to let go, and Josh had followed my lead. It was time.

With a sigh, not of sadness, but of acceptance, I removed the claddagh ring from my finger and turned it around, heart turned outward. One chapter of my life had ended, and another was beginning. It didn't mean I was looking, but I had to live all the facets of my life.

A loud crash from the kitchen jolted me upright.

"It's okay," came three voices in unison.

AUTHOR'S NOTE

This story is a work of fiction. The people Robyn works with, the disaster scenario, and the murder and investigation are from the author's imagination and bear no resemblance to her actual experiences. The patients Robyn encounters in her role as a patient rep are composites based on real cases.

Many hospitals and medical centers have patient representatives who function much the way Robyn Kelly does. If you or a family member have a problem with medical care, do not hesitate to ask for their assistance.

ABOUT THE AUTHOR

For fifteen years, **Liz Osborne** managed the Patient Relations department for a large healthcare organization in western Washington. Her book, *Resolving Patient Complaints: A Step-by-Step Guide to Effective Service Recovery,* is considered a primer on the subject. She lives near Seattle with her husband and Brittany spaniel.